LEED® AP BD+C

V4 EXAM

COMPLETE STUDY GUIDE

(BUILDING DESIGN & CONSTRUCTION)

A. Togay Koralturk

ISBN-13: 978-0994618023 (paperback)
ISBN-10: 0994618026

Printed in the United States of America

CONTENTS

CHAPTER 1

LEED GREEN BUILDING CERTIFICATION PROGRAM

This chapter will explain how a project can receive certification through the Leadership in Energy and Environmental Design certification program, what the requirements and processes are, and what types of LEED certifications are available.

However, before diving into the details, it is essential to mention some important issues to consider beforehand.

Chapter 1, chapter 2, and the first few topics of chapter 3 of this book are also in the scope of the LEED Green Associate exam. People who are confident about these topics from the LEED Green Associate exam—if they have already earned the LEED® Green Associate™ credential—may want to skip these chapters and start reading from the "Integrative Project Planning and Design" prerequisite. However, it is strongly recommended that the reader go through these chapters to reinforce knowledge and fill in any missing information, as these sections are also in the scope of the LEED AP BD+C exam. As you progress through the chapters, the book will provide strong guidance on the topics that need attention.

Another important issue to mention is the format of the LEED AP BD+C exam.

This exam is designed to assess knowledge about implementing LEED prerequisites and credits with respect to real-life projects, performing credit calculations, and making design and construction decisions for LEED projects. To summarize, the major part of the LEED BD+C exam is based on detailed knowledge of the LEED BD+C prerequisites and credits.

The necessary preparation for the LEED BD+C exam can be divided into two parts. The first part is about truly understanding the whole LEED process and the LEED requirements, which is also a necessity in actively applying them in real-life projects. (This way there is no need to memorize any information.) The second part is the information that needs to be retained while taking the exam, such as the formulas, thresholds, or standards that are relevant to each prerequisite and credit.

In order to ease the LEED AP BD+C exam experience, this book contains prerequisite/credit summaries that will demonstrate the whole process before diving into the prerequisite/credit details. Next, the reader will be exposed to the prerequisite/credit requirements without any need for searching additional resources. The end of each prerequisite and credit contains a "Key Things to Remember" section that will point out the details that are most likely to be dismissed as not so important but that can be encountered in the exam as questions. Once the reader has finished the book, the summary sheets will filter out the most important sections that must truly be grasped in each prerequisite and credit.

As in every book, the parts written in bold are important. However, in this book they're even more important since there is a high chance that this information will be encountered on the exam.

Even though the book may contain lots of pages, that doesn't mean that preparation for the LEED AP BD+C exam will be a hard journey. Once diving into the details, you'll find that the most seemingly complex topics will actually appear to be regular topics. Let's get started!

LEED STRUCTURE OVERVIEW

Just like a car rental company categorizing its rental vehicles in categories such as SUVs, minivans, compact cars, standard-sized cars, etc., LEED categorizes projects under LEED rating systems according to their types of construction and space usage. For example, a newly built school project may fall under the "LEED Building Design + Construction: Schools" rating system, but a hotel interior renovation project would fall under the "LEED Interior Design + Construction: Hospitality" rating system.

The first thing project teams should do is choose the LEED rating system that's appropriate for their project before registering the project for the LEED certification process. Then the project teams can proceed with registering the project at LEED Online.

No one can blame a sports car for not handling the road properly on a dusty mountain road. However, an SUV would be required to perform well on mountain roads.

Just like we have different expectations from each vehicle category, LEED has different expectations from each rating system in terms of awarding the LEED certification. To summarize, after a rating system is chosen, project teams need to work on fulfilling its requirements.

Let's take a look at the first group of requirements, which are applicable to all the LEED rating systems. In other words, they're applicable to all projects pursuing LEED certification. They're called the Minimum Program Requirements (MPR). These will also be discussed in the following sections in more depth, but to summarize, a project must be in a permanent location on existing land, must use reasonable LEED boundaries, and must comply with LEED's project-size requirements. Without fulfilling those three MPRs, a project cannot qualify for a LEED certification, and this is applicable for all ratings systems.

After the project complies with the MPRs, it's time to comply with the requirements of the selected rating system. There are two things a project should accomplish under each rating system. The first is to satisfy all the prerequisites of that rating system. You can think about them as if they're MPRs inside each rating system. Without achieving all of the prerequisites, a project cannot achieve a LEED certification. The second thing a project should do is collect points by achieving the credits of that rating system. A minimum of 40 points out of 100 is required for a LEED certification. (All LEED rating systems are scored on a basis of 100 total points, and 40 points are the minimum number needed to become LEED Certified, which is the base level.) Please note that satisfying prerequisites does not result in the award of any points; only satisfying credits leads to points.

Every credit has a different requirement, and every credit awards a point or points. Project teams decide on choosing the credits they want to pursue, preferably during the beginning of the project. There are 52 credits (and 16 prerequisites) under the LEED Building Design + Construction rating systems, and each has a different point value. After achieving the chosen credits, the project teams need to have documentation prepared in order to show that they achieved their MPRs, the prerequisites, and enough credits, and then those documents should be uploaded to LEED Online. Done!

To summarize, in order to achieve a LEED certification, first there are the MPRs (just three), which every project must comply with regardless of the rating system. Then there are prerequisites of each rating system that are mandatory to achieve for LEED certification. Then the project teams must choose credits to pursue and collect more than 40 points. And all of that should be documented.

What if a project satisfies all the MPRs and prerequisites and gets a total of 80 points?

Then it will gain more than a status of LEED Certified, and it will be given a LEED Platinum certificate! According to the total number of points a project receives, LEED certification levels are determined as follows:

- **LEED Certified™: 40–49 points** (This is the base certification level.)
- **LEED Silver: 50–59 points**
- **LEED Gold: 60–79 points**
- **LEED Platinum: 80+ points**

To see the complete list of prerequisites/credits and the point values for credits, it's recommended that you review the LEED scorecard for each rating system from the US Green Building Council's website below.

- usgbc.org/resources/LEED-v4-building-design-and-construction-checklist

The LEED scorecard (or LEED Building Design and Construction checklist or LEED project checklist) is an important document. Which the project teams can choose the credits to be pursued and see if the total expected points will be enough to achieve the target level of LEED certification.

For all the LEED BD+C rating systems, the prerequisites and credits are categorized under nine categories, which are called the credit categories. The following are the credit categories:

- Integrative Process (1 point)
- Location and Transportation (16 points)
- Sustainable Sites (10 points)
- Water Efficiency (11 points)
- Energy and Atmosphere (33 points) (**Category containing the highest points!**)
- Materials and Resources (13 points)
- Indoor Environmental Quality (16 points)
- Innovation (6 points)
- Regional Priority (4 points)

💡 Did you notice that there are 110 total points available? Just like some exams have bonus questions, LEED has 10 bonus points. Credit categories for Innovation (6 points) and Regional Priority (4 points) award the bonus points in LEED. But still, every project will be <u>scored</u> on the basis of 100 points, not 110.

LEED RATING SYSTEMS

Just like individuals have credentials such as LEED Green Associate or LEED AP BD+C, all the LEED projects are certified under a single LEED rating system.

All the LEED rating systems are grouped under five broad categories in accordance with their construction types:

1. LEED for Building Design + Construction (LEED BD+C)
2. LEED for Interior Design + Construction (LEED ID+C)
3. LEED Building Operations + Maintenance (LEED O+M)
4. LEED for Neighborhood Development (LEED ND)
5. LEED for Homes

Under these categories, rating systems are differentiated based on their space usage type in order to address specific needs of different project types:

1- LEED for Building Design and Construction (LEED BD+C) rating systems

a) LEED BD+C: New Construction and Major Renovation
b) LEED BD+C: Core and Shell Development
c) LEED BD+C: Schools
d) LEED BD+C: Retail
e) LEED BD+C: Data Centers
f) LEED BD+C: Warehouses and Distribution Centers
g) LEED BD+C: Hospitality
h) LEED BD+C: Healthcare

2- LEED for Interior Design and Construction (LEED ID+C) rating systems

a) LEED ID+C: Commercial Interiors
b) LEED ID+C: Retail
c) LEED ID+C: Hospitality

3- LEED Building Operations and Maintenance (LEED O+M) rating systems

a) LEED O+M: Existing Buildings
b) LEED O+M: Retail
c) LEED O+M: Schools
d) LEED O+M: Hospitality
e) LEED O+M: Data Centers
f) LEED O+M: Warehouses and Distribution Centers

4- LEED for Neighborhood Development (LEED ND) rating systems

   a) LEED ND: Plan

   b) LEED ND: Built Project

5- LEED for Homes rating systems

   a) LEED BD+C: Homes and Multifamily Low-rise

   b) LEED BD+C: Multifamily Mid-rise

Projects can also choose to use the rating system selector inside LEED Online, which helps project teams choose the most appropriate system for their project.

Some projects may also seem appropriate for more than one rating system. Think about a forty-story high-rise project that contains a hotel on the first twenty floors and residential units on the floors above twenty. Half of the building can be certified under LEED BD+C: Hospitality, while the other half can be certified under LEED BD+C: New Construction and Major Renovation. But in LEED, projects cannot be divided into different rating systems by section, and the whole project should be certified under one rating system. If more than one rating system seems applicable to a project, the 40/60 rule, which is the next topic, should be used to decide on the rating system.

40/60 RULE

This rule is used to choose the appropriate rating system for the project if the project seems to fit under multiple rating systems. In the 40/60 rule, a project should be divided into sections according to the appropriate rating system each section fits. Then the total floor area corresponding to each rating system should be calculated.

If the total floor area of one of the applicable rating systems is less than 40% of the project's total floor area, that rating system cannot be used. If the total floor area of one of the applicable rating systems is more than 60% of the project's total area, that rating system must be used. If it falls between 40% and 60%, then the project teams can decide on the rating system to be used for the project.

Let's consider the forty-story high-rise building project example. It contains a hotel on the first twenty floors and residential units on the floors above twenty. Since 50% of the project's total area is appropriate for one rating system and the other 50% is appropriate for the other, the project teams will decide which rating system to use.

The project teams can look at the requirements of LEED BD+C: Hospitality and LEED BD+C: New Construction and Major Renovation to decide on the rating system they will pursue. USGBC may ask the project teams to change their rating system if it's not chosen appropriately.

LEED RATING SYSTEMS IN DETAILS

LEED FOR BUILDING DESIGN AND CONSTRUCTION (LEED BD+C) RATING SYSTEMS

All types of buildings—whether newly constructed or going through major renovations while keeping the core structures of the buildings—will fall under the LEED BD+C category. **Single-family and multifamily homes between one and eight stories will be classified under the "LEED for Homes" category.**

To be eligible for the rating systems under LEED BD+C, **at least 60% of the project's gross floor area** should be completed by the time of LEED certification, with the exception of LEED BD+C: Core and Shell Development (which will be mentioned shortly). What is meant by "complete" is that there should be no additional work left for those spaces. For incomplete spaces, projects should submit a letter of commitment declaring that the remaining spaces will satisfy the requirements of the prerequisites and credits achieved by the project, and this declaration will need to be signed by the project owner.

a) **LEED BD+C: New Construction and Major Renovation**

   This is the most general rating system that addresses design and construction activities for both new buildings and major renovations of existing buildings. For existing buildings, this rating system includes major HVAC improvements, significant building envelope modifications, and major interior rehabilitation.

   This rating system is for buildings that do not fall under the other LEED BD+C rating systems described below, which are buildings that primarily serve K–12 education, retail, data centers, warehouses and distribution centers, hospitality, or healthcare.

b) **LEED BD+C: Core and Shell Development**

   This rating system is for projects in which the developer controls the design and construction of the building core and the mechanical, electrical, plumbing, and fire protection systems. However, it does not involve the design and construction of the tenant fit-out (which is called the core and shell construction). An example would be an office-building project in which the common spaces are constructed by the developer, and the tenant spaces are left out, allowing the tenants to construct their own custom designs in their office spaces.

   The requirement to be eligible for this rating system is to construct **less than 40% of the interior total gross floor area**. For all the other BD+C ratings systems, 60% of the project's gross floor area should be completed by the time of LEED certification.

The "LEED BD+C: Core and Shell" rating system is also eligible for **precertification**. Once the developer has established a goal to develop a "LEED BD+C: Core and Shell" project, USGBC will grant a precertification to aid in marketing the project to potential tenants and financiers for the unique and valuable green features of the proposed building. Precertification will be granted after USGBC reviews the early design documents of the project. However, the precertification will not guarantee the LEED certification since the LEED certification will be given at the end of construction, when all the requirements are met.

c) LEED BD+C: Schools

This rating system is for buildings made up of core and ancillary learning spaces on K–12 school grounds. It can also be used for higher education and nonacademic buildings on school campuses.

d) LEED BD+C: Retail

This rating system is for retailers such as banks, restaurants, apparel stores, electronics outlets, big-box stores, and everything in between.

e) LEED BD+C: Data Centers

This is specifically designed and equipped to meet the needs of high-density computing equipment.

f) LEED BD+C: Warehouses and Distribution Centers

This is for buildings that are used to store goods, manufactured products, merchandise, raw materials, or personal belongings (in self-storage).

g) LEED BD+C: Hospitality

This is for hotels, motels, inns, or other businesses within the service industry that provide transitional or short-term lodging with or without food.

h) LEED BD+C: Healthcare

This is for hospitals that operate twenty-four hours a day, seven days a week and provide inpatient medical treatment, including acute and long-term care.

LEED FOR INTERIOR DESIGN AND CONSTRUCTION (LEED ID+C) RATING SYSTEMS

LEED ID+C rating systems apply to projects that are a complete interior fit-out. If a company rents an office building and decides to design and construct the interior office space, the "LEED ID+C: Commercial Interiors" rating system can be used to LEED-certify the office.

a) LEED ID+C: Commercial Interiors

This is for interior spaces dedicated to functions other than retail or hospitality. Think about a LEED-certified core and shell office building project in which the developer was not involved in the design and construction of the tenant spaces. In that scenario, the tenants may decide to get a "LEED ID+C: Commercial Interiors" certification for their office spaces, which would only cover the interior fit-out design and construction work.

b) LEED ID+C: Retail

This is for the design and construction of interior spaces used to conduct the retail sale of consumer goods. It includes both direct customer service areas (showroom) and preparation or storage areas that support customer service.

c) LEED ID+C: Hospitality

This is for the design and construction of interior spaces dedicated to hotels, motels, inns, or other businesses within the service industry that provide transitional or short-term lodging with or without food.

LEED BUILDING OPERATIONS AND MAINTENANCE (LEED O+M) RATING SYSTEMS

The greenest building is the one already built. It can take up to eighty years to make up for the environmental impacts of demolishing an old building and constructing a new one, even if the newly constructed building is environmentally friendly.

The LEED O+M rating systems apply to existing buildings that are undergoing improvement work or <u>little to no construction</u>. LEED O+M certifies the operations and maintenance of the building and creates a plan to ensure high-performance building operations. LEED O+M monitors the building's systems (HVAC, electrical, automation systems, etc.) as well as the building's performance.

A LEED ID+C: Commercial Interiors-certified office located in a LEED BD+C: Core and Shell- certified building, can also receive a "LEED O+M: Existing Buildings" certification. By getting such a certification, the project gets proof that the ongoing building operations are efficient and building operations are high in performance.

LEED O+M rating system certifications expire **every five years**, and in order to keep a LEED O+M certification, a project needs to be recertified every five years. Certifications of the other rating systems do not expire and do not need a recertification.

a) **LEED O+M: Existing Buildings**

This is specifically for projects that do not primarily serve uses for K–12 education, retail, data centers, warehouses and distribution centers, or hospitality.

b) **LEED O+M: Retail**

This is for existing retail spaces, both showrooms and storage areas.

c) **LEED O+M: Schools**

This is for existing buildings made up of core and ancillary learning spaces on K–12 school grounds. It can be used for higher education and nonacademic buildings on school campuses as well.

d) **LEED O+M: Hospitality**

This is for existing hotels, motels, inns, or other businesses within the service industry that provide transitional or short-term lodging with or without food.

e) **LEED O+M: Data Centers**

This is for existing buildings specifically designed and equipped to meet the needs of high-density computing equipment such as server racks used for data storage and processing.

f) **LEED O+M: Warehouses and Distribution Centers**

This is for existing buildings used to store goods, manufactured products, merchandise, raw materials, or personal belongings (such as in self-storage).

LEED FOR NEIGHBORHOOD DEVELOPMENT (LEED ND) RATING SYSTEMS

This rating system is designed to certify new land-development projects or the development of land that contains residential uses, nonresidential uses, or both. The LEED ND rating system is designed to ensure that the developing neighborhood integrates the principles of smart growth, urbanism, and green building.

LEED ND contains two rating systems:

a) **LEED ND: Plan**

This is for neighborhood-scale projects that are currently in any phase of planning and design and up to 75% constructed. This was designed to help developers market and fund the project among prospective tenants, financiers, and public officials by affirming the intended sustainability strategies.

b) **LEED ND: Built Project**

This is for neighborhood-scale projects that are near completion or were completed within the last three years.

LEED FOR HOMES RATING SYSTEMS

This rating system category is designed to certify single-family and multifamily homes that are between **one and eight stories**. Residential buildings over eight stories should use the "LEED BD+C: New Construction and Major Renovation" rating system.

The two rating systems under this category are the only rating systems that require in-field verification. This means that a Green Rater (also mentioned in the "LEED Professional Credentials" section) is going to conduct a site visit to verify that the home is designed and built to the rating system's requirements.

a) **LEED BD+C: Homes and Multifamily Low-Rise**

This rating system is for single-family homes and multifamily residential buildings that are **one to three stories**.

b) **LEED BD+C: Multifamily Mid-Rise**

This rating system is for multifamily residential buildings with four to eight stories above grade. Residential buildings with **nine stories or more** should use the "LEED BD+C: New Construction and Major Renovation" rating system.

MINIMUM PROGRAM REQUIREMENTS (MPR)

The minimum program requirements are the minimum standards/characteristics that every LEED project should meet to pursue LEED certification. MPRs state whether a project can pursue LEED certification or not. They provide guidance on the types of projects that are eligible for LEED certification, protect the integrity of the LEED program, and reduce the number of issues that arise during the certification process. They define the types of buildings, spaces, and neighborhoods that a LEED rating system is designed to evaluate. (It is important to thoroughly know the MPRs for exam purposes.)

There are three MPRs:

1) Every project must be in a permanent location on existing land.

A project that is designed to move at any point in its lifetime is not eligible for LEED certification. Since a significant portion of LEED's prerequisites and credits are dependent on the project's location, the certification is awarded according to that particular location. Prefabricated or modular structures can be LEED-certified as long as they are installed permanently. However, boats or mobile homes are not eligible for a LEED certification.

It is also important to locate the projects on existing land to avoid artificial landmasses, which can displace and disrupt ecosystems in the future. Buildings located on previously developed infill, docks, piers, or jetties in or above water can be eligible for a LEED certification, as long as the artificial land was previously developed, and the land supported another building or hardscape that was constructed for a purpose other than the LEED project.

2) Every project must use reasonable LEED boundaries.

The LEED project boundary must include all contiguous land that is associated with the project and that supports its typical operations. These will include the landscaping, septic or stormwater treatment equipment, parking, sidewalks, and any other development that is used by the project. Any project space cannot be shown to be excluded in order to give the project an advantage in complying with credit requirements.

Noncontiguous parcels of land and facilities outside of the LEED project boundary may be included if they directly serve the project.

Projects inside phased sites with a master plan for multiple buildings should determine a LEED project boundary for each building. Or if the project consists of multiple structures that are connected only by circulation, parking, or mechanical rooms and have programmatic dependency—meaning that the buildings cannot function independently without the other buildings—it can be considered a single building for LEED certification purposes.

An addition to a building can be certified independently, excluding the building in its entirety, or the entire building can be certified as one single project.

Finally, the gross floor area of the LEED project should not be less than **2%** of the gross land area within the LEED project boundary. The "LEED project boundary" is defined by the platted property line of the project, including all land and water within it.

3) Every project must comply with project size requirements.

All LEED projects must meet the following size requirements according to their rating system:

LEED BD+C and LEED O+M rating systems: The project must include a minimum of 1,000 square feet (93 square meters) of gross floor area.

LEED ID+C rating systems: The project must include a minimum of 250 square feet (22 square meters) of gross floor area.

LEED for Neighborhood Development rating systems: The project should contain at least two habitable buildings and be no larger than 1,500 acres.

LEED for Homes: The project must be defined as a "dwelling unit" by all applicable codes. A dwelling unit should include permanent provisions for living, sleeping, eating, cooking, and sanitation. The LEED for Homes rating system additionally refers to the LEED for Homes Scope and Eligibility Guidelines for extra requirements.

PREREQUISITES AND CREDITS

Whether deciding to pursue LEED certification or not, all project teams should first take a look at the MPRs to see if their project can be eligible for a LEED certification. Then the project teams will need to determine the rating system that their project fits into. After the rating system is selected, project teams should evaluate the prerequisites and credits of that rating system.

Prerequisites are the minimum requirements that all buildings under a certain rating system must meet in order to achieve LEED certification. For example, all the projects that are certified under the LEED BD+C: Healthcare rating system must meet all the prerequisites of that rating system, while a project registered under LEED O+M: Retail must meet all of its prerequisites. To illustrate, let's take a look at the one of the prerequisites under the LEED BD+C: New Construction and Major Renovation rating system.

Prerequisite—Fundamental Refrigerant Management: Briefly, this prerequisite requires projects not use CFC-based refrigerants in their HVAC&R (heating, ventilating, air conditioning, and refrigeration) systems.

Therefore, every project under the LEED BD+C: New Construction and Major Renovation rating system will not use any CFC-based refrigerants—period. Any project that cannot meet this requirement will not be eligible for a LEED certification. While projects can pick and choose the credits they want to pursue, prerequisites are mandatory. Fulfilling the requirements of prerequisites will also not result in the award of any points.

Now let's look at the **credits**, which are also a part of each rating system. Project teams are free to go for any credit they want within the selected rating system. Each credit has requirements to be fulfilled, and once the requirements are met, the project will earn points. The higher the total points a project earns, the higher the level of LEED certification that will be awarded. To illustrate how a credit works, let's take a look at the one of the credits under the "LEED BD+C: New Construction and Major Renovation" rating system.

Credit—Access to Quality Transit: Briefly, this credit requires the project to be located within walking distance of public transportation to reduce greenhouse gas emissions resulting from single-occupancy vehicle use.

Hence, any LEED BD+C: New Construction and Major Renovation project located within walking distance of public transportation will earn points under this credit. Projects that do not comply with this credit will not receive any points.

The prerequisites and credits are also sometimes categorized as **design prerequisites/credits** and **construction prerequisites/credits,** according to the project phase they are performed in. For example, the previously mentioned "Access to Quality Transit" credit is a design credit since the project's location will not be decided during the construction phase. (See Appendix D—Prerequisite/Credit Classifications.)

PILOT CREDITS

Besides the prerequisites and credits, there are also Pilot Credits, which are credits being tested for the updated version of LEED. According to the feedback received by USGBC from the projects that pursue these credits, these pilot credits can become actual credits of the updated LEED rating system, which would be LEED v5.

Pursuing any pilot credit is optional to team members, but if the project chooses to earn a pilot credit, bonus points will be awarded. The points will be awarded under the "Innovation" credit, which is under the "Innovation" credit category. (Further details will be discussed under the "Innovation" credit.) The pilot credits available to each rating system can be accessed from the **LEED Pilot Credit Library** at this website:

- http://www.usgbc.org/pilotcredits

POINT ALLOCATION PROCESS

By looking at the LEED BD+C: New Construction section of the LEED scorecard, you can see that each credit contains a different number of points. For example, the "Optimize Energy Performance" credit contains 18 points while the "Site Assessment" credit only contains 1 point.

To better understand the system that LEED uses to distribute the 100 total points to each credit, we first need to understand the key elements that a LEED project should accomplish.

Impact Categories, also called **system goals**, are the key elements that every LEED project aims to accomplish. Impact categories consist of seven items:

1. **Reverse contribution to global climate change**
2. **Enhance individual human health and well-being**
3. **Protect and restore water resources**
4. **Protect, enhance, and restore biodiversity and ecosystem services**
5. **Promote sustainable and regenerative material resources cycles**
6. **Build a greener economy**
7. **Enhance social equity, environmental justice, and community quality of life**

Each credit in LEED will make a contribution to one or more of these impact categories. The more a credit makes a total contribution to each of these impact categories, the more points that credit will contain. To illustrate, let's say that credit A contributes to the following three impact categories at different levels:

- Reverse contribution to global climate change (high contribution)
- Protect and restore water resources (low contribution)
- Build a greener economy (medium contribution)

LEED v4 will determine the total contribution level to each impact category and then calculate the total points that will be allocated to that credit. All the credits in the rating systems contain a minimum of 1 point.

CREDIT INTERPRETATION RULINGS (CIR)

After the project is registered at LEED Online, if project teams have questions about the technical details of a prerequisite, credit, or MPR, a CIR is issued to ask for clarification.

Sometimes the reference guide will not be able to provide all the information regarding the achievement of a particular prerequisite/credit, and in that case, the project teams would submit a CIR through LEED Online and ask for a clarification. One CIR can be sent to clarify a single question, and project teams can submit an unlimited number of CIRs. A CIR has a fixed cost of $220 for both USGBC members and nonmembers.

CIRs are administered by Green Business Certification Inc. (GBCI), and the Credit Ruling Committee reviews the CIR in two to five weeks, concluding the process by clarifying the question asked.

LEED INTERPRETATIONS

In a process similar to the handling of CIRs, when project teams have questions about the technical details of a prerequisite, credit, or MPR, a LEED interpretation can be issued to ask for clarification. Just like the CIRs, LEED interpretations can be sent using LEED Online.

But the difference between LEED interpretations and CIRs is that LEED interpretations are **precedent-setting**, which means that every LEED project will be able to use it and will also adhere to that LEED interpretation. In other words, the clarification made in the LEED interpretation will be incorporated into the whole LEED rating system. A LEED interpretation will be published online on USGBC's website for general access, and it will be subject to a USGBC consensus-based review, which will take longer than the review of a CIR (approximately three to six months longer).

On the other hand, CIRs are not posted online, and they are not applicable to other projects. The fixed cost of issuing a LEED interpretation is $180 more than the cost of issuing a CIR for both USGBC members and nonmembers. CIRs are administered by GBCI, and LEED interpretations are administered by USGBC. (That distinction is important to know for exam purposes.)

LEED interpretations can become a part of Addenda, which will be the next topic.

ADDENDA

"Addenda" is the term that combines all the changes, improvements, issued LEED interpretations, and modifications made to a LEED rating system. Just as a piece of software updates itself once a week or so to incorporate the latest updates, LEED rating systems are updated with addenda.

After LEED v4 was released, addenda have been continuously issued at USGBC's website, which combines all the updates made to that rating system through LEED interpretations, modifications, and improvements. In addition, a project that registers with LEED Online after any issued addenda will be automatically subject to the addenda's requirements.

LEED CERTIFICATION PROCESS FOR LEED BD+C PROJECTS

1. PROJECT REGISTRATION

The first step for LEED-certifying a building is to register the project through LEED Online, which means completing the registration form and paying the flat registration fee, which is $900 for USGBC members and $1,200 for nonmembers. In this phase, a **LEED Project Administrator** needs to be assigned.

A LEED Project Administrator is the primary project contact for USGBC and GBCI. The LEED Project Administrator is the team member who acts as a project manager, overseeing the LEED project and organizing team members for certain tasks, credits, or prerequisites. The project administrator makes sure the LEED submission is complete and accurate before submitting the project to GBCI for review, and the project administrator accepts the review results once the review is complete. To avoid confusion, a LEED Project Administrator does not need to be a LEED Green Associate or a LEED AP. The duties of LEED Green Associates, LEED APs, and LEED Project Administrators in the project are completely different.

2. APPLICATION

After the project registration phase, the project teams will identify LEED credits to pursue and assign responsibility for the various credits to project team members. Then the project teams will collect information, perform calculations, prepare documentation, fill out the credit templates demonstrating the achievement of the prerequisites/credits, and upload all the documentation to LEED Online. At the end, the LEED Project Administrator will verify that everything is complete, and the project teams will pay the review (certification) fees to submit the application.

Review (certification) fees change according to the gross floor area of the project and membership status; they are not a flat fee like the registration fee. Once the review (certification) fees are received, GBCI will start the project review process. (Using credit cards for payments is faster than using checks since the review will not start before the check clears).

3. REVIEW

There are two types of review options for LEED BD+C projects. The first option is the **combined review**, in which documentation for all the design and construction prerequisites/credits are submitted for review at the end of the construction phase. At the end of the combined review, GBCI will mark the submitted prerequisites/credits as **awarded** or **denied**.

If there is more information needed by GBCI about a prerequisite/credit, GBCI will mark it as "**clarify**," and the project teams will submit the requested clarification. It is a little riskier than the second option, which is the **split review**. If some of the expected credits are not awarded, there will not be a makeup since the project is already completed and no change in design or construction can be made. If a prerequisite is not awarded, then the project will not be able to receive a LEED certification at all.

In the second option, **split review**, the design prerequisites/credits are submitted for review during the design phase, and both the additional design prerequisites/credits and all the construction prerequisites/credits are submitted at the end of the construction phase. When the design review is complete, GBCI will either mark the design prerequisites/credits as **anticipated** or **denied**. No prerequisite/credit will be awarded during the design phase since the design will also need to be implemented on-site during the construction phase. If a design prerequisite/credit is marked as **anticipated**, it means that the project will earn it at the end of the construction phase once that design is implemented on-site. If it's marked as **denied**, in order to earn the prerequisite/credit, the project teams will need to come up with a design alternative rather than proceeding with that design. At the end of the construction phase, the additional design prerequisites/credits (if applicable) and the construction prerequisites/credits are sent for review. GBCI will at that time mark all of them as **awarded** or **denied** unless clarification is needed. If more information is needed about a prerequisite/credit, it will be marked as "**clarify**," and the project teams will submit the requested clarification.

The review fees will depend on the gross floor area of the project. Expedited review is also available for an extra flat fee of $10,000 for a combined review and $5,000 per design and construction review under the split review. The fees are flat fees for both USGBC members and nonmembers and will reduce the review duration from 20–25 days down to 10–12 days.

To summarize the review process, let's list all the steps for a combined review and a split review:

Combined review:

At the end of the construction phase the following steps are taken:

1. Both design and construction submittals are sent by the project team.
2. There's a **preliminary review** by GBCI.
3. If additional information is needed to evaluate the application, GBCI will ask for clarifications, and the project team will send the clarifications.
4. GBCI will proceed with the **final review** to evaluate the clarifications and to report the awarded/denied prerequisites and credits to the project team.
5. The project team will either accept or appeal the result.

<u>Split review</u>:

During the design phase:

1. Design submittals are sent by the project team.
2. **Preliminary design review** is conducted by GBCI.
3. If additional information is needed to evaluate the application, GBCI will ask for clarification, and the project team will send the clarification.
4. GBCI will proceed with the **final design review** to evaluate the clarifications and report the <u>anticipated</u>/<u>denied</u> prerequisites/credits to the project team.
5. The project team will either accept or appeal the result.

At the end of the construction phase, the following occurs:

1. Both construction and extra design submittals (if applicable) are sent by the project team.
2. **Preliminary construction review is conducted** by GBCI.
3. If additional information is needed to evaluate the application, GBCI will ask for clarification, and the project team will send the clarification.
4. GBCI will proceed with the **final construction review** to evaluate the clarifications and report the <u>awarded</u>/<u>denied</u> prerequisites/credits to the project team.
5. The project team will either accept or appeal the result.

An unlimited number of appeals can be made for any LEED project. Appeals have a flat fee of $800 for each of the complex prerequisites/credits and $500 for each of the other prerequisites/credits. Expedited review is also available for an additional $500, and it will reduce the review duration from 20–25 business days down to 10–12 business days. Being a USGBC member does not reduce the appeal fee. (It is recommended to know that the review fees depend on the gross floor area of the project, but fees for appeals, registration, CIR, and LEED interpretation are flat fees.)

4. CERTIFICATION OR DENIAL

This is the last step of LEED certification. GBCI issues the final certification report, which will show the level of LEED certification awarded unless the certification is denied. The project teams can appeal the results if necessary, and if no appeals are made, then the project will be deemed "**closed out**," which means the project team will no longer be able to appeal the certification level or review decisions for specific credits or prerequisites.

As mentioned, the total number of earned points will determine the level of LEED certification, assuming all the prerequisites and MPRs are met.

This point system applies to all the rating systems in LEED. Any project that earns 80 points will get the LEED Platinum designation regardless of whether it is a "LEED O+M: Hospitality" project or a "LEED BD+C: Schools" project or belongs to any other category.

LEED VOLUME AND LEED CAMPUS

The LEED Volume Program is a streamlined certification process for organizations that plan to certify more than twenty-five prototype-based construction projects within three years. An example of this would be a coffee-shop chain that plans to open up twenty-five coffee shops with uniform designs. Such a project could use the LEED Volume Program to pay lower certification fees to help streamline the certification process.

The LEED Campus Program is not for projects uniform in design, but for multiple projects that are located on a single campus owned by the same entity. An example of this would be a university planning to construct several educational buildings on the same campus. These projects can use the LEED Campus Program to pay lower certification fees and streamline the certification process.

There are two ways to certify multiple buildings under the LEED Campus Program:

1. <u>Group approach</u>: This approach allows substantially similar buildings in a single location to be certified under a single LEED certification.
2. <u>Campus approach</u>: This approach allows buildings that are in a single location to achieve separate LEED certifications for each building space, project, or group on the master site.

CHAPTER 2

GREEN BUILDINGS AND LEED

According to the US Environmental Protection Agency (EPA), green building is the practice of creating structures and using processes that are environmentally responsible and resource-efficient throughout a building's life cycle, from siting to design, construction, operation, maintenance, renovation, and deconstruction. This practice expands and complements the classical building design concerns of economy, utility, durability, and comfort. Green building is also known as the practice of creating a sustainable or high-performance building.

Green buildings are more environmentally sensitive, provide more comfort to building occupants, and also remain resource-efficient and high-performance buildings throughout their entire life cycle. But how does that happen?

To highlight the major concept of green buildings, we must first observe the natural system.

In the natural cycle, there isn't any waste. Even what we term "animal waste" is actually a sustainable product, which is an organic fertilizer in agriculture that improves plant nutrition and assists the growth of plants. The key factor of animal waste is its sustainability; it is produced by nature and is continuously reused in a never-ending loop. Nevertheless, is the waste of man-made products also like that?

Think about a plastic bag, which takes about five hundred years to break down in the environment and creates a great deal of environmental harm during its lifetime.

Now, let's think about the "built environment," which refers to all the man-made surroundings that are needed for human activity, from roads, to buildings, to neighborhoods. We use most of the world's resources to develop our built environments, but do they end up like the plastic bag in the previous example, or can they continue sustainably in nature?

Green building is really a system that evolves by continuously enhancing a building's level of performance in order to get as close as possible to the natural system, which is by far the most efficient system known to man.

ENVIRONMENTAL IMPACTS OF BUILT ENVIRONMENTS

There is not a single building in the world that does not have an impact on the environment. That being said, the way we build can make a great contribution toward reducing this impact.

In the Unites States, buildings account for the following:

- 14% of potable water consumption[1]
- 30% of waste output
- 40% of raw materials use[2]
- 38% of carbon dioxide (CO_2) emissions
- 24% to 50% of energy use
- 72% of electricity consumption[3]

Accounting for 38% of carbon dioxide emissions, buildings are on top of the list and produce even more carbon dioxide (CO_2) than transportation and industrial emitters. And the total built environment contributes to 67% of all greenhouse gas emissions.[4]

But why do our buildings harm the environment? First, when we clear the land to make way for a development, the wildlife habitat in that area is destroyed, and the preexisting permeable soil becomes an impermeable surface. Second, we manufacture building products that pollute water and air, release toxic chemicals, and emit greenhouse gases. Furthermore, during the building operations phase, the building consumes energy, which further increases greenhouse gas emissions and adds to the consumption of potable water, which later becomes a waste product. With the commuting of building users and visitors to the building, the use of single-occupancy vehicles results in increased energy consumption and greenhouse gas emissions.

The list of aspects related to environmental impact is seemingly endless.

BENEFITS OF GREEN BUILDINGS

When looking at the statistics of green buildings, a study by the New Buildings Institute found that average energy use intensity of green buildings is 24% lower than typical buildings.[5]

Additionally, a US General Services Administration survey of twelve green buildings states that green buildings have:

- 26% energy use reduction
- 27% higher levels of occupant satisfaction
- 13% lower maintenance costs
- 33% lower carbon dioxide emissions

Occupants of green buildings are exposed to far lower levels of indoor pollutants and are exposed to superior air, lighting, and acoustical qualities than occupants of regular buildings.

According to the EPA, people in the United States spend, on average, 90% of their time indoors.[6] That means that developing green buildings will make a serious contribution to the health and comfort of the building occupants and their productivity.

ABOUT USGBC

Founded in the early 1990s and based in Washington, DC, the US Green Building Council (USGBC) is a nonprofit organization committed to a sustainable future through cost- and energy-efficient green buildings.

USGBC is made up of tens of thousands of member organizations, chapters, and student and community volunteers. Currently, there are more than 76 chapters, 16,000 member organizations, and 197,000 LEED professionals, and those numbers continue to grow. Members of USGBC include engineers, architects, building owners, contractors, facility managers, building product manufacturers, designers, utility managers, college students, college faculties, government agencies, and more.

USGBC promotes buildings that are environmentally responsible, profitable, and supportive of human health.

USGBC accomplishes this mission through the following:

- **LEED:** The most widely known and used green building program across the world.
- **Credentials:** The LEED Green Associate credential and the various LEED AP credentials offer professionals a designation to help them stand out in the building industry.
- **Greenbuild International Conference & Expo:** The world's largest expo, launched in 2002, dedicated to green buildings.
- **Education:** USGBC provides educational programs about green buildings to further spread environmental principles and design.

➣ **Advocacy:** At every level of government, USGBC provides policymakers and community leaders with all the tools, strategies, and resources necessary to inspire action toward a sustainable built environment.

➣ **Chapters & Committees:** USGBC contains more than 76 regional USGBC chapter organizations for involvement from the local level to the national level.

ABOUT LEED

LEADERSHIP in ENERGY and ENVIRONMENTAL DESIGN is a system developed by USGBC to certify high-performance buildings and sustainable neighborhoods.

The LEED Green Building Rating System™ is a **voluntary, consensus based rating system that provides third-party verification** that a building or community was designed and built to establish energy savings, water efficiency, location efficiency, improved indoor environmental quality, stewardship of resources, and sensitivity to their impacts. LEED addresses all building types through different rating systems and evaluates a building's performance throughout the building's life cycle.

The creation of the LEED green building rating system is led by USGBC member-based volunteer committees, subcommittees, and working groups in conjunction with USGBC staff. After development, LEED's green building rating systems are subject to review and approval by the LEED steering committee and the USGBC board of directors prior to a vote by USGBC membership.

LEED was created to do the following:

➣ Define "green building" by establishing a common standard of measurement
➣ Promote integrated, whole-building design practices
➣ Recognize environmental leadership in the building industry
➣ Stimulate green competition
➣ Raise consumer awareness of green building benefits
➣ Transform the building market

The number of LEED-certified projects in the United States and around the world is increasing each day. The US General Services Administration required all new federal government construction projects and renovations to achieve at least LEED Silver certification and currently requires these projects to achieve LEED Gold certification.

ABOUT GBCI

Green Business Certification Inc. (GBCI), formerly known as Green Building Certification Institute (GBCI), changed its name on April 16, 2015; it is the sister organization of USGBC; GBCI administers LEED building certifications and LEED professional accreditations.

When a project submits all the necessary documents for a LEED application, GBCI is the organization that will review the application and determine if all the requirements set forth in a LEED rating system are fully met or not. And if the requirements are fulfilled, GBCI will grant the LEED certificate.

LEED professional exams are also administered by GBCI, and LEED professional credentials are awarded according to exam results.

LEED CERTIFICATION BENEFITS

LEED-certified buildings are proven to be environmentally friendly and to respect human health. However, there are other major benefits of a LEED certification that can be summarized as money savings over the lifetime of a project, increased project value, and increased building-occupant satisfaction.

Additionally, LEED projects are known to be much more energy efficient than regular buildings and to have lower operating costs. The same thing applies for water consumption, as LEED-certified buildings consume less potable water than regular buildings. LEED-certified projects have an increased building value, which means more return on investment. LEED certification is a great marketing tool for developers, which results in higher occupancy rates. Since the building systems in LEED-certified projects are commissioned during the design and construction phases as a requirement, the building systems create fewer problems during the operations phase. Furthermore, people who work in LEED-certified buildings have increased productivity due to the healthier environment of the buildings, which is the result of increased exposure to natural daylight, increased ventilation rates inside the building, less contaminated indoor air, more open spaces, increased acoustic performance, and many other advantages.

Even though the initial cost of a LEED-certified building may be slightly higher than a regular building (because of the commissioning activities, LEED consulting, and LEED application costs), the life-cycle cost of a regular building typically turns out to be much higher than a LEED-certified building.

GREEN BUILDING INCENTIVES

In order to promote green developments, many municipalities award structural or financial incentives to developers or homeowners who practice green building techniques.

The structural incentives provide rewards for green building projects by making available additional density bonuses or expedited permitting processes. Even though the review and permitting processes vary from one jurisdiction to another, they are generally lengthy processes. By reducing the review and permitting durations in exchange for developers' establishment of green building standards, municipalities encourage developers to design green buildings.

Density and height bonuses are another incentive. Many municipalities allow for percentage increases in floor-to-area ratio or other measures of density contingent upon certification or proof of green building practices.

The financial incentives are direct incentives in the form of tax credits or grants to developers that build green buildings. Some municipalities offer reductions or waivers for permit review or other less onerous permitting processes in exchange for developers' use of green building standards. Revolving loan funds can also be available to those seeking to build or renovate to green building standards.

If a developer is unfamiliar with green building practices, many municipalities provide free planning or certification training and assistance.

Marketing assistance is also offered to promote green buildings, and many municipalities offer free marketing assistance via signage, awards, websites, and/or press releases.

LEED PROFESSIONAL CREDENTIALS

LEED credentials offer professionals a designation to help them stand out in the building industry. There are three main LEED professional credentials:

- **LEED Green Associate**: GBCI has created the LEED Green Associate credential for professionals who want to demonstrate green building knowledge and expertise in non-technical fields of practice. It has been created to denote basic knowledge of green design, construction, and operations. LEED Green Associates have a proven, up-to-date understanding of green building principles and practices.

- **LEED Accredited Professional with specialty**: The LEED AP with specialty credential is created for professionals with advanced knowledge in green building practices and with specialization in a particular LEED rating system. The LEED AP credential is divided into different specialties, and each credential is designed to show in-depth knowledge of a particular rating system. Below is the list of all LEED AP specialties:

  - LEED AP Building Design + Construction (LEED AP BD+C)
  - LEED AP Interior Design + Construction (LEED AP ID+C)
  - LEED AP Operations + Maintenance (LEED AP O+M)
  - LEED AP Neighborhood Development (LEED AP ND)
  - LEED AP Homes

There is also a LEED AP credential without any specialty, called LEED AP or Legacy LEED AP, which was granted to professionals who passed the LEED AP exam before 2009. The Legacy LEED AP credential is not offered anymore, and all the new LEED APs should choose a specialty.

➤ **LEED Fellow**: According to USGBC, the LEED Fellow credential designates the most exceptional professionals in the green building industry, and it is the most prestigious designation awarded. Outstanding LEED APs who have demonstrated exceptional achievement in key mastery elements related to technical knowledge and skill are eligible for the honor. LEED Fellows have also made significant contributions in teaching, mentoring, or research with proven outcomes and have a history of exemplary leadership, impactful commitment, service, and advocacy in green building and sustainability.

Other than those mentioned credentials, there are also LEED professional certificates that are needed to become **LEED for Homes Green Raters** or just Green Raters. Green Raters provide **in-field verification** to every LEED for Homes project. (The other rating systems do not require any in-field verification.)

LEED APs or LEED Green Associates may also choose to become **LEED Pro Reviewers** to evaluate the educational LEED courses at **EDUCATION@USGBC**, which is the education portal of USGBC. In exchange, USGBC provides a complimentary yearlong subscription to the USGBC's education portal.

CREDENTIAL MAINTENANCE PROGRAM (CMP)

LEED Green Associates and LEED APs with specialty should maintain their credentials by meeting the requirements of the Credential Maintenance Program (CMP) every two years, or otherwise the credential will expire, and retaking the exam will be necessary to maintain the LEED professional credential.

Under the CMP, all the LEED Green Associates must earn **15 continuing education (CE) hours every two years,** and LEED APs must earn **30 continuing education hours every two years** after earning their credential.

LEED ONLINE

LEED Online is the online platform of USGBC and is shared by both <u>USGBC and GBCI</u>. In LEED Online, project teams can register their project; pay their certification fees; upload their LEED submittals, documentation, and photos; access their credit templates and calculators; contact their project reviewers; contact customer support; send a credit interpretation ruling (CIR); and more.

For documenting the LEED prerequisites/credits, the project teams should fill in the **credit templates** available at LEED Online. With the use of credit templates, every LEED project team prepares LEED submittals in the same format, which streamlines the preparation of LEED applications and the review durations. For the prerequisites/credits that require any calculation, **credit calculators** are also built into the credit templates, and the project teams can use those calculators to input their calculation data.

All the project team members can have access to the prerequisites/credits uploaded to LEED Online.

CHAPTER 3

INTEGRATIVE PROCESS (IP)

A major concept of sustainable thinking is the integrated process, which is the key to applying sustainable thinking to real-life situations.

Every system is a composition of its individual parts. Let's take the human body as an example: cells form tissues, tissues form organs, organs form the organ systems, and organ systems form human bodies. A lung is made up of cells; however, only lung cells together will not do anything. The whole system needs to be there.

Assembling the project owner, key stakeholders, architects, civil engineers, and mechanical and electrical engineers will not create a successful project; rather, a system needs to be formed in which there is a flow of information and collaboration between each member for each phase of the project. To better understand the topic, we will discuss the conventional building process and then return to explain the details of the integrated building process.

CONVENTIONAL BUILDING PROCESS

In the conventional building process, project teams work in isolation and collaborate when problems occur. Usually, the process starts with a project owner hiring an architectural firm to develop the design.

As the design progresses, the architectural firm hires electrical and mechanical designers, who then start integrating the electrical and mechanical parts of the design separately. Then construction plans are issued, and the owner starts the bidding process. In this phase, different general contractors are requested to bid, and once all the bids are submitted, the owner chooses the general contractor and awards the construction of the project. This is called the **design-bid-build** process.

With this approach, the general contractor is not involved in the design phase at all, and furthermore, the general contractor doesn't have any collaboration with the architectural firm. In addition, the general contractor doesn't have any collaboration with the mechanical and electrical designers. During the construction phase, as problems arise, the general contractor invites the architectural firm to provide input. In turn, the architectural firm might invite the electrical and mechanical designers to the meetings in order to solve the problems at hand. The outcome of this process will usually be construction delays and extra project costs.

Referring to the human body example, all the cells were there, but the system was not working.

INTEGRATED BUILDING PROCESS IN DETAILS

To establish an integrated building process, a working system needs to be created. And the system should be active as early as possible during the **predesign phase** or even before deciding on the project location. Think about the following questions:

- What is the climate in the project's location, and what type of heating and cooling system should be installed?
- How should the building be oriented in order to get more sunlight into the building and to reduce the operating costs and provide natural daylight?
- Is there enough rainfall at the location to capture and use rainwater for irrigation?
- What are the goals and requirements of the project's owner?
- How will the building occupants commute once the project is finished, and what are the public transportation options?
- How will the resources and construction materials be transported to the project site?
- What are the building code requirements at the project's location?
- How does energy get to the site?
- What is the type of soil on-site?
- What type of vegetation exists on-site?

They're really the types of questions that should be addressed during the earliest phase of the project.

This is why the key in the integrated process is to integrate the whole project team early in order to develop an efficient project design and allow the project team to discover strategies. Taking actions late in the process only results in delays and additional costs.

IMPORTANCE OF THE PROJECT'S LOCATION

Most of the questions from the previous topic depend on the project's location. To turn the project goals into reality, a strong evaluation of the project location is mandatory. The project location should assist the project teams rather than creating challenges.

The preferred sequence is to set the project goals first and then choose the location that best fits those goals. If the sequencing is reversed, project teams still need to discover ways to establish project goals; however, they can also face more problems.

Understanding the whole community is essential for successful project integration. If people need to drive single-occupancy vehicles to commute to a building, the project will generate more greenhouse gas emissions. The climate in the project location is another factor, since it will impact all the building systems. The soil type will also change according to the location, and that soil type will affect the whole structural calculation of the building and lead to changes in the whole structural design. (For instance, with weak soil, a building can need a deep foundation; however, this may not be the case with other types of soil.)

Even the level of the underground water for a particular location can make a huge impact on the design and construction of the basement levels and the building as a whole. When evaluating the site, the project teams should work with experts such as engineers, hydrologists, ecologists, and project development consultants. Evaluating zoning and local codes, International Code Council (ICC) standards, Americans with Disabilities Act (ADA) requirements, and all other regulations at that location during the beginning of the project is also essential. Most of the mentioned laws and regulations will depend on the project's location, and they will take precedence over LEED requirements. For example, zoning and local codes—not LEED—will determine the building height, type of project to be constructed, size, and minimum parking requirements for a particular location.

ITERATIVE PROCESS

In the integrated process, the ideas are developed by the all members of the project teams. With the discovery of an idea, smaller groups are assigned to research and refine the topic, and then the idea is brought back to the table for all members to make the final decision. Hence an iterative process exists that contains lots of feedback loops in order to establish a working system.

Below is a list of stages for the iterative process:

- Establish clear goals.
- Brainstorm and develop creative and effective solutions.
- Research and refine ideas.
- Explore synergies between different strategies.
- Establish metrics to measure success.
- Set new goals based on the work that has been done.

This approach is unlike the conventional building approach, in which a project team member completes a work individually and then passes it to the next person (which is called **a linear approach**.) To establish an integrative process, it is useful to conduct different types of meetings. Such meetings would include charrettes, team meetings, small task groups, and stakeholder meetings (charrettes are intense workshops that are generally held in the beginning of a project and during project milestones).

TEAM SELECTION

The outcome of the project will depend on the professionals working on the project and the system created. Team members with green building knowledge and experience will make a big impact on the results. LEED Green Associate and LEED Accredited Professional credentials can be sought in team members to ensure adequate knowledge.

The duty of a LEED AP project team member is to support and encourage integrated design and to streamline the LEED application and certification process. A LEED Green Associate team member will have the general knowledge of green building practices and will provide support to other project team members. If there are inexperienced people on the team, it will be necessary to provide training and orientation.

PHASES OF THE INTEGRATED PROCESS

The whole integrated process can be summarized by three main phases:

1. **Discovery phase**: This is the most important phase, which also includes predesign to ensure green building goals are set early and cost-effectively. The risks are identified, and the triple bottom line (economic prosperity, social responsibility, and environmental stewardship) of the project is assessed. A system is created that enables the efficient collaboration of every participant in the project. The location of the project is well chosen, and applicable codes and standards are evaluated. The level of LEED certification desired and its requirements are thoroughly considered in this phase. Life-cycle costing,

life-cycle assessment, and computer modeling of the project are used to evaluate different strategies and alternatives.

2. **Design and construction phase**: The system continues to work, and charrettes, team meetings, small task groups, and stakeholder meetings are continuously conducted. Necessary actions required to protect the construction workers, building occupants, neighborhood, and surrounding environment from construction pollution are taken. The green building goals are turned into reality, with the exception of maintaining them throughout the whole life cycle of the building. All the requirements for LEED certification are documented. The project team conducts both the training and orientation of the building operations personnel.

3. **Occupancy, operations, and performance feedback phase**: The performance of all the building systems should be checked throughout the lifetime of the building. The data that the building systems provide are monitored and evaluated. Orientation and training of the building personnel and occupants are conducted repeatedly as tenants and personnel change and new lessons are learned. Building occupants are educated about the green features of the building and sustainable practices. Continuous feedback from all the building users and personnel is received, and the system continues for the whole life of the building.

Integrative Project Planning and Design—Prerequisite

■ Applicable to: **Healthcare**

PREREQUISITE SUMMARY

Hospitals throughout the world are known to consume much more energy and water per square foot than average buildings, and they make a serious contribution to greenhouse gas emissions. In addition, hospitals are the most critical facilities for serving and improving human health. That being said, planning and design of hospitals should require different principles than other building types. Utilizing an integrative process in healthcare projects should be mandatory rather than a choice, and making such a process mandatory is the main goal of this prerequisite.

The prerequisite forces project teams to implement an integrative process for the project planning and design phases of healthcare projects, and it encourages optimization of green strategies across all aspects of design, construction, and building operations with the commitment of all members of the project team, including the owner's representative. In order to fulfill the prerequisite, an owner's project requirements (OPR) should be developed, and a health mission statement should be created (which should also address the triple bottom line) to be incorporated into the OPR. Moreover, the project teams should conduct a preliminary LEED meeting to set the preliminary rating goals, preferably <u>before the schematic design phase</u>.

The project teams should also determine the level of LEED certification to be pursued and LEED credits to be met, and they should identify the responsible parties that will oversee meeting the LEED prerequisites and credits.

Next, the project teams should assemble the integrated process team, and preferably before the schematic design phase, conduct a minimum of four hours of design charrette with the involvement of the owner, or owner's representative. To reinforce knowledge, let's describe what a "charrette" is.

Charrettes are intense workshops that are generally held in the beginning of a project and during project milestones. These workshops bring together the entire project team, facility manager, and all the stakeholders and outside experts/consultants. (The facility manager is the person who will be responsible for running the operations of the buildings after the completion of construction.) Charrettes allow brainstorming and collaboration among different disciplines and experiences. An agenda and list of project goals are discussed in charrettes in order to make important decisions and agree on project goals. With brainstorming and collaboration of the teams' members, charrettes also allow the discovery of new project goals. Since charrettes are highly structured, a facilitator is recommended when conducting charrettes.

Below are the typical stages of a charrette:

- Background briefing: To make sure all participants have the basic information about the project and the topics that will be discussed
- Brainstorming
- Synthesis of work: Discussion of concerns and development of recommendations
- Initial response from the owner or the developer about the discussed strategies and goals
- Follow up: A written report stating the identified actions that should be sent to all participants

With the charrette, the project team will be encouraged to find more innovative ways for approaching design and construction.

To become familiar with the integrative process, project teams are encouraged to review the **ANSI Consensus National Standard Guide 2.0 for Design and Construction of Sustainable Buildings and Communities**, both for this prerequisite and for the "Integrative Process" credit, which is also important to know for exam purposes.

As being the only prerequisite under the "Integrative Process" credit category, Integrative Project Planning and Design is only applicable to the "LEED BD+C: Healthcare" projects. It is important not to confuse this prerequisite with the next credit, which is the "Integrative Process" credit, which is applicable to all the LEED BD+C rating systems, including healthcare.

💡 For exam purposes, knowing which prerequisites and credits apply to certain rating systems is essential. Once you've finished reading the book, go through the appendices to see the summary of applicable rating systems for each prerequisite and credit. However, the best way to study for this exam is to thoroughly understand the prerequisites/credits and try to avoid memorization. This way, a test taker will naturally feel the corresponding rating system for each prerequisite and credit and also apply those principles in real life more effectively. Since most of the prerequisites and credits mentioned in the book apply to all the LEED BD+C rating systems, while reading the book, it's much easier to watch out for the ones that do not apply to all the rating systems and really question the idea behind every prerequisite and credit. For example, the "Interior Lighting" credit that will be discussed in a later chapter requires projects to provide lighting controls, and it sets thresholds for lighting quality and aims to increase occupant productivity and well-being. The credit applies to all the LEED BD+C rating systems except "LEED BD+C: Core and Shell." Since the scope of the core and shell projects do not cover the tenant interior fit-out work, why would the credit award point(s) to the core and shell projects?

PREREQUISITE INTENT

Maximizing opportunities for integrated, cost-effective green design and construction strategies. Emphasizing human health as a fundamental evaluative criterion for building design, construction and operational strategies. Implementing innovative approaches and techniques for green design and construction.

💡 Being able to distinguish the "intent" of each prerequisite and credit is essential for exam purposes. Be aware that the intent of some of the prerequisites and credits may seem very similar and can be hard to distinguish.

PREREQUISITE REQUIREMENTS

Beginning in the <u>programming</u> and <u>predesign phase</u>, at a minimum, project teams should implement the following processes to address the owner's project requirement documents, preliminary rating goals, integrated project teams, and design charrette:

Owner's Project Requirements Document:

Projects should prepare the owner's project requirements (OPR) and a health mission statement to be incorporated into the OPR. The triple bottom line should be addressed by the health mission statement, and all the goals and strategies to protect the health of building occupants, the community, and the environment should be evaluated while creating the documents.

Preliminary Rating Goals:

Preferably before the schematic design phase, project teams should conduct a preliminary LEED meeting with a minimum of four key members and the owner or owner's representative to create a **LEED action plan**. During the meeting, project teams should at a minimum accomplish the following:

- Determine the level of LEED certification to pursue (Silver or Platinum?)
- Select the LEED credits to earn the desired level of LEED certification
- Identify responsible parties to oversee the LEED requirements for each prerequisite and credit

Integrated Project Team:

Projects should assemble the integrated project teams, which should include the following professionals (as many as are feasible, but the number cannot be fewer than four members) in addition to the owner or owner's representative:

- Architect or building designer, facility managers, construction manager, general contractor, owner's capital budget manager, green building or sustainable design consultants, facility green teams, environmental services staff, civil engineer, mechanical engineer, functional and space programmers, structural engineer, commissioning agent, energy modeler, community representatives, equipment planner, acoustical consultant, landscape architect, telecommunications designer, ecologist, controls designer, land planner, food service consultant, infection control staff, life-cycle cost analyst, construction cost estimator, lighting designer, physician and nursing teams, and other disciplines necessary to the project type.

Design Charrette:

As early as possible, preferably before the schematic design, projects should conduct, at a minimum, a **four-hour charrette** that includes as many of the previously described professionals as feasible. The main goal of the charrette should be to optimize the integration of green strategies across all aspects and disciplines of building design.

Projects starting the process after the predesign are still eligible to earn the prerequisite, but this prerequisite's requirements should be completed as early as possible.

> 📄 To document this prerequisite, project teams should submit a narrative about how the health mission statement addresses the prerequisite requirements, and they should submit the LEED action plan.

> 💡 During the exam, it is possible to get questions about documenting prerequisites and credits. However, again, the best way to study for this exam is to thoroughly understand the prerequisites/credits and try to avoid memorization. After reading the prerequisite/credit requirements, you will find it very helpful to match the required documentation with the prerequisite/credit requirements. For this prerequisite, creating a LEED action plan is a requirement, and from the GBCI's perspective, there is no way to confirm that the project really fulfilled this requirement without documentation of that LEED action plan. Also, without a narrative demonstrating how a health mission statement corresponds with the prerequisite requirements, it would be impossible for the GBCI to evaluate the work done. That is the top reason that so many prerequisites/credits will require a narrative for their documentation.

KEY THINGS TO REMEMBER

- This prerequisite addresses four main sections: "owner's project requirements documents," "preliminary rating goals," "integrated project teams," and the "design charrette."
- Project teams are advised to review the **ANSI Consensus National Standard Guide 2.0 for Design and Construction of Sustainable Buildings and Communities** to implement a successful integrative process.
- Preferably before the schematic design phase, project teams should conduct a preliminary LEED meeting with a minimum of four key members of project team member and the owner or owner's representative to create a **LEED action plan** and address preliminary rating goals.

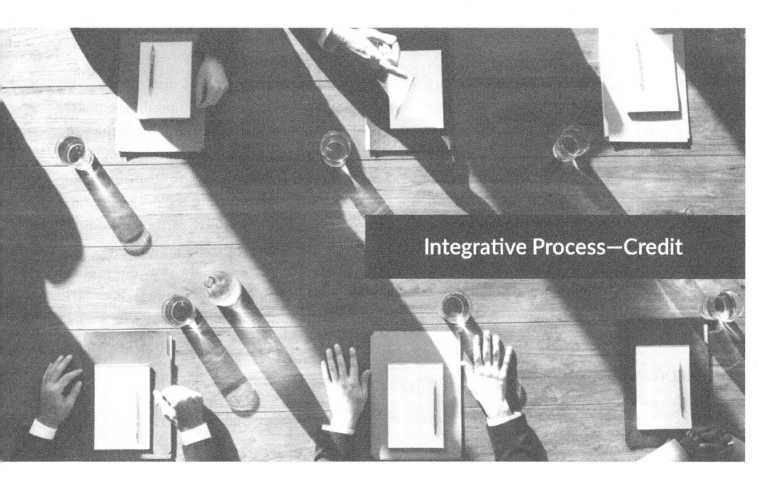

Integrative Process—Credit

■ Applicable to: All the LEED BD+C Rating Systems

New Construction	1 point	Retail	1 point	Hospitality	1 - 5 points
Core and Shell	1 point	Data Centers	1 point	Healthcare	1 - 5 points
Schools	1 point	Warehouses & Dist. Centers	1 point		

CREDIT SUMMARY

Integrative process, which is a major concept of sustainable thinking, emphasizes the importance of connection and communication among all the professionals and stakeholders in the project. Consider the human lung, which is made of lots of cells. However, when the cells are put together, without the whole system in place, these cells cannot perform the breathing function of the lung. Without a working system, an emergent property cannot be created.

As discussed, assembling the project owner, key stakeholders, architects, civil engineers, and mechanical and electrical engineers will not create a successful project; rather, a system should be formed that incorporates flow of information and collaboration between each member for each phase of the project.

This credit encourages the coordination of all the project team members, starting from the predesign phase, to discover unique opportunities for project design, enhanced building performance, and green features.

In order to earn this credit, project teams need to conduct preliminary research and analysis for the <u>energy-</u> and <u>water-related systems</u> of the building, starting from the predesign phase. Project teams also need to evaluate the possible energy and water strategies to achieve the project's goals and the targeted LEED credits. This really means brainstorming and value engineering the energy- and water-related building systems beforehand to not only avoid encountering unforeseen conditions but also to find the most effective solutions meeting the project's goals. Next, there is the implementation phase, which requires the project teams to turn their findings into reality.

In order to implement a successful integrative process, this credit (and the previous prerequisite), recommends that project teams review the **ANSI Consensus National Standard 2.0 for Design and Construction of Sustainable Buildings and Communities**.

CREDIT INTENT

Support high-performance, cost-effective project outcomes through an early analysis of the interrelationships among building systems.

CREDIT REQUIREMENTS

Starting from the **predesign phase** and continuing throughout all the design phases, project teams should implement an integrative process to enable project teams to discover unique opportunities for enhancing project performance and environmental benefits. In other words, the project teams should identify and use opportunities to achieve synergies across disciplines and building systems.

Project teams should perform the following analyses for both **energy-** and **water-related systems** in what we will call the "discovery" phase. And with these findings, project teams should inform the owner's project requirements (OPR), basis of design (BOD), and design and construction documents in what we call the "implementation" phase. (BOD describes the information necessary to accomplish the owner's project requirements, which includes system requirements, design criteria, standards, guidelines, etc. The BOD is developed by the architect or engineer.)

1. Energy related systems:

Discovery phase:

Before completing the schematic design, project teams should perform a **"simple box" energy modeling** that will enable the project teams to see the approximate energy usage of the building and evaluate strategies on how to reduce the energy use by questioning the default assumptions. A simple box energy modeling is a preliminary building model used to analyze the building's energy loads. Project teams can use the EPA's Target Finder tool or a similar tool in order to benchmark energy performance. Target Finder allows projects to set target goals for a building design's energy demands. And according to the enhancements in the design, project teams can see the savings in energy demand.

Project teams should assess **at least two strategies** related with each of the following:

- Site conditions: Evaluate shading, exterior lighting, landscaping, hardscape, and adjacent site conditions.

- Massing and orientation: Evaluate and optimize the massing and orientation effect on the HVAC (heating, ventilation, and air-conditioning) sizing, energy consumption, lighting, and renewable energy opportunities. Evaluate the number of floors, building footprint, and configuration.

- Basic envelope attributes: Evaluate the wall and roof insulation values, thermal mass, glazing characteristics, window-to-wall ratios, shading, and window operability.

- Lighting levels: Evaluate interior surface reflectance values, lighting needs and levels in the occupied spaces, daylighting, high-efficiency lighting fixtures, and controls.

- Thermal comfort ranges: Evaluate thermal comfort range options and thermal comfort parameters.

- Plug and process load needs: Evaluate reducing plug and process loads through programmatic solutions, such as equipment and purchasing policies, layout options, and more.

- Programmatic and operational parameters: Evaluate multifunctioning spaces, space allotment per person, operating schedules, reduction of building area, and anticipated operations and maintenance.

One possible strategy might be to change the building's base location orientation in order to get more sunlight to the interior spaces so that the lighting energy loads can be reduced.

Or the envelope of the building can be optimized according to the project's location in order to reduce the HVAC loads. And while the project teams look for ways to improve the project performance, they also need to consider strategies of how to achieve the corresponding LEED credits.

Implementation phase:

Lastly, project teams should document how these analyses and findings informed the project's OPR, BOD, and design, including the following as applicable:

- Building and site program
- Building form and geometry
- Building envelope and facade specifications on different orientations
- Elimination and/or significant downsizing of building systems (e.g., lighting controls, HVAC, etc.)
- Other systems

2. Water related systems:

Discovery phase:

Similar to the "simple box" energy modeling, which shows the building's energy demand, projects should this time perform a **preliminary water budget analysis** before completing the schematic design and calculate the project's water demand volume. Next, project teams should look for strategies for reducing the potable water consumption, including assessment of the nonpotable water sources. Project teams should evaluate all of the following:

- Indoor water demand: Evaluate the design demand volumes of the flow and flush fixtures in accordance with the "Indoor Water Use Reduction" prerequisite (which will be discussed in the following chapters).
- Outdoor water demand: Evaluate landscape irrigation demand volume in accordance with the "Outdoor Water Use Reduction" prerequisite (which will be discussed in the following chapters).
- Process water demand: Evaluate the cooling tower, laundry, kitchen and laundry equipment, and other equipment-process, water-demand volumes, as applicable.
- Supply sources: Evaluate all the potential nonpotable water sources that can be used to reduce potable water usage such as on-site rainwater graywater, municipally supplied nonpotable water, HVAC equipment condensate, and more.

The credit requires projects to find at least one nonpotable water source and reduce the burden on the municipality-supplied water or wastewater treatment systems by contributing **to at least two** of the water demand components listed above.

For example, the project teams can decide to install a graywater system and use the captured rainwater as a portion of the irrigation water and toilet water.

<u>Implementation phase</u>:

Lastly, project teams should document how these analyses and findings informed the project's OPR, BOD, and design, including the following as applicable:

- Plumbing systems
- Sewage conveyance and/or on-site treatment systems
- Rainwater quantity and quality management systems
- Landscaping, irrigation, and site elements
- Roofing systems and/or building form and geometry
- Other systems

With the completion of the preliminary energy and water research and analysis, the credit requires project teams to conduct a **goal-setting workshop** to identify the <u>targeted LEED credits</u>, identify <u>performance targets</u>, share the findings that were previously found, and identify initial responsibilities. Next, the project teams can effectively proceed with evaluating the agreed-upon project goals by exploring strategies.

As will be discussed in the following chapters, LEED has other credits tied to the energy- and water-related system items mentioned previously. For example, the "Indoor Water Use Reduction" credit will enable the project teams to earn points in accordance with the percentage of potable water reduction they establish. If a project team decides to pursue this credit, a preliminary water budget analysis will be a good starting point to evaluate all the alternatives for reducing the building's potable water demand. In addition, by implementing the integrative process, the project owner will also be informed about the suggested changes while the owner's project requirements (OPR), basis of design (BOD), design documents, and construction documents can be adjusted accordingly.

> Projects should document the "Integrative Process" worksheet. The elements of the "Integrative Process" worksheet are as mentioned under the credit requirements under the "Implementation" phases.

EXEMPLARY PERFORMANCE

This credit does not qualify for exemplary performance.

> 💡 During the exam, expect to see questions about exemplary performance requirements of eligible credits. Before the exam, it is strongly recommended to go through the "exemplary performance" section of each credit.

KEY THINGS TO REMEMBER

- Project teams are advised to review the **ANSI Consensus National Standard Guide 2.0 for Design and Construction of Sustainable Buildings and Communities** to implement a successful integrative process, both for this credit and the previous "Integrative Project Planning and Design" prerequisite.
- Under the requirements for the energy-related systems, projects should evaluate site conditions, massing and orientation, basic envelope attributes, lighting levels, thermal comfort ranges, and plug and process load needs. (Project teams need to assess at least two strategies under each category.)
- Under the requirements for water-related systems, projects should evaluate indoor water demand, outdoor water demand, process water demand, and supply sources. (Project teams need to assess all of the mentioned strategies under each category.)
- Project teams should find at least one nonpotable water source on-site and reduce the burden on the municipality-supplied water or wastewater treatment systems by contributing **to at least two** of the water-demand components listed in the credit requirements.

CHAPTER 4

LOCATION AND TRANSPORTATION (LT)

This chapter will discuss the importance of location and the transportation features of the building and their effects on the green building design.

The location of a green building project should first promote smart growth, which refers to the approach that protects undeveloped lands and contributes to developments in projects near jobs, schools, shops, and other destination points with diverse uses. An example would be a residential project located very close to a downtown with several public transportation options. On the other hand, a residential project in a suburban area that requires driving many commuting miles to a downtown area would not contribute to smart growth, and that project would be considered to be supporting suburban sprawl.

To discourage suburban sprawl, we should pay special attention to the neighborhood pattern and design. A healthy neighborhood should contain wide sidewalks and bicycle networks. Business centers, retail services, educational facilities, and other diverse uses should be close enough to minimize travel. Public transportation options should be easily accessible. Street layouts should allow for easy connectivity, and if community gardens, farmers markets, and agricultural programs are established, a neighborhood would also be able to support access to sustainable food.

The aforementioned strategies are also a part of compact development strategies, which promote efficient neighborhoods and reduce greenhouse gas emissions.

To promote smart growth, some municipalities offer increased floor-to-area ratios (FAR) in urban areas. The floor-to-area ratio is also a very important term for the exam, and it is calculated by dividing the total square feet of a building by the total square feet of the lot of the building. For example, 10,000 square feet of land that has a FAR of 2 would allow the construction of a 20,000-square-foot building. If the building had two stories, each story could contain 10,000 square feet of space. In this case, the building would cover the whole lot since the lot also measured 10,000 square feet. (These types of buildings, which are built on the entire lot, are called zero-lot-line projects.)

Another 10,000 square feet of land that had a FAR of 1 would allow construction of a 10,000-square-foot building. Again, if the building had two stories and each story contained 5,000 square feet of space, then the remaining 5,000 square feet of the lot could contain parking or landscaping. Hence, a higher FAR allows for more building space and a denser development.

Protecting the habitat should be a major goal of a green building, and protecting the habitat also depends on the project's location. To protect the habitat, green buildings should not be developed inside sensitive lands; instead, infill sites should be preferred. Infill sites, or infill developments, are sites that were either previously developed or were already being used for other purposes in urban areas. An example of an infill site would be a project location at a parking lot downtown. Or it could be at the site of a demolished building. Since infill sites have existing infrastructure and also have public transportation options, locating the project at an infill site would not create the negative consequences of suburban sprawl.

Another key component of LEED is transportation. It accounts for 50% of a typical project's total greenhouse gas emissions and 33% of greenhouse gas emissions in the United States, according to the US Energy Information Administration.[1] The transportation sector is also responsible for about one-quarter of energy-related greenhouse gas emissions globally.[2]

A project should reduce the consequences of transportation by ensuring access to alternative modes of transportation to reduce single-occupancy vehicle use; by encouraging walking and bicycling; and by actively promoting alternative-fuel vehicles. For instance, projects can provide fueling facilities for the green vehicles and/or offer discounted parking.

The "Location and Transportation" credit category contains the following credits. (Note that this credit category does not contain any prerequisite.):

- LEED for Neighborhood Development Location—Credit
- Sensitive Land Protection—Credit
- High-Priority Site—Credit
- Surrounding Density and Diverse Uses—Credit
- Access to Quality Transit—Credit
- Bicycle Facilities—Credit
- Reduced Parking Footprint—Credit
- Green Vehicles—Credit

DOCUMENTING LOCATION AND TRANSPORTATION CREDITS

Before diving into the credits, it is essential to mention the rules that need to be considered for credit compliance under this credit category. Related credit documentation and calculations should be prepared with the following considerations:

Calculations for walking and bicycling distances:

Some credits in the LT credit category require calculations of the walking and bicycling distances to a destination, such as the "Surrounding Density and Diverse Uses" credit or the "Bicycle Facilities" credit.

Walking and bicycling distances are measurements to show how far a pedestrian and bicyclist would travel to a destination such as the nearest grocery store.

The walking distance, also called the **shortest path analysis**, must be measured along infrastructure that is safe and comfortable for pedestrians (such as sidewalks and crosswalks). And cycling distances must be measured along infrastructure that is safe and comfortable for cyclists (such as bicycle lanes, off-street bicycle paths, etc.).

When calculating these distances for both walking and bicycling, the sum of the continuous segments of the route will give the total distance from the origin to the destination. A straight-line radius that does not follow safe pedestrian and bicyclist infrastructure will not be accepted.

All the walking and bicycling distances should be available to all building users in order for the project to be eligible for credit compliance.

Calculations for total vehicle parking capacity:

Some credits in the LT credit category require calculations of total vehicle parking capacity, such as the "Reduced Parking Footprint" credit or the "Green Vehicles" credit.

The following parking spaces must be included in total parking capacity:
- New and existing surface parking spaces
- New and existing garage or multilevel parking spaces
- Any off-street parking spaces both inside and outside of the project boundary that serve the building users

The following parking spaces should not be included in total parking capacity:
- Public on-street parking spaces
- Parking spaces assigned to fleet and inventory vehicles (unless these vehicles are used by employees for commuting as well as business purposes)
- Motorbike or bicycle spaces

If there are shared parking spaces among two or more buildings (which is also called pooled parking), then the project's share in the parking spaces should be included in the calculations.

If there isn't any parking area assigned to the project, the project will be awarded the "Reduced Parking Footprint" credit; however, such a situation would not merit the award of the "Green Vehicles" credit.

Calculations for preferred parking:

Some credits in the LT credit category, such as the "Reduced Parking Footprint" credit or the "Green Vehicles" credit, require projects to assign preferred parking locations for particular vehicles. When determining the preferred parking locations, project teams should consider the following requirements:

First, the preferred parking spaces should have the shortest walking distance to the main entrance of the project (exclusive of spaces designated for people with disabilities).

If parking is provided in a multilevel facility, the preferred spaces should be located on the level that is closest to the **main entrance** of the building. If there are different parking areas for different kinds of building users (customer parking, staff parking, etc.), then a project either can distribute the required preferred parking spaces proportionally across each different type of parking area, or it can provide one general preferred parking zone with enough parking space for all user types and can still separate the remaining parking spaces by user type.

The "Reduced Parking Footprint" credit requires projects to assign preferred parking locations to carpool or vanpool vehicles, while the "Green Vehicles" credit requires projects to assign preferred parking locations to green vehicles. Projects pursuing both credits will need to provide a higher number of preferred parking spaces. And when locating these parking spaces, it is up to the project teams to decide whether to place the "green vehicles" preferred parking closer to the main entrance or the "carpool" preferred parking closer to the main entrance. Some project teams may locate the green vehicles' preferred parking spaces closer to the main entrance and locate the carpool vehicles' preferred parking spaces next to them. Other project teams may decide to do the opposite.

Finally, projects pursuing both the "Reduced Parking Footprint" credit and the "Green Vehicles" credit can also combine the signage that indicates preferred parking locations—if that's needed.

LEED for Neighborhood Development Location—Credit

■ Applicable to: All the LEED BD+C Rating Systems

New Construction	8 - 16 points	Retail	8 - 16 points	Hospitality	8 - 16 points
Core and Shell	8 - 20 points	Data Centers	8 - 16 points	Healthcare	5 - 9 points
Schools	8 - 15 points	Warehouses & Dist. Centers	8 - 16 points		

CREDIT SUMMARY

The LEED for Neighborhood Development (LEED ND) rating system is designed to provide smart growth and promote sustainability in neighborhoods. And if a LEED BD+C project is located inside one of those LEED ND certified sites, the project will receive points under this credit.

The points will be awarded according to the located land's level of LEED ND certification (see table 1 for point distribution). For example, if the project is inside a LEED ND Platinum site, the project will get full points from this credit.

Since a project located inside the boundaries of LEED ND-certified land will mostly cover the goals of the other "Location and Transportation" credits, projects pursuing this credit will not be eligible to receive any other LT credits. This is also the reason why this credit contains lots of points. However, if the project teams see that they can earn more total points from the other LT credits, then they should pursue those credits instead of this credit.

CREDIT INTENT

To avoid development on inappropriate sites, to encourage the reduction of vehicles miles traveled, and to encourage the enhancement of livability and improvement of human health by spurring daily physical activity.

CREDIT REQUIREMENTS

In order to be eligible for this credit, the project has to be located inside a boundary of one of the following:

a. LEED ND Pilot—Stage 2 LEED for Neighborhood Development Certified Plan
b. LEED ND Pilot—Stage 3 LEED for Neighborhood Development Certified Project
c. LEED 2009—Stage 2 Precertified LEED for Neighborhood Development Plan
d. LEED 2009—Stage 3 LEED ND Certified Neighborhood Development
e. LEED v4—LEED for Neighborhood Development Certified Plan
f. LEED v4—LEED for Neighborhood Development Certified Built Project

If the project is inside the boundary of any of the following sites, no points will be awarded under this credit:

a. LEED ND Pilot—Stage 1 LEED for Neighborhood Development Prereviewed Plan
b. LEED 2009—Stage 1 Conditional Approval of LEED ND Plan
c. LEED v4—LEED for Neighborhood Development Conditional Approval

Basically, the LEED ND sites need to be <u>Stage 2</u> or <u>Stage 3</u> under the LEED Pilot or LEED 2009 rating systems or <u>Certified Plan</u> or <u>Certified Project</u> under the LEED v4 rating system. Conditional approvals or prereviewed LEED ND sites will not earn the credit.

To locate a LEED ND site, project teams can check the USGBC's website, local chapters in the United States, or other green building councils located in other countries. The following table shows the points that will be awarded for locating the project inside a LEED ND site.

	LEED ND Certified	LEED ND Silver	LEED ND Gold	LEED ND Platinum
BD+C	8 points	10 points	12 points	16 points
BD+C Core and Shell	8 points	12 points	16 points	20 points
BD+C Schools	8 points	10 points	12 points	15 points
BD+C Healthcare	5 points	6 points	7 points	9 points

Table 1. Points awarded for locating a project inside an LEED ND site

Project teams, should also consider the certification timelines of the LEED BD+C project, and the associated LEED ND project. Note that the LEED ND site that the project is located on should have achieved the LEED ND certification in order to earn this credit. The following are the certification timelines of the LEED BD+C project and the LEED ND project:

- If the neighborhood project that the LEED BD+C project is located on is certifying to LEED ND, both certifications need to be submitted at approximately the same time since each depends on the certification of the other.
- If the associated neighborhood project is certifying to a LEED ND Plan, and the building designs that are located on that neighborhood project are substantially complete, in order to streamline the application, it is recommended that project teams complete the building design review first and then complete the LEED ND Plan certification.
- If the associated neighborhood project is certifying to a LEED ND Plan, project teams should make sure to register the LEED BD+C project located in the neighborhood project before submitting the LEED ND project application.

> 📄 To document the credit, project teams should submit the LEED ND project information (name, ID number, level of certification, etc.) and a vicinity base map showing the LEED project boundary and the LEED ND certified neighborhood project or certified plan boundary.

EXEMPLARY PERFORMANCE

This credit does not qualify for exemplary performance.

KEY THINGS TO REMEMBER

- Projects pursuing this credit will not be eligible to receive any other LT credits, since a project located inside a LEED ND-certified land will mostly cover the goals of the other LT credits.
- LEED ND sites needs to be Stage 2 or Stage 3 under the Pilot or 2009 rating systems and Certified Plan or Certified Project under the LEED v4 rating system in order to gain points under this credit. Conditional approvals or pre-reviewed LEED ND sites will not earn this credit.
- Certification timelines of the LEED BD+C project and the associated LEED ND project should be known.

Sensitive Land Protection—Credit

■ Applicable to: All the LEED BD+C Rating Systems

New Construction	1 point	Retail	1 point	Hospitality	1 point
Core and Shell	2 points	Data Centers	1 point	Healthcare	1 point
Schools	1 point	Warehouses & Dist. Centers	1 point		

CREDIT SUMMARY

This credit is designed to prohibit site development in ecologically sensitive areas. Ecologically sensitive areas have a variety of benefits not only for human health but also for the environment. By locating the building's footprint on a previously developed area, ecologically sensitive areas will be saved.

If the project is located on previously developed land, it will earn the credit since the land had already lost its ecological value. However, if the land, or <u>a portion of the land</u>, has not been previously developed, then any portion of the project should not be located on any sensitive areas that are prime farmland, floodplain areas, habitat, water bodies, or wetlands in order to earn the credit.

For LEED, the term "development footprint" applies to the sum of all the areas that are affected by the project's activity in the project site. Surfaces paved with permeable pavement (at least 50% permeable) are exempt.

It is strongly recommended to go through this credit very slowly since it contains very detailed information that may be asked on the exam.

CREDIT INTENT

Avoiding development of environmentally sensitive lands and the reduction of the ecological impact from the location of a building project on a site.

CREDIT REQUIREMENTS

OPTION 1 — (1 Point)

Under this option, the development footprint must be located on previously developed land. If the development footprint or a portion of it is not located on previously developed land, project teams should pursue option 2.

> 📄 Project teams should provide documentation with site maps, indicating the project boundary, development footprint, sensitive areas, and previous development and minor improvements, and they should submit a narrative explaining the previous developments on the site.

OR

OPTION 2 — (1 Point)

If the land is not previously developed, then the development footprint or <u>a portion</u> of it should not be located on land that falls under any of the following categories:

a. **Prime farmland**: Prime farmland, unique farmland or farmland of statewide or local importance, which is defined by the "**US Department of Agriculture, United States Code of Federal Regulations** Title 7, Volume 6, Parts 400 to 699, Section 657.5", and identified in a state **Natural Resources Conservation Service (NRCS)** soil survey. If the project is located outside the United States, the project team should find a local equivalent and conduct a soil survey with an equivalent methodology to that of the NRCS to first identify the soil characteristics to compare it with the equivalent local codes.

b. **Floodplains**: The project should not be inside a <u>floor hazard area</u>—shown on a legally adopted flood hazard map—generally defined by the **Federal Emergency Management Agency (FEMA)** or local agencies. If no map exists, then the project teams should work with a hydrologist, engineer, or other qualified professional to ensure the area is not subject to 1% or greater chance of flooding in any year. Projects located outside the United States should find a local equivalent to show that the project is not inside a flood hazard area, or they can work with a professional to conduct a flood-risk assessment.

c. **Habitat**: No development can be made inside land identified as "habitat." For land to be identified as "habitat," it should meet one of the following criteria:

  ▪ It should contain species listed as threatened or endangered under the **US Endangered Species Act** or the **state's endangered species act**.

  ▪ It should contain species or ecological communities identified by **NatureServe** as GH (possibly extinct), G1 (critically imperiled), or G2 (imperiled). For international projects, a local equivalent—such as the **International Union of Conservation of Nature Red List** or something similar—should be documented.

  ▪ For projects outside the United States, the land should contain threatened or endangered species under the local equivalent code standards that are not covered by the NatureServe data. (Projects outside the United States should work with a qualified biologist or ecologist and conduct a biological survey to assess the site's status.)

d. **Water bodies**: No development can be made within **100 feet** (30 meters) of water bodies, with the exception of some minor improvements that will be specified shortly. For projects inside the United States, project teams should consult the **US Army Corps of Engineers Wetlands Delineation Manual** for guidance on delineating wetlands.

e. **Wetlands**: No development can be made within **50 feet** (15 meters) of wetlands, with the exception of some minor improvements specified below.

The following are the minor developments that are acceptable <u>within</u> water bodies and wetlands—with the requirement of <u>being available to all building users.</u> (On the exam, for any question asking for the acceptable minor developments under this credit, look first for the answer choice that is **not** available to all building users.):

  ➥ Brownfield areas can be remediated.

  ➥ Grading can be performed to allow for public access.

  ➥ Any activity to maintain or restore natural hydrology, or native natural communities can be implemented.

  ➥ Bicycle and pedestrian pathways, which can be constructed up to 12 feet wide (3.5 meters), of which no more than 8 feet (2.5 meters) can be impervious.

  ➥ One single-story structure per 300 linear feet (90 linear meters) on average, with the structure not exceeding 500 square feet (45 square meters).

- Trees that meet any of the following ratings can be removed:
  - Trees that are under 40% condition rating
  - Trees whose diameters are less than 6 inches (150 millimeters) at breast height
  - Hazardous trees
  - Up to 75% of dead trees
  - Up to 20% of the trees whose diameters are more than 6 inches (150 millimeters) at breast height, with a condition rating of 40% or higher
    The tree conditions mentioned above must be assessed by an arborist certified by the International Society of Arboriculture (ISA), and the ISA measures should be used (or a local equivalent for projects outside the United States).
- Clearings that do not exceed 500 square feet (45 square meters). This is limited to one clearing per 300 linear feet (90 linear meters) on average.

> 📄 Project teams should provide documentation with site maps showing the project boundary, development footprint, sensitive areas, previous development, and minor improvements, and project teams should submit a narrative explaining how the project teams verified the prime farmland and sensitive habitat criteria.

EXEMPLARY PERFORMANCE

This credit does not qualify for exemplary performance.

KEY THINGS TO REMEMBER

- US Department of Agriculture, United States Code of Federal Regulations Title 7, Volume 6, Parts 400 to 699, Section 657.5—defines prime farmlands
- Federal Emergency Management Agency (FEMA)—defines floodplains
- US Endangered Species Act—defines endangered/threatened species
- NatureServe—defines endangered/threatened species
- International Union for Conservation of Nature Red List—global list for endangered/threatened species
- No development can be made within **100 feet** (30 meters) of water bodies except for some minor improvements that are specified
- No development can be made within **50 feet** (15 meters) of wetlands, except for some minor improvements that are specified

- Acceptable minor developments within water bodies and wetlands must be available to **all building users**
- Types of acceptable minor developments that can be made within water bodies and wetlands

High Priority Site—Credit

■ Applicable to: All the LEED BD+C Rating Systems

New Construction	1 – 2 points	Retail	1 – 2 points	Hospitality	1 – 2 points
Core and Shell	2 – 3 points	Data Centers	1 – 2 points	Healthcare	1 – 2 points
Schools	1 – 2 points	Warehouses & Dist. Centers	1 – 2 points		

CREDIT SUMMARY

Just like the "Sensitive Land Protection" credit, this credit aims to preserve greenfields and ecologically sensitive lands; however, with this credit the requirements are different. To encourage development in high-priority areas, this credit requires a project to be developed either on an infill location inside a historic district, inside one of the high-priority development areas determined by communities and governments, or in a brownfield site that needs to be remediated before use.

Locating the project inside a historic district would promote redevelopment of the historic district. Locating the project inside one of the high-priority development areas would promote the improvement of a socially and economically depressed neighborhood, and locating the project in a brownfield would promote the recovery of a polluted site and provide lots of benefits to the environment.

CREDIT INTENT

To encourage the project location inside areas with development constraints and to promote the health of the surrounding area.

CREDIT REQUIREMENTS

OPTION 1: HISTORIC DISTRICT — (1 Point)

Under this option, the project site must be located on an infill location inside a historic district. For a piece of land to be qualified as an infill site, **at least 75% of the land should be already developed within a half mile (800 meters) of the project boundary.** After confirming the infill status, project teams should confirm that the land is inside a "historic district," which should be identified by the historic preservation entity that designates local historic districts.

> 📄 Project teams should provide documentation with a vicinity map showing the previously developed land within a half mile (800 meters) of the project boundary, and they should submit a statement from a historic preservation entity that confirms the project is located inside a historic district.

OR

OPTION 2: PRIORITY DESIGNATION — (1 Point)

Under this option, the project site must be located in one of the following priority development areas:

- A site listed by EPA National Priorities List
- A Federal Empowerment Zone site
- A Federal Enterprise Community site
- A Federal Renewal Community site
- A site within a Department of the Treasury Community Development Financial Institutions Fund Qualified Low-Income Community (a subset of the New Markets Tax Credit Program)
- A site in a US Department of Housing and Urban Development's Qualified Census Tract (QCT) or Difficult Development Area (DDA)
- For projects outside the United States, sites that meet the same types of specifications of a local equivalent program administered at the national level

The project can earn this credit under this option even if a portion of the project site is inside a high-priority designated area.

📄 Project teams should provide documentation with a vicinity map or other documentation that confirms the priority site designation.

OR

OPTION 3: BROWNFIELD REMEDIATION — (2 Points)

To pursue this option, the project site must be located on a brownfield and identified with soil or groundwater contamination, and the local, state, or national authority must require remediation at this site. (Asbestos or other contaminants do not count as contamination.) **Project teams pursuing this option should remediate the brownfield to the satisfaction of the oversight authority**, and since remediation is a long process, projects that have not been able to complete remediation at the time of LEED certification will still earn the credit. Projects pursuing this option will qualify even if a portion of the site is contaminated.

In order to identify contamination, project teams need to conduct a **Phase I** or **Phase II Environmental Site Assessment** (or a local equivalent for projects outside the United States) or consult a biologist or environmental scientist. A Phase I Environmental Site Assessment (ESA) is a survey to identify potential or existing site contamination, and it generally includes reviewing the historical records, a site visit for visually identifying any sign of contamination, and a narrative that indicates whether a Phase II ESA is required. A Phase II ESA covers the testing of the on-site soil, groundwater, and more, and it determines how much contamination exists on-site. A Phase III ESA is the first step for the remediation process, and it covers the evaluation of the remediation options and costs. That being said, project teams that are sure about site contamination can directly conduct a Phase III ESA after the Phase I ESA, therefore skipping the Phase II ESA.

Once the contamination is confirmed, the project team should obtain a declaration from the authority having jurisdiction and complete remediation to the satisfaction of that authority.

If the project site is already assessed and remediated, the project can earn the credit by submitting complete documentation.

📄 Project teams should document a declaration from the authority that indicates the existence of site contamination, and they should submit confirmation stating that the remediation has been completed to the authority's satisfaction.

💡 For exam purposes, it is very important to know the titles of the options for the prerequisites/credits if those options are named. (The options under the "Sensitive Land Protection" credit are not named.) It is also very important to know the relationships between the options. For this credit, any question regarding one of the three options can be asked by naming the title of the options. In this case, those names are "Historic District," "Priority Designation," and "Brownfield Remediation." Project teams will choose one of them since the options are separated by an "OR." Only for exemplary performance (see below) can projects pursue more than one option. However, in some credits, pursuing more than one option can bring additional points, and in those instances the options are separated by an "AND/OR." It is recommended that you know the path that project teams can pursue to get maximum points out of a credit.

EXEMPLARY PERFORMANCE

To qualify for exemplary performance under this credit, project teams need to pursue option 2 or option 3 in addition to option 1. Any other combinations will not result in an award of an exemplary performance point.

KEY THINGS TO REMEMBER

- For a piece of land to be qualified as an infill site, at least 75% of the land should be already developed within a half mile (800 meters) of the project boundary.
- US Environmental Protection Agency, National Priority List—defines National Priority sites.
- US Housing and Urban Development—defines Federal Empowerment Zone, Federal Enterprise Community, and Federal Renewal Community.
- US Department of the Treasury, Community Development Financial Institutions Fund—provides funds for low-income communities.
- Project teams pursuing option 2 can qualify their project even if a portion of the project site is inside a high-priority designated area.
- Project teams pursuing option 3 can qualify their project even if a portion of the site is contaminated.
- Project teams pursuing option 3 should remediate the brownfield to the satisfaction of the authority having jurisdiction.

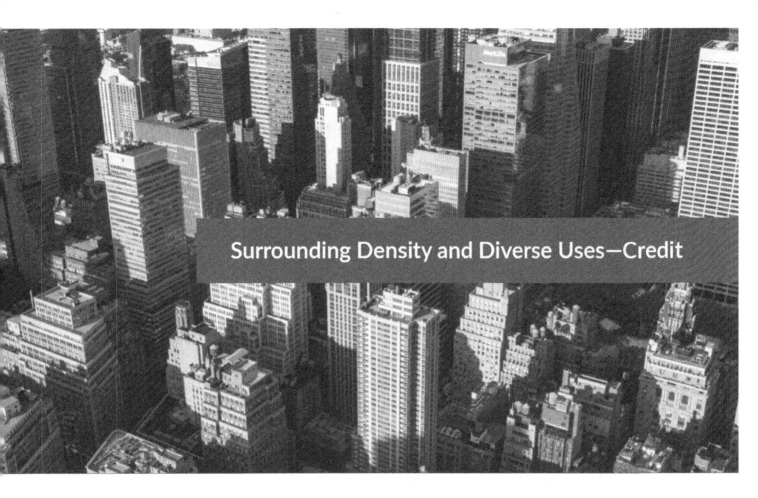

Surrounding Density and Diverse Uses—Credit

■ Applicable to: All the LEED BD+C Rating Systems

New Construction	1 – 5 points	Retail	1 – 5 points	Hospitality	1 – 5 points
Core and Shell	1 – 6 points	Data Centers	1 – 5 points	Healthcare	1 point
Schools	1 – 5 points	Warehouses & Dist. Centers	1 – 5 points		

CREDIT SUMMARY

A project located inside existing built density and/or which is at a walkable distance to diverse uses such as banks, restaurants, supermarkets, etc., has great benefits for both the project users and the environment since such a project will also contribute to compact development. Increasing the residential and nonresidential densities in an area will reduce vehicle use and consequently also reduce the air pollution and greenhouse gas emissions. Car accidents will also be less likely to occur.

In addition, this credit will award points for projects that are located inside surrounding areas of dense development and/or are at a walking distance to diverse uses. If the project satisfies both criteria, then the total points of both options will be awarded.

As will be discussed shortly, for the "LEED BD+C: Warehouses and Distribution Centers" and the "LEED BD+C: Healthcare" projects, the credit requires different criteria.

CREDIT INTENT

To conserve land and to protect sensitive farmlands and wildlife habitat by promoting development in areas with existing infrastructure. To encourage walkability, transportation efficiency, and reduction of vehicle distance traveled. To improve people's health by encouraging daily physical activity.

CREDIT REQUIREMENTS

For all LEED BD+C projects, except "LEED BD+C: Warehouses and Distribution Centers" and "LEED BD+C: Healthcare":

OPTION 1: SURROUNDING DENSITY — (2-3 Points)

Under this option, the project site should be located so that the **quarter-mile** (400 meter) radius of the project boundary meets the values in the following table. Project teams should either use "separate residential and nonresidential densities" or the "combined density" values on the following table. (If the project teams cannot collect the density information for residential and nonresidential uses separately, they can use the combined density values.) Please note that in the following table, nonresidential density will be calculated as FAR, but residential density will be calculated according to number of dwelling units.

Combined density	Separate residential and nonresidential densities		Points (except Core and Shell)	Points for Core and Shell
Square feet per acre of buildable land	Residential density (DU/acre)	Nonresidential density (FAR)		
22,000	7	0.5	2	2
35,000	12	0.8	3	4

Table 2. Points awarded according to location density

If the quarter-mile (400 meter) radius of the project also contains mixed uses (both residential and nonresidential), projects can calculate a weighted average for them. For example, if a mixed-use building has a land area of 2 acres, and the building contains 40% residential and 60% nonresidential uses, project teams can allocate 0.8 acres to the residential density and the remaining 1.2 acres to the nonresidential density in the credit calculations.

Following is the equation that would be used to calculate combined density, which basically divides the total floor area by the total buildable land in the quarter-mile (400 meter) radius of the project site:

Combined density (ft²/acre or m²/hectare) = **Total floor area** (ft² or m²) / **Total buildable land** (acres or hectares)

Equation 1. Calculation of "combined density"

Please note that in LEED, buildable land excludes public right-of-way and any other land that is not considered buildable by the local code or other codes.

Only with regard to the "LEED BD+C: School" projects, project teams should neglect any physical education spaces (such as playgrounds or playing fields) from the development density calculations.

> 🗎 For documentation, project teams should submit the area plan or map that shows the project site and the location of residential and nonresidential buildings within a quarter mile (400 meters), and they should submit a narrative describing the previous development on the site.

AND/OR

OPTION 2: DIVERSE USES — (1-2 Points)

Under this option, the building's **main entrance** should be within a **half mile** (800 meter) <u>walking distance</u> of the main entrance of **four to seven** (1 point) or **eight or more** (2 points) existing and publicly available diverse uses, as shown on the following table.

Category of diverse use	Use type
Food retail	Supermarket
	Grocery
Community-serving retail	Convenience store
	Farmers market
	Pharmacy
	Hardware store
	Other retail
Services	Bank
	Family entertainment venue (theater)
	Gym, health club, exercise studio
	Laundry, dry cleaner
	Hair care
	Restaurant, cafe, diner
Civic and community facilities	Adult or senior care (licensed)
	Child care (licensed)
	Community or recreation center
	Cultural arts facility (museum, performing arts)
	Education facility (K—12 school, university)
	Education center, vocational school, community college
	Government office that serves public on-site
	Medical clinic or office that treats patients
	Place of worship
	Police or fire station
	Post office
	Public library
	Public park
	Social services center
Community anchor uses	Commercial office (100 or more full-time equivalent jobs)

Table 3. Diverse uses

However, there are several rules that LEED requires while counting diverse uses. First, the same type of store cannot be counted more than twice. For example, if there are four supermarkets within walking distance, they can only be counted as two diverse uses. Second, a diverse-use outlet selling products in several categories can only be counted as one diverse use.

For example, a retailer that contains a pharmacy and a supermarket within the same store cannot be counted as two diverse uses. Finally, the counted diverse uses must be present under **at least three** of the five diverse use categories shown on the left column of the previous table, exclusive of the building's primary use.

Project teams can also count the planned but currently not-operating diverse uses, but each diverse use must be active within **one year** of the date when the project accepts its initial certificate of occupancy.

As is the case with all walking-distance calculations, projects should confirm walkability on a map by the use of paths that provide a safe and comfortable environment for pedestrians and provide a continuous network of sidewalks.

> 📄 For documentation, project teams should submit the area plan or map that shows the project site, the location and type of each diverse use, and the walking routes.

For "LEED BD+C: Warehouses and Distribution Centers" projects:
The project teams have two options and can pursue either one or both of them.

In option 1, the project teams have two paths and can choose either one of them. In the first path, projects can earn points if the project site is located on a previously developed site that was used for industrial or commercial purposes. In LEED, for a site to be considered as "previously developed," a minimum of 75% of the land area should have been previously developed.

But in order to get full points under option 1, project teams need to choose the second path, which requires the construction or renovation of the project on a site that is both a previously developed site and an adjacent site. And the adjacent site must be used at the time for industrial or commercial purposes. In LEED, an "adjacent site" refers to the site having at least a continuous stretch of 25% of its boundary bordering parcels with a previously developed site. Intervening rights-of-way will not be considered a bordering parcel. (Any part of the boundary bordering a water body can be excluded from the adjacent site calculation.)

In option 2, on the other hand, the project teams should construct or renovate the project close to transportation resources, as will be discussed shortly.

OPTION 1: DEVELOPMENT AND ADJACENCY — (2-3 Points)

Construct or renovate the project site on a previously developed site that was used for industrial or commercial purposes (2 points).

OR

Construct or renovate the project on a site that is both a previously developed and adjacent site; the adjacent sites must be used at the time for industrial or commercial purposes (3 points).

📄 For documentation, project teams should submit the area plan or map that shows the project site, the previous development, and the adjacent industrial or commercial properties.

AND/OR

OPTION 2: TRANSPORTATION RESOURCES – (1-2 Points)

Under this option, project teams should construct or renovate the project on a site that satisfies **two** or **three** (1 point), or **four** (2 points) of the following transportation resources requirements:

- ☞ The site is located within a **10-mile** (16-kilometer) driving distance of a <u>main logistics hub</u>, defined as an <u>airport</u>, <u>seaport</u>, <u>intermodal facility</u>, or <u>freight village with intermodal transportation</u>.
- ☞ The site is located within a **1-mile** (1.6-kilometer) driving distance of an on-off ramp to a <u>highway</u>.
- ☞ The site is located within a **1-mile** (1.6-kilometer) driving distance of an access point to an active <u>freight rail line</u>.
- ☞ The site is served by an active <u>freight rail spur</u>.

Under this option, <u>planned</u> transportation resources can also be counted as long as they are sited, funded, and under construction by the date of the certificate of occupancy and complete within **24 months** of that date.

📄 For documentation, project teams should submit the area plan or map showing the project site and the driving routes to the transportation resources, and they should indicate the driving distances. Again, a straight-line radius from the project site to the transportation resource will not be accepted. If any planned transportation resources are used for credit compliance, project teams should submit verification indicating that the transportation resources will be funded and under construction by the date of the certificate of occupancy and will be complete within two years of that date.

<u>For "LEED BD+C: Healthcare" projects:</u>

To earn points under this credit, healthcare projects either should be located inside a surrounding area that is densely developed or should be located close to diverse uses. One thing to note is that the project teams for healthcare projects cannot pursue both options, and they need to choose either one of the two options. Let's take a closer look at the requirements.

OPTION 1: SURROUNDING DENSITY — (1 Point)

Under this option, the project site must be located on a site for which the surrounding existing density within a **quarter-mile** (400-meter) radius of the project boundary is:

- at least 7 dwelling units per acre (17.5 DU per hectare) with a 0.5 floor-to-area ratio (the counted density must be existing density, not zoned density); or
- at least 22,000 square feet per acre (5,050 square meters per hectare) of buildable land.

For previously developed existing rural healthcare campus sites, projects should achieve a minimum development density of **30,000 square feet per acre** (6,890 square meters per hectare).

> 🗎 For documentation, healthcare project teams should submit the area plan or map that shows the project site and the location of residential and nonresidential buildings within a quarter mile (400 meters), and they should submit a narrative describing the previous development on the site.

OR

OPTION 2: DIVERSE USES — (1 Point)

Under this option, the project site should be located so that the building's main entrance is within a **half-mile** (800 meter) walking distance of the main entrance of **at least seven** operational and publicly accessible diverse uses shown on table 3.

Healthcare projects should also comply with LEED's rules for counting diverse uses. Again, that means the same type of store cannot be counted more than twice. A diverse use selling products in several categories can only be counted as one diverse use. And the counted diverse uses must be present under at least three of the five diverse-use categories shown on the left column of table 3, exclusive of the building's primary use.

Again, project teams can count the planned but currently not-operating diverse uses, but the diverse use must be active within **one year** of the date that the project accepts the initial certificate of occupancy.

> 🗎 For documentation, healthcare project teams should submit the area plan or map that shows the project site, the location and type of each diverse use, and the routes.

EXEMPLARY PERFORMANCE

This credit does not qualify for exemplary performance.

CASE STUDY 1

To illustrate, let's say that a "LEED BD+C: New Construction and Major Renovation" project aims to pursue this credit and decides to calculate the "residential" and "nonresidential" densities instead of calculating the combined density in its quarter-mile (400 meter) radius. The project team finds the following values:

Residential land area: 120 acres

Nonresidential land area: 40 acres

Mixed-use land area: 40 acres

Total land area: 200 acres

At this point, the project team should figure out the residential and nonresidential portion of the mixed-use land area in order to calculate the total residential and nonresidential land area. The project teams determine that 50% of the mixed-use land area is allocated to residential use, and the remaining 50% is allocated to nonresidential use. With this information, the project team calculates the land area for both the residential and the nonresidential portions within the mixed use.

Residential portion of the mixed use land area: 20 acres

Nonresidential portion of the mixed use land area: 20 acres

Then the project team calculates the total residential and nonresidential area.

Total residential area: 140 acres

Total non-residential area: 60 acres

The project team determines that there are **1,400 dwelling units** (including the dwelling units on the mixed-use land) in its quarter-mile (400 meter) radius, and with this information, the residential density can be calculated.

Residential density: 1400 DU / 140 acres = **10 DU/acre**

Next, the project team determines that the nonresidential space (including the nonresidential units on the mixed-use land) in its quarter-mile (400 meter) radius is **2,200,000 square feet**. The project team performs the following calculations:

If the total nonresidential area, 60 acres, is converted to square feet, it will equal **2,613,600 square feet**.

Nonresidential density (FAR): 2,200,000 / 2,613,600 = **0.84**

From these results, we can say that the project can receive 2 points under this credit. If the residential density value of the project was 12 DU/acre instead of 10 DU/acre, the project would be able to receive three points under this credit since its nonresidential density, which is 0.84, is above the three-point-level threshold (see table 2). But in this situation, since its residential density is below the three-point threshold, the project can only receive 2 points.

CASE STUDY 2

In this case study, let us assume that a "LEED BD+C: Retail" project aims for this credit under "Option 2: Diverse Uses." The project team checks the diverse uses within a **half-mile** (800 meter) walking distance of the building's main entrance and finds the following results:

Category of diverse use	Food retail		Services	Community anchor uses	Total
Type of diverse use	Supermarket	Grocery	Hair care	Commercial office	
Number of diverse uses	3	4	2	3	12

But since the same type of store cannot be counted more than twice, the project team adjusts its result with the following table:

Category of diverse use	Food retail		Services	Community anchor uses	Total
Type of diverse use	Supermarket	Grocery	Hair care	Commercial office	
Number of diverse uses	3	4	2	3	12
Number of eligible diverse uses	2	2	2	2	8

Since the counted diverse uses are also under three of the five diverse-use categories (which are food retail, services, and community-anchor uses in this example), the project receives 2 points under this credit.

KEY THINGS TO REMEMBER

- Categories and types of diverse uses.
- Walking distances to the diverse uses are measured from the main entrance of the building, not the functional entrance.
- In the "Surrounding Density" option, if the quarter-mile (400 meter) radius of the project contains mixed uses, project teams should calculate a weighted average of them.
- With regard to only the "LEED BD+C: Schools" projects, project teams should neglect any physical education spaces (such as playgrounds or playing fields) from the development density calculations.
- For the diverse-uses calculations, the same type of store cannot be counted more than twice, a diverse-use establishment selling products in several categories can only be counted as one diverse use, and the counted diverse uses must be present under the **at least three** of the five diverse-use categories, exclusive of the building's primary use.
- Project teams can also count the planned but currently not-operating diverse uses, but the diverse use must be active within **one year** of the date that the project gets the initial certificate of occupancy.
- In LEED, for a site to be considered "previously developed," the minimum **75%** of the land area should have been previously developed.
- In LEED, an "adjacent site" refers to the site having at least a continuous stretch of **25%** of its boundary bordering parcels with a previously developed site. Intervening rights-of-way will not be considered as a bordering parcel. (Any part of the boundary bordering a water body can be excluded from the adjacent-site calculation.)
- Even though this credit contains two options for healthcare projects as well, healthcare project teams need to choose either one of the two options.

■ Applicable to: All the LEED BD+C Rating Systems

New Construction	1 – 5 points	Retail	1 – 5 points	Hospitality	1 – 5 points
Core and Shell	1 – 6 points	Data Centers	1 – 5 points	Healthcare	1 – 2 points
Schools	1 – 4 points	Warehouses & Dist. Centers	1 – 5 points		

CREDIT SUMMARY

As in the previous credit, locating the project at a walking distance from quality transit would reduce the single-occupancy vehicle use, thereby reducing air pollution and greenhouse gas emissions.

The environmental harms of public transport are known to be far less than that of single-occupancy vehicles. Additionally, access to quality public transit is considerably helpful to people who do not own a car or to elderly people who can't drive.

As will be discussed shortly, for the "LEED BD+C: Schools" and the "LEED BD+C: Healthcare" projects, the credit requires different criteria.

CREDIT INTENT

To encourage development in locations that contain multimodal transportation choices or provide reduced motor vehicle use, therefore reducing greenhouse gas emissions, air pollution, and other environmental and public health harms related to motor vehicle use.

CREDIT REQUIREMENTS

For all LEED BD+C projects, except "LEED BD+C: Schools" and "LEED BD+C: Healthcare": Project teams should locate **any functional entry** of the building within a **quarter-mile** (400 meter) walking distance of existing or planned **bus, streetcar**, or **rideshare stops**. Or any functional entry of the building must be located within a **half-mile** (800 meter) walking distance of existing or planned **bus rapid transit stops, light or heavy rail stations, commuter rail stations**, or **commuter ferry terminals**.

"Planned" stops or stations are those stops or stations that are planned but at the time are nonoperational and can be counted under this credit if they're sited, funded, and under construction at the time of the certificate of occupancy and will be completed within **24 months** from that date. (This is similar to option 2 of the "Surrounding Density and Diverse Uses" credit for the "LEED BD+C: Warehouses and Distribution Centers" rating system requirements. In that instance, project teams are also able to count the planned transportation resources.)

In order to earn the credit, the transit service in those stops and stations in **aggregate** must meet the minimum values on tables 4 and 5:

Minimum daily transit service for <u>multiple transit types</u> (bus, streetcar, rail, or ferry)			
Weekday Trips	Weekend Trips	Points (except LEED BD+C: Core and Shell)	Points for LEED BD+C: Core and Shell
72	40	1	1
144	108	3	3
360	216	5	6

Table 4. Minimum daily transit service for multiple transit types

Minimum daily transit service for commuter rail or ferry service <u>only</u>		
Weekday Trips	**Weekend Trips**	**Points**
24	6	1
40	8	2
60	12	3

Table 5. Minimum daily transit service for commuter rail or ferry service only

💡 Please note the differences in the previous tables. The first table can be used if the project contains multiple transit types, such as bus, streetcar, rail, or ferry. The second table is to be used for projects that only contain either a commuter rail station or a ferry service close by.

As can be seen from the previous tables, LEED has different requirements for minimum daily transit service numbers for weekdays and weekends, and both should be met. If the number of transit trips vary each day during <u>weekdays</u>, the project teams should count the trips from the weekday with the <u>lowest number</u> of trips. However, if the number of trips for the <u>weekends</u> also vary, in that instance the project teams should calculate their <u>average</u> and use that number to determine credit compliance.

The qualifying transit route should have paired-route service, which means that the service should operate in opposite directions. However, in the credit calculations project teams will calculate a round trip as one trip. And for the walking distance calculations, project teams will be free to choose which of the two (opposite) stops to consider.

If a qualifying transit has more than one stop at a walking distance, only one stop will be counted.

If any of the transit types, located at a walking distance from the project, is temporarily rerouted (for less than 2 years), it can still be counted toward credit compliance as long as the local transit agency has committed to restoring the routes and the project team can provide supporting documentation.

Projects served by two or more transit routes such that no one route provides more than **60%** of the documented levels can earn one additional bonus point up to the maximum number of points. (See the case study under this credit for a demonstration.) But if the project already receives full points under this credit, satisfying the 60% rule will not lead to an award of a bonus point. Even though the project teams may at that point decide to pursue exemplary performance and still earn an additional point by satisfying its requirements. (See "Exemplary Performance" under this credit.)

As discussed under "Documenting LT Credits," each walking distance should be calculated according to the LEED walkability requirements.

> 📄 For documentation, project teams should submit maps showing the project boundary, transit stop locations, and walking routes to the stops. And they should submit the transit timetables and, if applicable, document the planned transit or restoration of temporarily rerouted service.

For LEED BD+C: Schools projects:

The project teams have two options, and the project teams can choose either one of them. Option 1 is more suitable for school projects whose students mainly don't live nearby and require public transit for commuting to the school. Option 2 is suitable for projects whose students mostly live within walking distance of the school.

OPTION 1: TRANSIT-SERVED LOCATION — (1-4 Points)

This option basically requires the same criteria as listed previously for other LEED BD+C project types, but with some minor adjustments. Since schools are typically closed during the weekends, teams for school projects are not required to evaluate weekend transit service as long as the students do not commute to school on weekends. In order to earn the credit, the transit service in those stops and stations in **aggregate** must meet the minimum values from tables 6 and 7.

Minimum daily transit service for projects with <u>multiple transit types</u> (bus, streetcar, rail, or ferry)	
Weekday Trips	**Points**
72	1
144	2
360	4

Table 6. Minimum daily transit service for projects with multiple transit types

| Minimum daily transit service for projects with commuter rail or ferry service <u>only</u> ||
Weekday Trips	Points
24	1
40	2
60	3

Table 7. Minimum daily transit service for projects with commuter rail or ferry service only

To avoid any confusion and to reinforce knowledge, let's also list the requirements for this option, even though the requirements are the same as the requirements on the previous page.

Under this option, "LEED BD+C: Schools" project teams should locate <u>any functional entry</u> of the building within a **quarter-mile** (400 meter) walking distance of existing or planned <u>bus</u>, <u>streetcar</u>, or <u>rideshare stops</u>. Or <u>any functional entry</u> of the building must be located within a **half-mile** (800 meter) walking distance of existing or planned <u>bus rapid transit stops</u>, <u>light or heavy rail stations</u>, <u>commuter rail stations</u>, or <u>commuter ferry terminals</u>. "Planned" stops or stations are those stops or stations that are planned but are at the time nonoperational and can be counted if they're sited, funded, and under construction at the time of the certificate of occupancy and will be completed within **24 months** from that date.

The qualifying transit route should have paired route service, which means that it should serve in opposite directions. However, in the credit calculations, project teams will calculate a round trip as one trip. And for the walking distance calculations, project teams will be free to choose which of the two stops to consider in the walking distance calculations.

If a qualifying transit has more than one stop at a walking distance, only one stop will be counted.

If any of the transit types, located at a walking distance from the project is temporarily rerouted (for less than 2 years), it can still be counted toward credit compliance as long as the local transit agency has committed to restoring the routes and the project can provide supporting documentation.

Projects served by two or more transit routes such that no one route provides more than 60% of the documented levels of transportation can earn one additional point up to the maximum number of points.

Again, each walking distance calculated should be done according to the LEED walkability requirements.

> 🗎 For documentation, project teams should submit maps showing the project boundary, transit stop locations, and walking routes to the stops, and they should submit the transit timetables, and if applicable, document the planned transit or restoration of temporarily rerouted service.

OR

OPTION 2: PEDESTRIAN ACCESS – (1-4 Points)

Under this option, "LEED BD+C: Schools" project teams should demonstrate that the specified percentages of students live within a **three-quarter-mile** (1200 meter) walking distance (for grades 8 and below, or ages 14 and below), and a **1 1/2-mile** (2400-meter) walking distance (for grades 9 and above or ages 15 and above) of <u>any functional entry</u> of the school building. To calculate compliance, project teams can use the school's **attendance boundary**, which basically shows where the students live on a map without showing the exact addresses. Points will be awarded according to the table below.

As the name of this option, "Pedestrian Access," implies, the project site should be located at a place that allows pedestrian access from all residential neighborhoods where the students live.

Points for student population within walking distance of any functional entry	
Percentage of students	**Points**
50%	1
60%	2
70% or more	4

Table 8. Points awarded for student population within walking distance of any functional entry

📄 Project teams should provide documentation with a map showing the walkshed boundary.

<u>For LEED BD+C: Healthcare projects:</u>

This option basically requires the same criteria as listed previously for other LEED BD+C project types and in option 1 of "LEED BD+C: Schools". The only difference for healthcare projects is that the point values for this option will be awarded according to tables 9 and 10. For healthcare projects, the number of weekend trips also needs to be addressed, unlike in option 1 of "LEED BD+C: Schools".

Minimum daily transit service for projects with **multiple transit types** (bus, streetcar, rail, or ferry)		
Weekday Trips	Weekend Trips	Points
72	40	1
144	108	2

Table 9. Minimum daily transit service for projects with multiple transit types

Minimum daily transit service for projects with commuter rail or ferry service <u>only</u>		
Weekday Trips	Weekend Trips	Points
24	6	1
40	8	2

Table 10. Minimum daily transit service for projects with commuter rail or ferry service only

📄 For documentation, project teams should submit maps showing the project boundary, transit stop locations, and walking routes to the stops, and they should submit the transit timetables, and if applicable, document the planned transit or restoration of temporarily rerouted service.

To summarize, even though school and healthcare projects are addressed separately inside this credit, their requirements are the same with the exception of varying numbers of points awarded to them according to the trip numbers required. For school projects, there are two options, and project teams have the chance to earn the credit under option 2 if the school is located at a walking distance from the students' residences. In option 1, project teams do not need to consider the number of transit trips during the weekends in their credit calculations if the students do not commute to school on the weekends.

EXEMPLARY PERFORMANCE

To qualify for exemplary performance under this credit, projects need to **double** the highest transit service threshold. "LEED BD+C: Schools" projects pursuing option 2 will not be eligible for exemplary performance.

CASE STUDY

To illustrate, let us say that team members of a "LEED BD+C: New Construction and Major Renovation" project decide to check the project's eligibility for earning points under this credit. The building contains three functional entries with the following walking distances to the quality transits:

- ❧ Functional entry #1 is within a quarter-mile (400 meter) walking distance of a bus station.
- ❧ Functional entry #2 is within a half-mile (800 meter) walking distance of a rideshare stop.
- ❧ Functional entry #3 is within a half-mile (800 meter) walking distance of an existing ferry terminal, but the ferry terminal at the time has been rerouted for a year for restoration purposes and is not operational.

In this scenario, functional entry #2 exceeds the walking limits under this credit and therefore should be ignored.

Even though the ferry terminal has been rerouted for a year, the project team can use it in the credit calculations as long as it can document that the terminal is temporarily rerouted. The project team will need supporting documentation from the local transit agency. (Remember that the rerouted transit items can be counted as long as the project teams can document that the rerouting duration is <u>less than two years</u>.)

Next, the project team would confirm that the bus station and the ferry terminal have service in opposite directions as well, which means that the teams can now proceed with figuring out the number of bus and ferry trips in <u>one</u> direction and determine how many points they can receive.

The project team creates the following table:

Type of Transit	No. of trips in one direction						
	Mon.	Tue.	Wed.	Thu.	Fri.	Sat.	Sun.
Bus	100	75	100	75	100	60	50
Ferry	30	30	30	30	30	3	3

Let's start with discussing the number of trips for the bus. With these numbers, the project team can say that during the weekdays, the project will have access to **75** bus trips. (Remember, if the number of transit trips vary each day during weekdays, the project teams should use the number from the weekday with the lowest number of trips available.) And for the weekend, the project will have access to **55** bus trips.

(Remember, if the number of trips for the weekends also vary, in this instance the project teams should calculate their average and use that number to determine credit compliance.)

With this scenario alone, even without counting the ferry trips, the project team can determine that the project can receive one point for the bus trips since the project's available trips are above the minimum threshold for both the required weekday and weekend bus trips (see table 4). Let's now continue with discussing the number of trips for the ferry, and see if the project can receive additional points with the addition of ferry trips.

The project team can say that the project will have access to **30** ferry trips during the weekdays and **3** ferry trips during the weekend (after the ferry is operational again). And in this case, the aggregate number of trips, including both bus and ferry trips, would be as follows:

Aggregate number of trips during the weekdays: 75 + 30 = **105** trips

Aggregate number of trips during the weekends: 55 + 3 = **58** trips

With these numbers, the project cannot go above the next threshold level (which is 144 weekday trips and 108 weekend trips), and it misses the chance to earn 3 points and ends up earning only one point. But remember, projects served by two or more transit routes such that no one route provides more than **60%** of the documented levels can earn one additional bonus point up to the maximum number of points. To figure out if the project can receive an additional point, the project team creates the following table:

Transit Type	Lowest number of weekday trips	Average number of weekend trips	Total
Bus	75	55	130 (78% of total trips)
Ferry	30	3	33 (22% of total trips)
		Number of total trips	166

Note that, for this calculation, the project teams will need to add the lowest number of weekday trips and the average number of weekend trips to determine the number of total trips for a particular transit type. LEED does not accept finding an average trip number by adding the number of trips for each day in a week and dividing it by 7.

With these results, the project cannot receive a bonus point, since bus trips make up **78%** of the total trips, which is above the 60% threshold.

KEY THINGS TO REMEMBER

- For all the LEED credits that require walking-distance calculations, walkability should be confirmed by the use of paths that provide a safe and comfortable environment for pedestrians and provide a continuous network of sidewalks. Any walking route that does not meet these requirements cannot be used to document walking distance.
- Walking distance is calculated from any functional entry of the building. In the "Surrounding Density and Diverse Uses" credit, the walking distance was calculated from the main entrance of the building. And for the next credit, which is the "Bicycle Facilities" credit, the walking distance will be calculated from the main entrance and from the functional entry, depending on the bicycle storage type.
- If any of the transit types, located at a walking distance from the project, is temporarily rerouted (for less than **two years**), that transit type can still be counted toward credit compliance as long as the local transit agency has committed to restoring the routes, and the project team can provide supporting documentation.
- Planned but, at the time, nonoperational stations can be counted if they're sited, funded, and under construction at the time of the certificate of occupancy and if they will be completed within **twenty-four months** from that date.
- The qualifying transit route should have paired route service, which means that it should serve in opposite directions. However, in the credit calculations, project teams will calculate it as one trip.
- If the number of transit trips vary each day during the weekdays, the project teams should use the number from the weekday with the lowest number of trips available. However, if the number of trips available for the weekends also vary from one day to the next, then in that instance the project teams should calculate the average number of trips for the two weekend days and use that number to determine credit compliance.
- Projects served by two or more transit routes such that no one route provides more than **60%** of the documented levels can earn one additional bonus point up to the maximum number of points.

Bicycle Facilities—Credit

■ Applicable to: All the LEED BD+C Rating Systems

All the LEED BD+C Rating Systems	1 point

CREDIT SUMMARY

We all know the great benefits to human health of bicycling, which extends human life and lowers the risk of cardiovascular diseases. This credit is aimed to promote the bicycle- friendly design of a project to support the health of the building users and to reduce air pollution that would otherwise be generated by vehicle use.

To earn this credit, projects will need to be located close to bicycle networks and contain bicycle storage and shower rooms. There should be both **long-term** and **short-term bicycle storage** since the project occupants and visitors will have different storage needs.

With LEED, to qualify as a **bicycle network**, a network should be continuous and consist of any combination of the following:

➤ Off-street bicycle paths or trails at least 8 feet (2.5 meters) wide for a two-way path, and at least 5 feet (1.5 meters) wide for a one-way path

➤ Physically designated on-street bicycle lanes that are at least 5 feet (1.5 meters) wide

➤ Streets that are designed for a target speed of 25 mph (40 kmh)

As will be discussed shortly, for projects within the LEED BD+C: Schools, LEED BD+C: Retail, and LEED BD+C: Healthcare rating systems, the credit requires different criteria.

CREDIT INTENT

To promote bicycling and transportation efficiency and thereby reduce vehicle distance traveled, and to improve public health by encouraging utilitarian and recreational physical activity.

CREDIT REQUIREMENTS

For all LEED BD+C projects, except "LEED BD+C: Schools", "LEED BD+C: Retail" and "LEED BD+C: Healthcare":

To earn this credit, projects need to satisfy both the bicycle network and the bicycle storage and shower room requirements.

Bicycle network requirements:

The project should be located so that the building's functional entry or bicycle storage is within **200 yards** (180 meters) walking distance or bicycling distance from a **bicycle network** that connects to **at least one** of the following:

- At least 10 diverse uses (see table 3 in the "Surrounding Density and Diverse Uses" credit)
- An employment center or school if the project's total floor area is 50% or more residential
- A light rail or heavy rail station, a bus rapid transit stop, a commuter rail station, or a ferry terminal

All these destinations should also be within a **3-mile** (4800 meter) bicycling distance of the project boundary. Planned but at the time nonexisting bicycle trails or lanes can be counted too if they're funded by the date of the certificate of occupancy and scheduled to be finished within a year of that date (not two years, as was the case with the previous credit).

AND

Bicycle storage and shower rooms requirements:

Case 1: Commercial or Institutional projects

(This case includes the retail portion of the project too, if it exists. However, the whole project should not be under the "LEED BD+C: Retail" rating system)

Commercial or institutional projects should provide **short-term bicycle storage** (typically used by visitors for less than two hours and which is not enclosed parking) for at least **2.5%** of all peak visitors (cannot be less than four spaces per building). Additionally, projects should provide **long-term bicycle storage** (protected storage from rain and snow and which is for residents and employees) for at least **5%** of all the regular building occupants (cannot be less than four spaces per building).

Finally, projects should provide at least one on-site shower room with a changing facility for the first **100 regular building occupants** and one additional shower for every **150 occupants** after the first 100.

Case 2: Residential projects

Residential projects should provide short-term bicycle storage for at least **2.5%** of all peak visitors (cannot be less than four spaces per building) and provide long-term bicycle storage for at least **30%** of all the regular building occupants, which **cannot be less than one storage space per residential unit**. Since residential projects will already have showers inside, LEED does not ask for any shower rooms with changing facilities.

Case 3: Mixed-use projects

Mixed-use projects should meet case 1 and case 2 requirements for the residential and nonresidential portion of the project respectively. For example, if the project contains residential, office, and retail space, the project teams will calculate the residential portion under case 2 and calculate the office plus the retail portion under case 1.

One thing to note under this credit is that, for all types of projects mentioned above, all the short-term bicycle storage should be within **100 feet** (30 meters) walking distance from any main entrance, and all the long-term bicycle storage should be within **100 feet** (30 meters) walking distance from any functional entry. And only the bicycle storage that is allocated to the building occupants will be included in the credit calculations; any bicycle storage allocated to any nonproject facility should be ignored.

The "LEED BD+C: Core and Shell" projects should refer to LEED's **Default Occupancy Counts** for the occupancy count requirements.

> 📄 Project teams should document the vicinity map showing the bicycle networks and distances from the project, and they should submit a site plan showing bicycle project locations and should submit calculations on bicycle storage and shower facilities.

For "LEED BD+C: Schools":

To earn this credit, "LEED BD+C: Schools" projects need to satisfy both the bicycle network and the bicycle storage and shower rooms requirements.

Bicycle network requirements:

The school project should be located so that the building's functional entry or bicycle storage is within **200 yards** (180 meters) walking distance or bicycling distance from a **bicycle network** that connects to **at least one** of the following:

- ➤ At least 10 diverse uses (see table 3 in the "Surrounding Density and Diverse Uses" credit)
- ➤ A light rail or heavy rail station, a bus rapid transit stop, a commuter rail station, or a ferry terminal

Again, all these destinations should also be within a **3-mile** (4800-meter) bicycling distance of the project boundary. Again, planned but at the time nonexisting bicycle trails or lanes can be counted too if they're funded by the date of the certificate of occupancy and scheduled to be finished within a year of that date.

Unlike the other rating systems, school projects should also provide dedicated **bicycle lanes** that extend at least to the end of the school property from the school buildings without any barriers such as fences.

AND

Bicycle storage and shower rooms requirements:

School projects should provide **long-term bicycle storage** for at least **5%** of all regular building occupants, excluding students in grade 3 and younger, which cannot be less than four spaces per building. In other words, when doing the long-term bicycle storage calculations, the school projects will only consider the staff and full-time students in grade 4 or above.

In addition to long-term bicycle storage, school projects should provide at least one on-site shower room with a changing facility for the first **100 regular building occupants** (excluding students this time) and one additional shower for every **150 occupants** after that (again, excluding the students).

All the long-term bicycle storage provided should be within **100 feet** (30 meters) walking distance from any main entrance. (For the other rating systems' requirements, the long-term storage should be within 100 feet of any functional entry, not the main entrance. As is the case with the previous rating systems' requirements, only the bicycle storage that is allocated to the building occupants will be included in the credit calculations; any bicycle storage allocated to any nonproject facility should be ignored.

(Note that "LEED BD+C: Schools" projects are not required to provide any short-term bicycle storage.)

> 📄 For documentation, project teams should submit a vicinity map showing the bicycle networks and distances from the project, submit a site plan showing bicycle project locations, and should submit calculations on bicycle storage and shower facilities.

For "LEED BD+C: Retail":

To earn this credit, "LEED BD+C: Retail" projects need to satisfy both the bicycle network and the bicycle storage and shower rooms requirements.

Bicycle network requirements:

The retail project should be located so that the building's functional entry or bicycle storage is within **200 yards** (180 meters) walking distance or bicycling distance from a **bicycle network** that connects to **at least one** of the following:

- ⮞ At least 10 diverse uses (see table 3 in the "Surrounding Density and Diverse Uses" credit)
- ⮞ A light rail or heavy rail station, a bus rapid transit stop, a commuter rail station, or a ferry terminal

Again, all these destinations should also be within a **3-mile** (4800 meter) bicycling distance of the project boundary. Again, planned but at the time nonexisting bicycle trails or lanes can be counted too if they're funded by the date of the certificate of occupancy and scheduled to be finished within a year of that date.

AND

Bicycle storage and shower rooms requirements:

Retail projects should provide **at least two** (not one) short-term bicycle storage spaces for every **5,000 square feet** (465 square meters). There cannot be fewer than two storage spaces per building. (Note that for the other rating systems, LEED requires a minimum of **four spaces**, not two.) And retail projects should provide long-term bicycle storage for at **least 5%** of regular building occupants. There cannot be fewer than two storage spaces per building. (Again, note that for the other rating systems, LEED requires a minimum of **four spaces**, not two).

For the requirement dealing with on-site shower rooms with a changing facility, projects should provide one shower for the first **100 regular building occupants** and one additional shower for every **150 regular building occupants** thereafter. One thing to note is that "LEED BD+C: Retail" projects will not include peak-time visitors (customers) in their calculations. The regular building occupants only include the employees.

As with the previous requirements of the other rating systems (except schools, since schools only require long-term parking storage, not short-term), all the short-term bicycle storage should be within **100 feet** (30 meters) walking distance to any <u>main entrance</u>, and all the long-term bicycle storage should be within **100 feet** (30 meters) walking distance of any <u>functional entry</u>. As is the case with other rating systems, only the bicycle storage that is allocated to the building occupants will be included in the credit calculations; any bicycle storage allocated to any nonproject facility should be ignored.

Unlike the other rating systems, retail projects are also required to provide a **bicycle maintenance program** for <u>employees</u> or **bicycle route assistance** for <u>employees</u> and <u>customers</u>. An example of a bicycle maintenance program would be to provide coupons for a bicycle tune-up, and an example of bicycle route assistance would be to provide a map that shows bicycle routes to the project site.

If the retail project is a part of a multitenant complex and contains bicycle storage spaces that are shared at the complex, project teams should determine the number of bicycle spaces that may be allocated to the project by dividing the project's floor area by the total floor area of the development (only the buildings) and multiplying the resulting percentage by the total number of spaces. Basically, they will need to calculate their own share of those bicycle spaces, and if this number does not meet the credit requirement, the project must provide additional bicycle storage.

📄 Project teams should provide documentation of a vicinity map showing the bicycle networks and distances from the project, and they should submit a site plan showing bicycle project locations. They should also submit calculations on bicycle storage and shower facilities, and they should submit a narrative describing the programs implemented to support bicycle use.

For "LEED BD+C: Healthcare":

To earn this credit, "LEED BD+C: Healthcare" projects need to satisfy both the requirements for a bicycle network and bicycle storage and shower rooms.

Bicycle network requirements:

The healthcare project should be located so that the building's <u>functional entry</u> or <u>bicycle storage</u> is within **200 yards** (180 meters) <u>walking distance</u> or <u>bicycling distance</u> from a **bicycle network** that connects to **at least one** of the following:

- At least 10 diverse uses (see table 3 in the "Surrounding Density and Diverse Uses" credit)
- A light rail or heavy rail station, a bus rapid transit stop, a commuter rail station, or a ferry terminal

Again, all these destinations should also be within a **3-mile** (4800 meters) <u>bicycling distance</u> of the project boundary. Again, <u>planned</u> but at the time nonexisting bicycle trails or lanes can be counted too if they're funded by the date of the certificate of occupancy and scheduled to be finished within a <u>year</u> of that date.

AND

Bicycle storage and shower rooms requirements:

Case 1: Commercial or Institutional projects

Commercial or institutional projects should provide **short-term bicycle storage** for at least **2.5%** of all **peak visitors** (cannot be less than four spaces per building). Additionally, projects should provide **long-term bicycle storage** for at least **5%** of all the **regular building occupants**, excluding patients, and there cannot be fewer than four spaces per building.

In addition to the short-term and long-term bicycle storage, projects should provide at least one on-site shower room with a changing facility for the first **100 regular building occupants**, excluding patients, and one additional shower for every **150 occupants** after that.

Case 2: Residential projects

Residential projects should provide secure, enclosed bicycle storage for at least 30% of all regular building occupants (excluding patients), measured at peak periods, and the bicycle storage cannot be less than one storage space per residential unit.

As with the other rating systems' requirements (except schools), all the short-term bicycle storage should be within **100 feet** (30 meters) walking distance from any <u>main entrance</u>, and all the long-term bicycle storage should be within **100 feet** (30 meters) walking distance from any <u>functional entry</u>. Only the bicycle storage that is allocated to the building occupants will be included in the credit calculations; any bicycle storage allocated to any nonproject facility should be ignored.

> 📄 Project teams should use documentation of a vicinity map showing the bicycle networks and distances from the project, and they should submit a site plan showing bicycle project locations. They should also submit calculations on bicycle storage and shower facilities.

Note that there are several requirements that are exactly the same for all the rating systems. Let's summarize them one by one:

For the bicycle network requirement, all the LEED BD+C projects should be designed or located so that the building's <u>functional entry</u> or <u>bicycle storage</u> is within **200 yards** (180 meters) <u>walking distance</u> or <u>bicycling distance</u> from a bicycle network that connects to at least **one** of the following:

- At least 10 diverse uses
- ~~An employment center or school if the project's total area is 50% or more residential~~ (this is not applicable to schools, retail, and healthcare projects)
- Light rail or heavy rail station, bus rapid transit stop, commuter rail station, or ferry terminal

All these destinations should also be within a **3-mile** (4800 meter) <u>bicycling distance</u> of the project boundary. <u>Planned</u> but at the time nonexisting bicycle trails or lanes can be counted too if they're funded by the date of the certificate of occupancy and scheduled to be finished within a <u>year</u> of that date.

All the short-term bicycle storage provided should be within **100 feet** (30 meters) walking distance from any main entrance, and all the long-term bicycle storage should be within **100 feet** (30 meters) walking distance from any functional entry. Regarding only schools, all the long-term bicycle storage provided should be within **100 feet** (30 meters) of walking distance from any <u>main entrance</u> (as opposed to a functional entry), and school projects will not provide any short-term bicycle storage.

For all LEED BD+C rating systems, the bicycle storage that is allocated to the building occupants will be included in the credit calculations; any bicycle storage allocated to any nonproject facility should be ignored.

All LEED BD+C projects, excluding the residential portion of a building, should provide at least one on-site shower room with a changing facility for the first **100 regular building occupants** and one additional shower for every **150 occupants** after those first 100. (School projects will exclude students, and healthcare projects will exclude patients from this calculation.)

Let's summarize the formulas that will be used for the credit calculations:

Short-term bicycle storage = Peak visitors x 0.025

Equation 2. Short-term bicycle storage

"LEED BD+C: Retail" short-term bicycle storage = 2 x (Building floor area (ft^2) / 5,000)

Equation 3. LEED BD+C: Retail short-term bicycle storage

Long-term bicycle storage = Regular building occupants x 0.05

Equation 4. Long-term bicycle storage

Residential long-term bicycle storage = Regular building occupants **x** 0.3
OR
Residential long-term bicycle storage = Number of dwelling units

Whichever is greater.
Equation 5. Residential long-term bicycle storage

School projects will not provide any short-term bicycle storage.

EXEMPLARY PERFORMANCE

This credit does not qualify for exemplary performance.

CASE STUDY 1

To illustrate, let's say that a residential project team pursuing the "LEED BD+C: New Construction and Major Renovation" rating system decides to check the project's eligibility for earning this credit.

The project's functional entry is within 50 yards (45 meters) bicycling distance to a bicycle network that connects to a heavy rail station. The project team calculates that the heavy rail station is within 2 miles (3200 meters) bicycling distance of the project boundary, which means that the project satisfies the first requirement. Next the team will need to calculate the amount of short-term and long-term bicycle storage it needs to provide.

The project has

- 350 peak visitors
- 200 residents; and
- 100 residential units.

In this case, the project will need to provide the following:

Short-term bicycle storage: 350 x 0.025 = 8.75 — rounded to **9 spaces** (in LEED, this number must be rounded up, not down)

Long-term bicycle storage: 200 x 0.3 = **60 spaces**

For residential projects, the amount of **long-term bicycle storage cannot be less than one storage space per residential unit.** That means that the project teams will need to provide 100 long-term bicycle storage spaces instead of 60. The project teams then confirm the following values:

Short-term bicycle storage: 9 spaces
Long-term bicycle storage: 100 spaces

Next, the project teams will need to locate the short-term spaces within 100 feet (30 meters) walking distance of any main entrance and the long-term spaces within 100 feet (30 meters) walking distance of any functional entry.

Since the project is residential, there will not be any shower-room requirements.

CASE STUDY 2

For this case study, let's say that a 50,000-square-foot "LEED BD+C: Retail" project team decides to check the project's eligibility for earning this credit. The project's functional entry is within 100 yards (90 meters) bicycling distance of a bicycle network that connects to a bus rapid transit stop. And the project team calculates that the bus rapid transit stop is within 1 mile (1600 meter) bicycling distance of the project boundary, which means the project satisfies the first requirement. Next, the team will need to calculate the amount of short-term and long-term bicycle storage and shower rooms that the project should provide.

The building has

➾ 20 full-time employees;

➾ 4 part-time employees (working 20 hours per week); and

➾ 200 peak visitors.

But actually, "LEED BD+C: Retail" project teams do not need to consider the peak visitors in their calculations since the credit only considers the employees, or in other words, the regular building occupants.

> ♥ If the project was under the "LEED BD+C: New Construction and Major Renovation" rating system, and part of the building contained a retail portion, then project teams would need the peak visitor values for the retail portion of the building (see Case Study 3).

The project team proceeds with calculating the full-time equivalent value of the building in order to find the number of regular building occupants, and ignoring the 200 peak visitors.

20 full-time employees **+** (**4** part-time employees **x 4** hours a day) **/ 8** hours per day = **22 regular building occupants**

"LEED BD+C: Retail" projects should provide at least two <u>short-term bicycle storage spaces</u> for every **5,000 square feet** (465 square meters), which cannot be fewer than two storage spaces per building. Additionally, retail projects should provide <u>long-term bicycle storage</u> for at **least 5%** of regular building occupants, which cannot be fewer than two storage spaces per building. The project team continues with the following calculation.

Short-term bicycle storage: 2 x (50,000 sf² / 5,000 sf²) = **20 spaces**

Long-term bicycle storage: 22 regular building occupants x 0.05 = 1.1 space, rounded to **2 spaces**

Next, the project team will need to locate the short-term spaces within 100 feet (30 meters) walking distance of any main entrance and locate the long-term spaces within 100 feet (30 meters) walking distance of any functional entry.

Finally, the project team will need to calculate the required number of shower rooms with changing facilities. "LEED BD+C: Retail" projects should provide one shower for the first **100 regular building occupants** and one additional shower for every **150 regular building occupants** thereafter. Since the project has 22 regular building occupants, providing **one** on-site shower with a changing facility will earn the credit.

But there is one thing missing here. "LEED BD+C: Retail" projects are also required to provide a "bicycle maintenance program" for <u>employees</u> or "bicycle route assistance" for <u>employees</u> and <u>customers</u>. So the project team also decides to provide a **bicycle maintenance program** for <u>employees</u> by providing coupons for a yearly bicycle tune-up, and it earns the credit.

CASE STUDY 3

With this case study, let's say that a <u>mixed-use</u> "LEED BD+C: New Construction and Major Renovation" project's team—which contains 60% residential space, 20% commercial space, and 20% retail space (according to the project's total floor area)—decides to check the project's eligibility for earning this credit. The project's functional entry is within 50 yards (45 meters) bicycling distance of a bicycle network that connects to an employment center. The project team calculates that the employment center is within 1 mile (1,600 meter) bicycling distance of the project boundary. Next, the team will need to calculate the amount of short-term and long-term bicycle storage to be provided.

The commercial part of the building contains
- 30 full-time employees ;
- 4 part-time employees (working 20 hours per week); and
- 20 peak visitors.

The retail part of the building contains
- 10 regular building occupants; and
- 30 peak visitors.

And the residential part of the building contains;
- 60 dwelling units;
- 100 residents; and
- 70 peak visitors.

Let's now summarize these values. The project team will need to combine the retail and the commercial part of the building and calculate the required number of bicycle storage spaces and shower rooms. And it will need to separately calculate the bicycle storage for the residential portion. Let's add the values for the commercial part of the building and the retail part of the building. But before that, we need to figure out the number of regular building occupants for the commercial part of the building.

30 full-time employees **+** (**4** part-time employees **x 4** hours a day) **/ 8** hours per day = **32 regular building occupants**

Now we can organize these values as follows:

Nonresidential portion (retail + commercial):
Regular building occupants: 32 + 10 = **42 regular building occupants**
Peak visitors: 20 + 30 = **50 peak visitors**

Residential portion:
60 dwelling units
100 residents
70 peak visitors

The project team proceeds with the credit calculations;

For the nonresidential portion (retail + commercial):

Short-term bicycle storage: 50 x 0.025 = 1.25 — rounded to 2 spaces — **adjusted to 4 spaces**

Since the credit requires projects to contain at least 4 short-term bicycle storage spaces, the number is adjusted to 4.

Long-term bicycle storage: 42 x 0.05 = 2.1 spaces — rounded to 3 spaces — **adjusted to 4 spaces**

Since the credit requires projects to contain at least 4 long-term bicycle storage spaces, the number is adjusted to 4.

Shower rooms:

There are 42 regular building occupants for the nonresidential portion, which means that the project team must provide **1** on-site shower room with a changing facility.

<u>For the residential portion:</u>

Short-term bicycle storage: 70 x 0.025 = 1.75 — rounded to **2 spaces** — **adjusted to 4 spaces**

Since the credit requires projects to contain at least 4 short-term bicycle storage spaces, the number is adjusted to 4.

Long-term bicycle storage: 100 x 0.30 = 30 spaces — adjusted to **60 spaces**

For residential projects, the amount of **long-term bicycle storage cannot be less than 1 storage space per residential unit**. Since there are 60 units, the project team will need to provide 60 long-term bicycle storage spaces instead of 30.

Finally, the project team will need to locate the short-term spaces within 100 feet (30 meters) walking distance of any main entrance and the long-term spaces within 100 feet (30 meters) walking distance of any functional entry.

KEY THINGS TO REMEMBER

- Definition of long-term bicycle storage, and short-term bicycle storage. Short-term bicycle storage is typically used by visitors for less than two hours, and it is not enclosed parking. Long-term bicycle storage is storage protected from rain and snow, and it is for residents and employees.

- Short-term bicycle storage distance is measured from the main entrance, and long-term bicycle storage is measured from any functional entry of the building except for "LEED BD+C: Schools" projects (as their long- term bicycle storage is measured from any main entrance).

- "LEED BD+C: Core and Shell" projects should refer to LEED's Default Occupancy Counts for occupancy count requirements.

- "LEED BD+C: Schools" projects don't provide any shower rooms and changing facilities to the students and exclude them from the on-site shower room calculations.

- "LEED BD+C: Schools" projects do not need to provide any short-term bicycle storage and instead provide long-term bicycle storage to all regular building occupants (excluding students grade 3 and younger).

- "LEED BD+C: Schools" projects should provide dedicated bicycle lanes that extend at least to the end of the school property from the school buildings without any barriers such as fences.

- Only for "LEED BD+C: Retail" projects, the minimum amount of short-term and long-term bicycle storage to be provided can be two spaces each for short-term and long-term storage. For the other rating systems, LEED requires a minimum of four spaces for each.

- "LEED BD+C: Retail" projects are required to provide a bicycle maintenance program for employees or bicycle route assistance for employees and customers.

- "LEED BD+C: Healthcare" projects exclude patients from their bicycle storage and shower-room calculations.

Reduced Parking Footprint—Credit

- Applicable to: All the LEED BD+C Rating Systems

All the LEED BD+C Rating Systems	1 point

CREDIT SUMMARY

Parking spaces create a considerable amount of harm to the environment. First, the surfaces (especially the dark-colored surfaces) of the parking lots trap heat. That results in heat island effects and increases the ambient air temperatures in urban areas. We have all seen that in hot climates, asphalt parking lots release air just like a hair dryer blowing hot air. However, if a greenfield was there, this effect wouldn't occur.

In addition, because of the impervious surfaces of the parking lots, rainwater runoffs will occur, which overwhelms the municipal stormwater systems and carries contaminants into the waterways. Again, if there was a greenfield instead of a parking lot, the soil would absorb all the rainwater without transferring it to the municipal stormwater systems. For those reasons, the aim of this credit is to reduce and limit the number of parking spaces to a minimum.

To allow for further reduction of the parking footprint, **transportation demand management strategies** can be implemented, which are:

- Telecommuting
- Compressed workweek schedule
- Provision of shuttles for employees

- Sale of parking separately from residential units
- Shared parking between uses
- Transit subsidy

CREDIT INTENT

To minimize the environmental harms related to parking facilities, automobile dependence, land development, and rainwater runoff.

CREDIT REQUIREMENTS

This credit requires projects not exceed the **minimum local code requirements** for the parking capacity. Additionally, projects should provide parking capacity that is a percentage reduction below the base ratios of the **Parking Consultants Council, as shown in the Institute of Transportation Engineers' Transportation Planning Handbook, 3rd edition, tables 18-2 through 18-4**. Projects without off-street parking will earn the credit automatically.

But what if the base ratios of the Parking Consultants Council are below the minimum local codes? Then project teams should work with the local municipality to secure zoning variances. If zoning variances cannot be secured, the credit will not be awarded.

The credit contains two cases, and they define the percent reduction from the base ratios.

Case 1: Baseline location

Projects that have not earned points under "Surrounding Density and Diverse Uses" or "Access to Quality Transit" credits should achieve a **20%** reduction from the base ratios.

Case 2: Dense and/or transit-served location

Projects that have earned 1 or more points under either the "Surrounding Density and Diverse Uses" credit or the "Access to Quality Transit" credit, should achieve a **40%** reduction from the base ratios.

In other words, if the project is in a dense and/or transit-served location, the project should further decrease its parking capacity from the base ratios of the Parking Consultants Council.

The calculations must also include all the out-of-the-project-boundary parking spaces that are leased or owned by the project. However, the public on-street parking is exempt from the calculations. For projects that use pooled parking, the project's share in the pooled parking should be calculated.

Project teams for mixed-use projects should determine the percentage reduction by calculating the number of parking spaces for each use specified by the base ratios.

Parking spaces for fleet and inventory vehicles are exempt from these calculations unless the vehicles are regularly used by employees for commuting.

Finally, projects need to provide preferred parking for carpools for **5%** of the total parking after the reductions have been made from the base ratios. (If no off-street parking is provided, preferred parking is not required.)

Below is the equation to be used for this credit.

$$\text{Percent parking reduction} = \frac{\text{Total baseline capacity} - \text{Total provided capacity}}{\text{Total baseline capacity}} \times 100$$

Equation 6. Percent parking reduction

📄 Project teams should document a site plan that shows the parking areas and the preferred parking spaces, submit calculations that demonstrate the threshold achievement, and document the drawings or photos of signage/pavement markings that show the reserved status of the preferred parking areas.

EXEMPLARY PERFORMANCE

To qualify for exemplary performance under this credit, projects pursuing case 1 need to achieve a 60% parking reduction from the base ratios. Projects pursuing case 2 need to achieve an 80% parking reduction from the base ratios.

KEY THINGS TO REMEMBER

■ Base ratios are referenced from the Parking Consultants Council, as shown in the Institute of Transportation Engineers' Transportation Planning Handbook, 3rd edition, tables 18-2 through 18-4.

■ Projects need to provide preferred parking for carpools for **5%** of the total parking after the reductions have been made from the base ratios.

■ Projects without off-street parking will earn the credit automatically.

■ Projects that have earned 1 or more points under either the "Surrounding Density and Diverse Uses" credit or the "Access to Quality Transit" credit should achieve a **40%** reduction from the base ratios.

Green Vehicles—Credit

■ Applicable to: All the LEED BD+C Rating Systems

All the LEED BD+C Rating Systems	1 point

CREDIT SUMMARY

This credit promotes the use of green vehicles (vehicles that score a minimum of 45 points on the **American Council for an Energy-Efficient Economy (ACEEE)** annual vehicle rating guide) by providing them exceptions, including preferred parking spaces, discounted parking rates, and **electric vehicle supply equipment (EVSE)**.

In the United States, transportation accounts for 27% of total greenhouse gas emissions from combustion of petroleum-based fuels.[3] The usage of petroleum-based fuels is a serious cause of climate change and is the main source of air pollution.

CREDIT INTENT

To reduce pollution by promoting alternative vehicles as opposed to conventionally fueled automobiles.

CREDIT REQUIREMENTS

For all LEED BD+C projects, except "LEED BD+C: Schools", and "LEED BD+C: Warehouses and Distribution Centers":

Project teams should designate **5% of all parking spaces** as preferred parking for sole use by green vehicles. Preferred parking spaces should be distributed proportionally among various parking sections, if exists, including short-term, long-term, customer, and visitor parking sections. Required signage should be posted on the preferred parking locations that clearly shows that those preferred locations are reserved for green vehicles.

Or instead of providing preferred parking to green vehicles, projects can provide a discounted parking rate of **at least 20%** to green vehicles. The discounted rate must be publicly posted at the entrance of the parking area and should be available to every green vehicle permanently.

To be considered a green vehicle, a vehicle must achieve a minimum green score of **45** on the **American Council for an Energy Efficient Economy** annual vehicle rating guide (or equivalent for projects outside the United States).

After a project has complied with the preferred parking or the discounted parking requirements, project teams should pursue one of the following two options:

OPTION 1: ELECTRIC VEHICLE CHARGING – (1 Point)

Under this option, projects should install **electric vehicle supply equipment** in **2% of all the parking spaces** used by the project. These parking spaces should be identified and reserved for sole use by plug-in electric vehicles. Project teams can decide on the location of these parking spaces at their own discretion. (These EVSE parking spaces will be provided in addition to the preferred parking spaces reserved for green vehicles that are mentioned above.)

The installed EVSE should have the following properties:

- Provide Level 2 charging capacity (208–240 volts) or greater.
- Comply with the relevant regional or local standard for electrical connectors, such as SAE Surface Vehicle Recommended Practice J1772, SAE Electric Vehicle Conductive Charge Coupler, or for projects outside the United States, IEC 62196 of the International Electrotechnical Commission.
- Be networked or accessible from the Internet (must have Wi-Fi, a cellular modem, or other capability to send usage data to a server) and be capable of participating in a demand-response program or time-of-use pricing to encourage off-peak charging.

📄 Project teams should document parking on a site plan indicating the building entrance, preferred parking spaces, and fueling stations, and the teams should submit the parking capacity calculations. To show the preferred parking spaces, vehicle charging stations, and posted discounted parking rates, project teams should submit photographs of the required signage or the pavement markings. For the vehicle charging stations, project teams should submit product specifications, Internet accessibility, and compliance with the relevant standard.

OR

OPTION 2: LIQUID, GAS, OR BATTERY FACILITIES – (1 Point)

Under this option, projects should install **liquid** or **gas alternative fuel** fueling facilities or a **battery switching station** that should be capable of refueling a number of vehicles per day equal to at **least 2% of the total parking spaces**. Alternative fuels are nongasoline, low-polluting fuels like hydrogen, electricity, propane, compressed natural gas, liquid natural gas, methanol, and ethanol.

📄 Project teams should document parking on a site plan indicating the building entrance, preferred parking spaces, and fueling stations, and they should submit the parking capacity calculations. To show the preferred parking spaces or the posted discounted parking rates, project teams should submit the photographs of the required signage or the pavement markings. For the liquid or gas fueling stations, project teams should submit the product specifications.

For "LEED BD+C: Schools":

OPTION 1: GREEN PASSENGER VEHICLES – (1 Point)

Under this option, the school projects should designate **5% of all parking spaces** used by the project as preferred parking for green vehicles. Again, the preferred parking spaces should be distributed proportionally among various parking sections, such as short-term and long-term parking sections. Again, the signage should be posted on the preferred parking locations, and it should clearly show that those preferred locations are reserved to green vehicles.

Again, instead of providing preferred parking to green vehicles, projects can provide a discounted parking rate of **at least 20%** to green vehicles. The discounted rate must be publicly posted at the entrance of the parking area and should be available to every green vehicle permanently.

After the project has complied with the preferred parking or the discounted parking requirements, project teams should pursue one of the following two paths:

PATH 1: ELECTRIC VEHICLE CHARGING

Under this path, projects should, again, install **electric vehicle supply equipment in 2% of all the parking spaces** used by the project. These parking spaces should be identified and reserved for the sole use of plug-in electric vehicles, and project teams can decide on their location at their own discretion. (These EVSE parking spaces should be provided separately and in addition to the preferred parking spaces reserved for green vehicles mentioned above.)

The installed EVSE should have the following properties:

- Provide Level 2 charging capacity (208–240 volts) or greater, such as Level 3 charging
- Comply with the relevant regional or local standard for electrical connectors, such as SAE Surface Vehicle Recommended Practice J1772, SAE Electric Vehicle Conductive Charge Coupler, or for projects outside the United States, IEC 62196 of the International Electrotechnical Commission
- Be networked or accessible from the Internet. And the project should also be capable of participating in a demand-response program or time-of-use pricing to encourage off-peak charging

OR

PATH 2: LIQUID, GAS, OR BATTERY FACILITIES

Under this path, projects should install **liquid** or **gas alternative fuel** fueling facilities or a **battery switching station** that should be capable of refueling a number of vehicles per day equal to **at least 2% of the total parking spaces**.

💡 As seen so far, the requirements for the "LEED BD+C: Schools" projects are exactly the same as other rating systems requirements (except the LEED BD+C: Warehouses and Distribution Centers" projects that we will discuss shortly). The difference with the "LEED BD+C: School" projects is that school projects have another option, which is the "Green Buses and School-Owned Vehicles" option.

📄 Project teams should document parking plan or site plan indicating the building entrance, preferred parking spaces, and fueling stations, and they should submit the parking capacity calculations. To show the preferred parking spaces, vehicle charging stations, and posted discounted parking rates, project teams should submit photographs of the required signage or the pavement markings. For the vehicle charging stations, project teams should submit product specifications, Internet accessibility, and compliance with the relevant standard (path 1). For liquid or gas fueling stations, projects should submit product specifications (path 2).

OR

OPTION 2: GREEN BUSES AND SCHOOL-OWNED VEHICLES — (1 Point)

Under this option, school projects should develop and implement **a plan for every bus serving the school** in order to meet the following emissions standards within <u>seven years of the building certificate of occupancy</u>:

- Nitrogen oxide (NOx) emissions of 0.50 grams or less per brake horsepower-hour; and
- Particulate matter emissions of 0.01 grams or less per brake horsepower-hour.

To summarize, if there are any school buses that cannot meet these emission standards, the school project teams should determine whether to retrofit or phase them out in order to meet these emission standards. If the school project teams choose to retrofit buses, the retrofitting must be approved by a relevant third party such as the **California Air Resources Board** or a local equivalent.

Additionally, project teams should develop and implement a plan for **100%** of all other (nonbus) vehicles owned or leased to serve the school as green vehicles.

📄 For documentation, project teams should submit the phase-in plan for the bus fleet, indicating the emissions evaluations, retrofitting strategies, and timeline. For nonbus vehicles, project teams should submit a phase-in plan showing the types of vehicles and timeline.

<u>For "LEED BD+C: Warehouses and Distribution Centers"</u>:

OPTION 1: ALTERNATIVE FUEL VEHICLES — (1 Point)

Project teams should provide an on-site fleet with at least **one yard tractor** powered by <u>electricity</u>, <u>propane,</u> or <u>natural gas</u>, and they should also provide <u>on-site charging</u> or <u>refueling stations</u> for the mentioned vehicle(s). Liquid or gas refueling stations should be separately ventilated if not located outdoors.

> 📄 Project teams should submit the manufacturer's documentation of the yard tractor model and fuel type.

OR

OPTION 2: REDUCED TRUCK IDLING — (1 Point)

Project teams should provide an electrical connection for at least **50% of all dock door locations** to limit truck idling at the dock. These electrical connectors are for shutting down the truck engines without shutting down the in-cab air-conditioning or the communications and entertainment systems.

> 📄 Project teams should submit a site plan showing the electrical connector locations at the loading dock doors and the manufacturer's documentation.

EXEMPLARY PERFORMANCE

This credit does not qualify for exemplary performance.

CASE STUDY

To illustrate, let's suppose that a "LEED BD+C: New Construction and Major Renovation" project decides to pursue this credit. The project has total parking capacity of 100 spaces, and 80 of those spaces are long-term while the remaining 20 are dedicated to short-term use. The project teams decide to designate preferred parking spaces for the sole use of green vehicles and also provide EVSE by pursuing option 1 of the credit.

Required number of preferred parking spaces to green vehicles: 100 x 0.05 = **5 spaces**

Since the preferred parking spaces should be distributed proportionally among the short-term and long-term parking sections, the project team calculates the following:

Required number of preferred short-term parking spaces to green vehicles:
5 x (20 / 100) = **1 space**

Required number of preferred long-term parking spaces to green vehicles:
5 x (80 / 100) = **4 spaces**

Now the project team calculates the required number of parking spaces with EVSE reserved for electric vehicles:

Required number of parking spaces with EVSE: 100 x 0.02 = **2 spaces with EVSE**

Finally, the project team documents the credit on a plan, showing the locations of the preferred parking spaces and the parking spaces with EVSE. Remember that the project team can choose the location of the EVSE parking spaces at its own discretion.

KEY THINGS TO REMEMBER

- Green vehicles must achieve a minimum green score of **45** on the ACEEE annual vehicle rating guide.
- Alternative fuels are nongasoline, low-polluting fuels like hydrogen, electricity, propane, compressed natural gas, liquid natural gas, methanol, and ethanol.
- To earn this credit, if school project teams choose to retrofit buses, the retrofitting must be approved by a relevant third party such as the **California Air Resources Board** or a local equivalent.
- EVSE parking spaces must be provided separately and in addition to the preferred parking spaces reserved for green vehicles.
- If the project does not contain any parking area, this credit cannot be pursued, as mentioned under the "Documenting Location and Transportation Credits" section.

CHAPTER 5

SUSTAINABLE SITES (SS)

This chapter will discuss both the importance of sustainable sites and their effects on green building design. Green buildings need to consider all the factors for creating a sustainable site and minimize the building's effect on the environment and the whole neighborhood.

During construction, the environmental impacts of construction activities should be minimized, and necessary strategies should be evaluated before the start of construction. Necessary precautions should be taken to prevent construction-related dust from polluting the neighborhood, and while grading the project site, the project teams should take measures to prevent erosion and sedimentation.

As an important aspect of the integrated process of creating a sustainable site, a site assessment needs to be conducted in order to have the relevant information that will be necessary for the site design. With the completion of the site assessment, the project team will have the necessary information to proceed with the site design.

When designing the site, the development footprint of the project should be considered as a whole.

Many people enjoy spending time with pristine views and natural surroundings. In light of this, when designing a development footprint, the project teams should always think about preserving open spaces, which will allow the occupants to spend time in the outdoors in a picturesque landscape.

Choosing the type of vegetation to be used in the project is also an important decision that will greatly impact outdoor water consumption. If the project teams choose to use native or adapted plants, the project will need less irrigation and maintenance. (The native or adapted plants will reduce the water use of the project since those plants are accustomed to naturally surviving in that climate.)

Lighting is another important factor that needs to be addressed during the site design. During the green building design, all types of light pollution should be avoided. Project teams should eliminate uplighting, glare, overlighting, and light trespass (light spilling out of the project boundary) in order to conserve energy and to not create discomfort for the adjacent properties.

As will be discussed under the "Light Pollution Reduction" credit, LEED started to request the use of the **backlight-uplight-glare (BUG)** rating method to show compliance with sustainable lighting measures as well as the standards of the **Illuminating Engineering Society of North America (IESNA)**, which sets lighting specifications for building design.

Rainwater management is another issue that all green buildings need to address. The first goal of a green building for rainwater management should be for it to contain the least number of impervious surfaces. Furthermore, the rainwater that falls onto the pervious surfaces should be collected and retained, or at least its flow should be slowed down. If the flow of rainwater cannot be slowed down, heavy rainfall will result in the overwhelming of the municipal storm sewer system.

The "Sustainable Sites" credit category contains the following prerequisites/credits:

- Construction Activity Pollution Prevention—Prerequisite
- Environmental Site Assessment—Prerequisite
- Site Assessment—Credit
- Site Development—Protect or Restore Habitat—Credit
- Open Space—Credit
- Rainwater Management—Credit
- Heat Island Reduction—Credit
- Light Pollution Reduction—Credit
- Site Master Plan—Credit
- Tenant Design and Construction Guidelines—Credit
- Places of Respite—Credit
- Direct Exterior Access—Credit
- Joint Use of Facilities—Credit

Construction Activity Pollution Prevention—Prerequisite

■ Applicable to: All the LEED BD+C Rating Systems

PREREQUISITE SUMMARY

In most parts of the world, there are codes to ensure that all construction projects implement an Erosion and Sedimentation Control (ESC) plan, which protects the environment and the neighborhood from the pollution created by construction activities. However, this prerequisite ensures, even if there is not a local code, that the project disturbances to the neighboring properties, to the site, and to the rainwater systems are minimized.

This prerequisite encourages projects to create and implement an ESC plan according to the erosion and sedimentation requirements of the **2012 US Environmental Protection Agency (EPA) Construction General Permit (CGP)** or local equivalent, whichever is more stringent.

Below are some of the issues addressed:
 ➥ The slope of the project site and where water will drain
 ➥ The total area and duration of ground disturbance to identify air quality and rainwater runoff effects on neighboring properties
 ➥ The location of existing rainwater management systems that must be protected
 ➥ Weather and soil conditions that can create rainwater runoff or generate dust
 ➥ Construction entrances and their effects on local roads servicing the project site
 ➥ Planned construction sequencing, which may require additional future ESC measures

The measures should be implemented before the commencement of construction, and as the construction progress, additional measures should be taken as necessary. Project teams should monitor the control measures and record the inspections by date-stamped site photographs and reports.

PREREQUISITE INTENT

To reduce the pollution created from construction activities by controlling <u>soil erosion</u>, <u>airborne dust</u>, and <u>waterway sedimentation</u>.

PREREQUISITE REQUIREMENTS

Projects should create and implement an erosion and sedimentation control plan (ESC) for all construction activities associated with the project. The plan should conform to the erosion and sedimentation requirements of the **2012 US Environmental Protection Agency (EPA) Construction General Permit (CGP)** or a local equivalent, whichever is more stringent, and it should describe the measures implemented.

Project teams should first review the local codes and see if the local jurisdictions require a construction general permit based on the National Pollutant Discharge Elimination System (NPDES) program criteria. If the local codes do require a CGP, projects can directly earn this prerequisite without any additional effort. However, if the local codes do not require a CGP, project teams should check and compare the local codes with the CGP and implement whichever is more stringent.

The main items that the CGP will address are erosion and sedimentation control, stabilization, and pollution prevention.

> 🗎 Project teams using the 2012 EPA CGP should document a description of compliance with the EPA CGP. For the zero-lot-line projects, a description of special conditions and compliance with any applicable ESC measure is also required.
>
> 🗎 Projects using local standards should document a comparison of local standards with the EPA CGP, describe how the project complies with local standards, submit drawings showing the ESC measure implemented, and send a declaration or photographs about the implemented plan. For zero-lot-line projects, a description of special conditions and compliance with any applicable ESC measure is also required.

KEY THINGS TO REMEMBER

- The ESC plan needs to conform to the erosion and sedimentation requirements of the 2012 US Environmental Protection Agency (EPA) Construction General Permit (CGP).
- The intent of this prerequisite is to reduce the pollution created from construction activities by controlling **soil erosion**, **airborne dust,** and **waterway sedimentation**.

Environmental Site Assessment—Prerequisite

■ Applicable to: **Schools** and **Healthcare**

PREREQUISITE SUMMARY

This prerequisite is designed for school and healthcare projects to ensure that the project site or any existing building in the project does not have any contamination or hazardous materials that can harm the health of students and patients.

The prerequisite requires an environmental site assessment, and if any contamination is found, the project teams must perform remediation activities in order to make the project suitable for school or healthcare use.

The prerequisite requirements mention the phases of environmental site assessment, just as the "High Priority Site" credit does. Remember that a Phase I Environmental Site Assessment (ESA) is a survey to identify potential or existing site contamination. It generally includes reviewing the historical records, a site visit for visually identifying any sign of contamination, and a narrative that indicates whether a Phase II ESA is required or not. A Phase II ESA covers the testing of the on-site soil, groundwater, and more, and it determines how much contamination exists on-site. On the other hand, a Phase III ESA is the first step of the remediation process, and it covers the evaluation of the remediation options and costs.

PREREQUISITE INTENT

To protect the health of vulnerable populations by ensuring that the project site is assessed for environmental contamination and that any environmental contamination has been remediated.

PREREQUISITE REQUIREMENTS

Project teams should conduct a Phase I Environmental Site Assessment, according to the **ASTM E1527-05 standard**, or a local equivalent, and they should determine if any environmental contamination exists on-site. If contamination is suspected, project teams can directly conduct a Phase II Environmental Site Assessment, according to the **ASTM E1903-11 standard** or a local equivalent.

If no contamination is found under the Phase I ESA, project teams will earn the prerequisite. However, if the Phase I ESA indicates existence of any recognized environmental condition, or if it suggests additional assessment, project teams must then conduct a Phase II ESA. And if any contamination is found, projects must remediate the site to meet local, state, or national environmental protection agency regional residential standards, using whichever standard is more stringent. Under this prerequisite, if any contamination is found on-site in the Phase II ESA, it is up to the project teams to conduct a Phase III ESA before proceeding with remediation.

For projects outside the United States, LEED also accepts local equivalents to the ESAs provided that they are equal or more stringent.

> 📄 Project teams will need to document the Phase I, II, and III ESAs as applicable, and they will need to provide a narrative about the contamination and with verification that the site has been remediated as applicable.

KEY THINGS TO REMEMBER

- The American Society of Testing and Materials (ASTM) ESA is the methodology used in LEED to investigate a project site's contamination.
- Scopes of the Phase I, II, and III Environmental Site Assessment are important.
- This prerequisite is only applicable to school and healthcare projects.

Site Assessment—Credit

- Applicable to: All the LEED BD+C Rating Systems

All the LEED BD+C Rating Systems	1 point

CREDIT SUMMARY

Site assessment is a part of the integrative process, which clearly shows the project teams the properties of the site, such as topography, hydrology, climate, soil types, vegetation, human use, and human health effects. By conducting a site assessment, teams can orient the building to take advantage of solar access or can decide which types of plants would be well suited to the site conditions for landscaping. Or teams can evaluate the project's rainfall data, optimize on-site rainwater management, and much more.

Therefore, a site assessment before the conceptual design can make a great contribution to reducing the project costs and promoting the building users' health.

CREDIT INTENT

To assess site conditions before project design to evaluate suitable options and inform decisions about the site design.

CREDIT REQUIREMENTS

Project teams should prepare and document a site survey or assessment that includes the following:

- **Topography**: This covers contour mapping, slope stability risks, and unique topographic features.
- **Hydrology**: This covers flood hazard areas, lakes, delineated wetlands, streams, shorelines, rainwater collection and reuse opportunities, and **Urban Hydrology for Small Watersheds Technical Release 55 (TR-55) initial water storage capacity of the site** (or local equivalent for projects outside the United States). With TR-55, project teams can model the watersheds to calculate the stormwater runoff volume, peak rate of discharge, and storage volumes. Project teams can also evaluate strategies on rainwater harvesting for irrigation or other uses with this assessment.
- **Climate**: This pertains to the site's solar exposure, heat island effect potential, seasonal sun angles, prevailing winds, monthly precipitation, and temperature ranges.
- **Vegetation**: This covers the site's primary vegetation types, significant tree mapping, threatened or endangered species, unique habitat, greenfield area, and invasive plant species.
- **Soils**: Project teams should determine the soil classification with **Natural Resources Conservation Service soils delineation** (which is a soil survey showing all the different types of soils), the US Department of Agriculture prime farmland status, healthy soils, disturbed soils, and previous development on-site.
- **Human use**: This includes views, the site's transportation infrastructure, adjacent properties, and construction materials with existing recycle or reuse potential.
- **Human health effects**: Project teams should evaluate the proximity of vulnerable populations that can be affected by the project, adjacent physical activity opportunities, and proximity to major sources of air pollution. Additionally, project teams should identify any source of noise, air, or water pollution that can affect the design. It is also very important that project teams assess green environments that can provide opportunities for physical activity and social interaction.

The assessment should document how the project design was influenced by the site assessment. If any of the topics above are not addressed, then an explanation should be provided by the project teams.

> Project teams should document a site survey or assessment plan with a site assessment worksheet or narrative.

EXEMPLARY PERFORMANCE

This credit does not qualify for exemplary performance.

KEY THINGS TO REMEMBER

- A site assessment includes evaluation of topography, hydrology, climate, vegetation, soils, human use, and human health effects.
- Projects can estimate the water storage capacity of the site using the Urban Hydrology for Small Watersheds Technical Release 55 (TR-55). International projects can use a local equivalent.

Site Development-Protect or Restore Habitat—Credit

■ Applicable to: All the LEED BD+C Rating Systems

New Construction	1 – 2 points	Retail	1 – 2 points	Hospitality	1 – 2 points
Core and Shell	1 – 2 points	Data Centers	1 – 2 points	Healthcare	1 point
Schools	1 – 2 points	Warehouses & Dist. Centers	1 – 2 points		

CREDIT SUMMARY

This credit is aimed to both protect the on-site greenfield during construction and restore the damaged habitat. In order to achieve the credit, during construction project teams should protect at least **40%** of their greenfield on-site, if it exists, in any option they choose to pursue. (To qualify as a greenfield, that area should have not been previously developed, graded, or disturbed.) Moreover, the project teams should restore at least **30%** of the previously disturbed land by revegetation in option 1, or instead provide financial support to a nationally or locally recognized land trust or conservation organization in option 2. But still, in order to earn the maximum number of points from the credit, project teams should choose option 1, which is on-site restoration.

CREDIT INTENT

To conserve existing ecological areas and restore damaged areas to provide habitat and promote biodiversity.

CREDIT REQUIREMENTS

Projects should preserve and protect **40%** of the greenfield area on the site, <u>if it exists</u>, from all development and construction activity. Next, project teams should pursue one of the following options:

OPTION 1: ON-SITE RESTORATION — (2 Points)

By using native or adapted vegetation, projects should restore **30%** (including the building footprint) of all portions of the site that were previously disturbed. Projects that achieve **at least a density of 1.5 floor-to-area ratio** may also include <u>vegetated roof surfaces</u> in this calculation if native and adapted plants are used and the vegetated roof provides habitat and promotes biodiversity.

Projects should restore all disturbed soils that will be revegetated to meet the following requirements:

- Soils (including imported soils) must be reused for functions similar to their original function.
- Imported topsoils, or soil blends designed to serve as topsoil, cannot include either of the following:

  - Soils defined regionally by the Natural Resources Conservation Service web soil survey (or equivalent for projects outside the United States) as prime farmland, unique farmland, or farmland of statewide or local importance
  - Soils from other greenfield sites, unless they are a byproduct of a construction process

- Restored soil should meet the criteria of **reference soils** (reference soils are the native soils of a site that were present before the development) in categories 1, 2, and 3 and meet the criteria of either category 4 or 5:

  1) Organic matter
  2) Compaction
  3) Infiltration rates
  4) Soil biological function
  5) Soil chemical characteristics

Vegetated landscape areas that are constructed to accommodate rainwater infiltration from the vegetation and soils are exempt from this calculation. But project teams must make sure that these areas are treated the same under the "Rainwater Management" credit as well. The areas that do not contain any vegetation naturally can be counted toward the greenfield or restored-area requirement; they include natural rock outcrops, natural desert, existing ponds, or similar areas if they are enhanced and restored.

Only for the "LEED BD+C: School" projects, the dedicated athletic fields that are used only for athletic purposes are excluded from the soil restoration criteria. Additionally, these areas cannot be counted toward the 30% minimum restoration requirement.

> 📄 Project teams should document greenfield calculations, provide a narrative about the greenfield area, submit a site plan showing the development and vegetation, describe the disturbed soil that was revegetated, submit the native or adapted vegetation calculations, and document reference soil characteristics and test results. Teams with projects with vegetated roofs should also provide the floor-to-area (FAR) ratio.

OR

OPTION 2: FINANCIAL SUPPORT – (1 Point)

Provide financial support equivalent to at least $0.40 per square foot ($4 per square meter) for the total site area, including the building footprint. Financial support must be provided to a land trust or conservation organization **within the same EPA Level III ecoregion** or the **project's state**. For projects in the United States, the land trust must also be accredited by the **Land Trust Alliance**, which is an organization that provides accreditation to land trust organizations. Land trust organizations are private, nonprofit organizations that work to conserve land by undertaking or assisting in conservation. In order to identify the Level III ecoregion and the project's native vegetation and soils, project teams can use the classification system of the EPA.

For projects outside the United States, the land trust or conservation organization must be located within **100 miles (160 kilometers)** of the project. These projects should also determine their ecoregion to make decisions about habitat restoration and protection. NatureServe Natural Heritage Program, Conservation International, and World Land Trust are all organizations that work internationally and can assist project teams with this issue.

> 📄 Project teams should document greenfield calculations, provide a narrative about the greenfield area, and submit financial support calculations and the agreement with the land trust with a confirmation stating that the land trust is accredited by the Land Trust Alliance.

> 📄 For projects outside the United States, project teams should confirm that the conservation organization is nationally or locally recognized.

EXEMPLARY PERFORMANCE

To qualify for exemplary performance under this credit, project teams pursuing option 1 need to double the 30% restoration requirement by restoring at least 60% of the previously disturbed site. And project teams pursuing option 2 need to double the financial donation requirement by donating at least $0.80 per square foot, or $8.00 per square meter, for the total site area.

CASE STUDY

To illustrate, let's say that the team for project A decides to earn 2 points from this credit by pursuing option 1. But in order for the team to pursue option 1, the project should have sufficient land to meet the credit's requirements, and that land should contain previously developed areas. If the project has sufficient land, but all the land is greenfield, again option 1 cannot be pursued. If the project's floor-to-area ratio is higher than 1.5, the project teams can choose to install a vegetated roof and qualify for option 1.

Now we will assume that the project contains sufficient land to pursue option 1, and some part of the site is previously developed. In this scenario, project teams will first categorize all the areas of the project site as either greenfield or previously developed. Then, the project team will take measures to protect at least 40% of the greenfield that exists on-site by developing a construction activity management plan for greenfield protection.

Next, it is time to work on the areas that were identified as previously developed. Project teams will first calculate the minimum required area that needs to be restored with the formula below, and the teams should make sure the area exceeds the 30% of the total previously developed site area.

$$\text{\% of Restoration area} = \frac{\text{Restoration area}}{\text{Total previously developed site area}} \times 100$$

Equation 7. Percentage of restoration area

In this case study, the project teams will determine the restoration strategies by using native or adapted plants. But before that, the soil conditions and the reference soils need to be determined.

If the project teams will import soil, they need to meet the credit's requirements, which can be done by conducting a soil test to demonstrate that the restored soil achieves the credit's requirements. Finally, the project teams will restore the soils by using native and adapted plants. Turf grasses (lawns) can count toward vegetation. However, the native and adapted plants should not require any maintenance such as irrigation, pesticides, etc.

Again, landscape areas that are constructed to accommodate rainwater infiltration from the vegetation and soils are exempt from this calculation. But project teams must make sure that these areas are treated the same in the "Rainwater Management" credit.

Now, let us assume that the project teams decided to pursue option 2 instead of option 1. In that scenario, the project teams would need to provide financial support to a qualifying land trust or conservation organization. To calculate the financial support required, the project teams could use the following formula:

$$\textbf{Minimum financial support}\ =\ \text{Total site area}\ \ \text{x}\ \ \$\ 0.40\ /\ ft^2$$

Equation 8. Minimum financial support

Next, the project team would do research to find out the qualifying financial support within the same EPA Level III ecoregion or the project's state, and then would send the financial support.

KEY THINGS TO REMEMBER

- For projects in the United States, the land trust must be accredited by the Land Trust Alliance.
- Only for the "LEED BD+C: School" projects, the dedicated athletic fields that are used only for athletic purposes are excluded from the soil restoration criteria. Additionally, these areas may not count toward the **30%** minimum restoration requirement.
- Projects can earn exemplary performance points by basically doubling up the requirements in both the options. The requirement to preserve and protect **40%** of the greenfield area on the site, if it exists, from all development and construction activity still applies to both options.
- Projects that achieve at least a density of **1.5 floor-to-area ratio** may include vegetated roof surfaces in this calculation if native and adapted plants are used.
- Under option 2, financial support must be provided to a land trust or conservation organization **within the same EPA Level III ecoregion** or the **project's state**. For projects outside the United States, the land trust or the conservation organization must be located within **100 miles (160 kilometers)** of the project.

Open Space—Credit

■ Applicable to: All the LEED BD+C Rating Systems

All the LEED BD+C Rating Systems	1 point

CREDIT SUMMARY

We all love to go to parks, lie on the grass, and spend time with our friends or read books. We also know that open spaces provide great health benefits to individuals. This credit encourages project teams to provide outdoor spaces, with vegetation. The outdoor spaces provided should be <u>accessible to all building users.</u>

CREDIT INTENT

To create open spaces that would promote interaction with the environment, passive recreation, social interaction, and physical activities.

CREDIT REQUIREMENTS

Projects should provide outdoor space **more than or equal to 30% of the total site area**, including the building footprint. **A minimum 25% of the provided outdoor space must be vegetated** (turf grass does not count as vegetation) or should have overhead vegetated canopy.

The outdoor space must be physically accessible and be one or more of the following:

- Pedestrian-oriented paving or turf area with physical site elements that accommodate outdoor social activities for building occupants
- Recreation-oriented paving or turf area with physical site elements to encourage physical activity for building occupants
- Garden space with different vegetation types and species that provide opportunities for year-round visual interest
- Garden space dedicated to community gardens or urban food production
- Preserved or created habitat that meets the criteria of the "Site Development—Protect or Restore Habitat" credit and also includes elements of human interaction

For projects that achieve a density of 1.5 floor-area ratio (FAR), **extensive** or **intensive vegetated roofs** can be used for the minimum 25% vegetation requirement, and the roof's physically accessible paving areas can be used toward credit compliance.

Extensive vegetated roofs are the types of roofs that do not include a variety of plants and require little maintenance. Their soil layer is thinner than intensive roofs since they're more designed for smaller-size vegetation. Intensive vegetated roofs have a wider variety of plants and also have more soil depth to support those plants.

Wetlands or naturally designed ponds can be counted as open space as well. But their side slope gradients should average 1:4 (vertical: horizontal) or less, and they need to be vegetated.

For projects that are part of a <u>multitenant complex</u>, open spaces can be at another location in the site master plan. But still, they should be protected from any development. If the open space is not adjacent to the building, documentation should be provided showing that the credit requirements have been met and that the land is in a natural state or will be returned to a natural state and will also be conserved for the whole life of the building.

> 🗎 Project teams should provide documentation with a site plan showing all types of open spaces inside the project boundary, open space and vegetated area calculations, and a narrative description of how open space is accessible and meets the credit criteria. For projects with vegetated roofs, the floor-to-area (FAR) ratio should be additionally submitted.

EXEMPLARY PERFORMANCE

This credit does not qualify for exemplary performance.

CASE STUDY

To illustrate, let us suppose that a team with a project located in Los Angeles aims for this credit and wants to calculate the required open space and vegetation area. With a project site of 80,000 square feet of total site area (including the building footprint), the credit calculations would be as follows:

Required open space: 80,000 x 0.3 = 24,000 square feet

Required vegetated area: 24,000 x 0.25 = 6,000 square feet

KEY THINGS TO REMEMBER

- Definitions of intensive and extensive vegetated roofs.
- For projects that achieve a density of 1.5 floor-area ratio (FAR), **extensive** or **intensive vegetated roofs** can be used for the 25% vegetation requirement.
- In LEED, an open space area should be a minimum of 30% of the total site area, and a minimum of 25% of the open space must be vegetated. Open spaces should be accessible to all building users.

Rainwater Management—Credit

■ Applicable to: All the LEED BD+C Rating Systems

New Construction	2 – 3 points	Retail	2 – 3 points	Hospitality	2 – 3 points
Core and Shell	2 – 3 points	Data Centers	2 – 3 points	Healthcare	1 – 2 points
Schools	2 – 3 points	Warehouses & Dist. Centers	2 – 3 points		

CREDIT SUMMARY

Most people have probably seen the gigantic pipes of storm sewers, which are responsible for carrying stormwater to avoid flooding. But what is the reason that municipalities are working so hard to get rid of this much water?

Think about an undeveloped piece of land with a ground surface of soil. In this scenario, there wouldn't be any flooding. Moreover, rainwater would not be considered an enemy, but a best friend.

After we started developing the world, soil was replaced by impervious surfaces through which the rainwater couldn't be absorbed by the soil. Now, all the rainwater that falls on impervious surfaces adds up to vast amounts of water that need to be transferred somewhere else. In turn, the transferal of such amounts of rainwater results in other consequences.

With the stormwater runoff, water gets contaminated by harmful chemicals and then flows into natural bodies of water such as seas, oceans, or lakes, resulting in a degraded quality of surface water, which consequently harms aquatic life and prevents recreational opportunities.

This type of pollution is also called **nonpoint source pollution** since the point of the pollution source cannot be identified.

Because the rainwater can't be absorbed and filtered by the soil, it cannot replenish the aquifers. To summarize, the natural hydrology of the ecosystem can't work anymore. Because of that, green buildings need to address rainwater management to protect the environment.

The first goal of a green building for rainwater management should be for it to contain the least number of impervious surfaces. Furthermore, the rainwater that falls onto the pervious surfaces should be collected and retained (this is called **on-site water retention**), or at least its flow should be slowed down. If the flow of the rainwater cannot be slowed down, heavy rainfall will result in the overwhelming of the municipal storm sewer system.

This particular credit aims to re-create the rainwater balance by promoting **green infrastructure** (GI) and **low-impact development** (LID) rainwater management strategies, which can be done by mimicking a site's natural hydrology, thus minimizing the disruption caused by the project.

To earn the credit, the total volume of rainwater run-off will be calculated according to the rainfall data of the project's location, and strategies will be implemented to manage that amount of rainwater.

CREDIT INTENT

To reduce the volume of rainwater runoff and improve water quality by replicating the natural hydrology and water balance of the project site, based on past climate data and undeveloped ecosystems in the region.

CREDIT REQUIREMENTS

OPTION 1: PERCENTILE OF RAINFALL EVENTS — (2-3 Points)

PATH 1: 95TH PERCENTILE — (2 Points)

Under this path, projects should manage the on-site rainwater runoff from the developed site for the **95th percentile of regional or local rainfall events** by using green infrastructure and low-impact development, to best replicate the natural site hydrology.

Project teams will use the **daily rainfall data** and EPA methodology to determine the 95th percentile amount. The mentioned methodology is the **US Environmental Protection Agency Technical Guidance on Implementing the Stormwater Runoff Requirements for Federal Projects under Section 438 of the Energy Independence and Security Act.**

OR

PATH 2: 98TH PERCENTILE — (3 Points)

Project teams pursuing this path should achieve path 1. But in this instance, for the **98th percentile of regional or local rainfall events**. Again, the on-site runoff volume should be managed by using <u>low-impact development</u> and <u>green infrastructure</u> to best replicate the natural site hydrology.

OR

PATH 3: ZERO-LOT-LINE PROJECTS ONLY—85TH PERCENTILE — (3 Points)

Only for the <u>zero-lot-line projects in urban areas with a minimum density of 1.5 floor-to-area ratio</u>, project teams should manage the runoff from the developed site for the **85th percentile of regional or local rainfall events**, again by using <u>low-impact development</u> and <u>green infrastructure</u> to best replicate the natural site hydrology. (Zero-lot-line projects are the projects in which their project boundary exactly aligns with the building footprint. In other words, the building sits on the whole project site.)

- 📄 Project teams should document rainfall data, rainfall calculations, runoff volume calculations, plans depicting site conditions, green infrastructure or low-impact development strategies, and calculations with a narrative. If 10 years of historic rainfall data are not available, project teams should provide an explanation.
- 📄 Multitenant complex projects should additionally document a summary of centralized approach and associated distributed techniques.
- 📄 Project teams pursuing path 3 should additionally provide a narrative of conditions that make the project zero-lot-line, and they should submit a floor-to-area (FAR) ratio.

OR

OPTION 2: NATURAL LAND COVER CONDITIONS — (3 Points)

Under this option, project teams should manage the annual increase in rainwater runoff on-site, from the natural land cover condition to the post-developed condition.

In this option, the project teams need to find the natural land condition of the project site and then make a calculation to find how much rainwater it was able to absorb for the 95th percentile of regional or local rainfall events. Next, the project teams should calculate how much rainwater the land at the time can absorb. The difference between those two values will give the runoff volume that occurred with the disturbance of the project to the site.

And that runoff volume needs to be managed in order to earn the credit under option 2. However, in order to pursue this option, project teams should have data showing the natural land cover conditions.

<u>Only for the projects that are a part of a multitenant complex</u>, the credit requirements can be met by using a **coordinated approach** for the multiple buildings within the project boundary. Distributed techniques based on a watershed approach are required. Project teams can use distributed LID strategies to manage runoff closest to its source.

> 📄 Project teams should document rainfall data, rainfall calculations, runoff volume calculations, plans depicting site conditions, GI or LID strategies, and calculations with a narrative. If 10 years of historic rainfall data are not available, project teams should provide an explanation.
>
> 📄 Multitenant complex projects should additionally document a summary of centralized approach and associated distributed techniques.
>
> 📄 Projects should submit documents that illustrate the natural land cover conditions.

EXEMPLARY PERFORMANCE

To qualify for exemplary performance under this credit, projects need to manage **100%** of the rainwater that falls within the project boundary.

CASE STUDY

To illustrate, let's suppose that a project aiming for this credit wants to pursue path 2 by managing the 98th percentile of the regional or local rainfall events and by using LID and green infrastructure.

First, the project team will need to obtain the historical rainfall data for the project's location, showing at least a period of 10 years of data. In order to find the data, projects teams located in the United States can use the **National Climatic Data Center**, and project teams outside the United States can use local sources or the **UN Food and Agriculture Organization** and **Aquastat**.

Next, the project teams will need to calculate the rainfall value for the 98th percentile (in inches or millimeters) of all rainfall events. And once this rainfall volume at the site is calculated, project teams will then calculate the runoff volume of the site in its post- developed condition. For calculating the runoff volume, the project teams can use the **US EPA Rainwater Management Model**, the **modified rational method**, or the **Natural Resources Conservation Service** method, as described in **TR-55**.

USGBC's rainfall event calculator can be used for this purpose as well. It can calculate the 85th, 95th, and 98th percentile rainfall events by inputting the daily historical precipitation data.

Finally, project teams should design green infrastructure and low-impact development strategies that will account for the calculated runoff volume. With this approach, the natural hydrology of the site will be replicated, and runoff volume will not be transferred into the municipality's sewer.

If the project teams aim for path 1, again these steps will be taken to manage the runoff volume, but for the 95th percentile of rainfall events.

Teams with zero-lot-line projects pursuing path 3 will also follow the same steps, but in this case they will be for the 85th percentile of rainfall events. And since the zero-lot-line projects cover the whole lot, the teams can install intensive or extensive vegetated roofs or can install rainwater-harvesting systems in order to manage that amount of rainwater.

KEY THINGS TO REMEMBER

- Green infrastructure (GI) and low-impact development (LID) strategies will be used to manage the on-site rainwater runoff volume.
- Only zero-lot-line projects can manage the 85th percentile of regional or local rainfall events.
- Only for the projects that are a part of a multitenant complex, the credit requirements can be met by using a **coordinated approach** for the multiple buildings within the project boundary. Distributed techniques based on a watershed approach are required.
- In order to find rainfall data, projects located in the United States can use the **National Climatic Data Center**, and projects outside the United States can use local sources or the **UN Food and Agriculture Organization** and its global water information system, **AQUASTAT**.
- For calculating the runoff volume, the project teams can use the **US EPA Rainwater Management Model**, the **modified rational method**, or the **Natural Resources Conservation Service** method as described in **TR-55**.

Heat Island Reduction—Credit

- Applicable to: All the LEED BD+C Rating Systems

New Construction	1 – 2 points	Retail	1 – 2 points	Hospitality	1 – 2 points
Core and Shell	1 – 2 points	Data Centers	1 – 2 points	Healthcare	1 point
Schools	1 – 2 points	Warehouses & Dist. Centers	1 – 2 points		

CREDIT SUMMARY

An example of the heat island effect would be the black asphalt surfaces radiating heat on a hot summer day, with the air rising from the asphalt like hot air from a hair dryer. If there was a grass or soil area instead of a black-colored asphalt, as it would have existed before the development, this effect would not occur, as soil cannot absorb the solar heat like black-colored asphalt does.

Disturbing the environment with dark-colored, nonreflective surfaces causes the heat island effect. These surfaces absorb heat during hot weather and release it into the atmosphere. Studies show that urban "heat islands" are responsible for 24.2% of global warming.[1] And because of this effect, urban areas can have air temperatures that are 1.8° F to 22° F warmer than surrounding suburban areas. Higher temperatures also lead to smog or ground-level ozone, which create consequences for human health.

Heat islands are also responsible for increased cooling loads in buildings, and they result in higher electricity usage and harm to plants and animals that are sensitive to temperature changes.

Think about wearing a black T-shirt on a hot summer day when walking under the sun at noon, and compare the difference of heat that would be absorbed by the black T-shirt versus a white T-shirt.

The black T-shirt would absorb all the heat from the sun while the white T-shirt would reflect back the heat. This can be explained by the differences in their **solar reflectance (SR)** and **solar reflectance index (SRI)** values.

A solar reflectance value will show the solar energy that is reflected by a surface on a scale of 0 to 1. A black surface will have an SR of 0 while a white surface will have an SR of 1.

A material's SRI value will indicate a material's ability to stay cool by reflecting solar radiation and emitting thermal radiation. Thus, both the solar reflectance and **emissivity** of a material are combined to rank the material. Emissivity (infrared or thermal emittance) is a measure that shows how much heat or infrared radiation a material can shed back into the atmosphere. The SRI value of a material is measured from a scale of 0 to 100, and within that scale, light-colored materials are closer to scoring a 100 SRI while darker-colored materials are closer to scoring a 0 SRI. **Thus, the higher the SRI or SR, the lower the heat island effect.**

In order to classify building materials according to their solar emissions and reflectance, the **solar reflectance index** will be used for <u>roofing materials,</u> and **solar reflectance** values will be used for <u>nonroof materials</u> (such as hardscape) in this credit's calculations. In addition to the initial SR and SRI values, <u>three-year-aged SR</u> and <u>SRI</u> values will also be needed since the materials' performance will drop as they age.

This credit awards points for minimizing a project's heat island effect by using vegetated roofs, light colored nonroof measures, high-reflectance roofs, or covered parking.

CREDIT INTENT

To minimize effects on microclimates, wildlife habitats, and humans by reducing heat islands.

CREDIT REQUIREMENTS

Projects should choose one of the following options.

OPTION 1: NON-ROOF AND ROOF — (2 Points)

Projects pursuing this option should meet the following formula:

$$\frac{\text{Area of non-roof measures}}{0.5} + \frac{\text{Area of high-reflectance roof}}{0.75} + \frac{\text{Area of vegetated roof}}{0.75} \geq \text{Total site paving area} + \text{Total roof area}$$

Equation 9. Heat Island Effect

Project teams will input the areas of nonroof measures, high-reflectance roof, and vegetated roof on the left side of the equation if they meet the requirements set forth for each of them, which will be mentioned shortly.

Alternatively, project teams can use the SRI and SR weighted average approach to calculate compliance.

Projects should use any combination of the following strategies to satisfy the previous equation. The strategies are grouped under nonroof measures, high-reflectance roof, and vegetated roof.

<u>For the non-roof measures on-site</u>:

> ➤ Use existing plants or install new plants that will provide shade over paving areas on the site within 10 years of planting. Install vegetated planters. However, plants must be in place at the time of the occupancy permit, and artificial turf cannot be included.

> ➤ Provide shade with structures covered by energy generation systems (e.g., solar thermal collectors, photovoltaics, wind turbines, etc.).

> ➤ Provide shade with architectural devices or structures that have a <u>three-year aged</u> solar reflectance value of at least **0.28**. If this information is not available, projects can use materials with an initial SR of at least **0.33**.

> ➤ Provide shade with vegetated structures.

> ➤ Use paving materials with a <u>three-year aged</u> solar reflectance value of at least **0.28**. If this information is not available, the projects can use materials with an initial SR of at least **0.33**.

> ➤ Use an open-grid pavement system that is at least **50% unbound**.

One thing to note for the nonroof measures is this: If the building contains parking on the top level, this area will be considered a nonroof surface. If the top level does not contain any parking, the project teams will consider it a roof measure.

<u>For high-reflectance roofs:</u>

Projects can use roofing materials that have an SRI and three-year aged SRI equal to or greater than the values in the following table. If a three-year aged SRI value is not available, projects can use materials that meet the initial SRI value. Projects should also consider maintaining the SRI value of the roof by regular cleaning and maintenance.

In the credit calculations, roof areas covered by mechanical equipment, solar energy panels, skylights, or similar items will be excluded.

	Minimum solar reflectance index value by roof slope		
	Slope	**Initial SRI**	**3-year aged SRI**
Low-sloped roof	≤ 2:12	82	64
Steep-sloped roof	> 2:12	39	32

Table 11. Minimum solar reflectance index value by roof slope

If the project has multiple roofs with different angles and cannot meet the credit's requirements with the previous equation, project teams should conduct a weighted nonroof or roof calculation and determine if the weighted calculation can satisfy the credit. This is useful for projects that contain roof or nonroof measures, both below and above the required SRI values.

Project teams for international projects that cannot obtain the SRI information from their manufacturers can identify a similar material from the **Cool Roof Rating Council** standard and can satisfy the documentation requirements.

<u>For vegetated roofs:</u>

Projects can install both intensive and extensive vegetated roofs. However, artificial turf grass will not meet the credit's requirements.

📄 Project teams should document nonroof and roof-area calculations, a site plan showing the areas of each roof and nonroof measure, and the manufacturer's documentation stating the SR, SRI, and paving permeability.

OR

OPTION 2: PARKING UNDER COVER — (1 Point)

Under this option, projects should place at least **75%** of parking spaces under cover. This would include locating the parking spaces under a deck, under a roof, or under a building.

Motorcycle spaces are included in the calculations; however, bicycle parking spaces are exempt. Any roof that is used to shade or cover parking must either

- ❧ have a three-year aged SRI of at least **32** (if this information is not available, projects can use materials with an initial SRI of at least **39**);
- ❧ be a vegetated roof; or
- ❧ be covered by energy-generation systems, such as solar thermal collectors, photovoltaics, and wind turbines.

Any of these requirements will also apply to the building's top-level parking spaces, if applicable.

> 📄 Project teams should submit the manufacturer's documentation stating the SR, SRI, and paving permeability, and they should submit the parking space calculations.

EXEMPLARY PERFORMANCE

To qualify for exemplary performance under this credit, projects need to achieve **both** <u>option 1</u> and <u>option 2</u> and locate **100%** of parking under cover.

CASE STUDY

To illustrate, let us say that a project team aiming for this credit under option 1 wants to confirm that its current design meets the intent of this credit. The project contains

- ❧ 5,000 square feet of total hardscape area;
- ❧ 1,000 square feet of permeable sidewalks that are 50% unbound and have a 3-year-aged SR value of 0.45;
- ❧ 1,200 square feet of shading by tree canopy;
- ❧ 7,000 square feet of intensive vegetated roof;
- ❧ 5,000 square feet of steep-sloped high-reflectance roof, with an initial SRI value of 81 and a 3-year-aged SRI of 72, of which 500 square feet is covered by mechanical systems; and
- ❧ 900 square feet of parking canopy covered by PV panels.

In this case, the project team first confirms that the unbound ratio, the 3-year-aged SR value of the permeable sidewalks, and the SRI values of the 5,000-square-foot, steep-sloped, high-reflectance roof satisfy the credit's requirements and can be used on the left side of the credit's equation.

However, since 500 square feet of the high-reflectance roof is covered by mechanical systems, the applicable roof area used in the formula is as follows:

Applicable high-reflectance roof area: 5,000 – 500 = 4,500 square feet

Total roof area including the vegetated roof: 4,500 + 7,000 = 11,500 square feet

The applicable area for the nonroof measures to be used on the left side of the equation will be the

- 1,000 square feet of permeable sidewalks that are 50% unbound and have a 3-year-aged SR value of 0.45;
- 1,200 square feet of shading by tree canopy; and
- 900 square feet of parking canopy covered by PV panels.

Next, the project teams will perform the heat island calculation with the credit's equation:

$$\frac{1,000 + 1,200 + 900}{0.5} + \frac{4,500}{0.75} + \frac{7,000}{0.75} \geq 5,000 + 11,500$$

And the project earns the credit under option 1.

KEY THINGS TO REMEMBER

- Equation 9.
- SR, SRI and also 3-year-aged SR and SRI values are both used in the credit.
- For nonroof measures, SR values are used; for roofs, SRI values are used.
- The use of lighter-colored surfaces reduces the heat island effect.
- If the project contains multiple roofs with different angles and cannot meet the credit's requirements with the previous formula, project teams should conduct a "weighted nonroof or roof calculation" and determine if the weighted calculation can satisfy the credit.
- Teams for international projects that cannot obtain the SRI information from their manufacturers can identify a similar material from the **Cool Roof Rating Council** standard and can satisfy the documentation requirements.

Light Pollution Reduction—Credit

■ Applicable to: All the LEED BD+C Rating Systems

All the LEED BD+C Rating Systems	1 point

CREDIT SUMMARY

Light pollution is another factor that creates environmental problems. Overexposure to artificial lighting causes sleeping problems in humans and causes birds to become disoriented, and light pollution is a waste of energy that can bring further environmental impacts.

This credit requires projects to establish efficient lighting designs, and in order to establish efficient lighting designs, project teams should reduce the uplight, glare, and light trespass. Backlight is the primary factor of light trespass onto adjacent sites by directing the light in the opposite direction; uplight is the cause of artificial glow; and glare is caused by high-angle front lights.

The **BUG rating method** is also used in the credit, which is a luminaire classification system that classifies a luminaire according to backlight, uplight, and glare. It indicates the luminaire's likelihood to create pollution.

The credit also mentions the Model Lighting Ordinance (MLO) lighting zones, which are prepared by the International Dark-Sky Association (IDA) and the Illuminating Engineering

Society of North America (IES). The MLO lighting zones were created using the BUG rating method to address outdoor lighting regulation in North America.

There are five lighting zones to classify land use, and there are appropriate lighting levels for each. They are LZ0, LZ1, LZ2, LZ3, and LZ4. LZ0 is for the areas where the natural environment would be negatively affected by lighting, while LZ4 is for areas where high light levels are needed, like Times Square in New York City. In this credit, project teams will first choose the lighting zone that is appropriate for their project's location and then work on fulfilling the credit requirements.

Projects need to meet the uplight, light trespass, and internally illuminated exterior signage requirements separately in order to earn the credit. For uplight and light trespass, projects have two options and can choose either one of them.

CREDIT INTENT

To increase night sky access, improve nighttime visibility, and reduce consequences of human development for wildlife and people.

CREDIT REQUIREMENTS

Projects need to meet uplight and light trespass requirements by either using the backlight-uplight-glare (BUG) method in option 1 or the calculation method in option 2. Projects may also use different options for uplight and light trespass. For example, a project may choose the BUG method (option1) for meeting the uplight requirements and choose the calculation method (option 2) for meeting the light trespass requirements. In addition to these requirements, projects also need to meet internally illuminated signage requirements if signage exists on site.

Project teams should consider all the **exterior luminaires** inside the project boundary when addressing the credit requirements (except those listed as "exemptions" in the following section) based on the following:

- The photometric characteristics of each luminaire when mounted in the same orientation and tilt as in the project design.
- The lighting zone of the project property at the time construction starts. Project teams need to classify the project under a lighting zone, using the lighting zones definitions provided in the **Illuminating Engineering Society of North America and International Dark-Sky Association (IES/IDA) Model Lighting Ordinance (MLO) User's Guide**.

Below are the types of lighting that are exempt from the credit requirements if they are controlled separately from the nonexempt lighting:

- Specialized signal, directional, and marker lighting for transportation
- Lighting solely used for facade and landscape lighting in MLO lighting zones 3 and 4 and that is automatically turned off from midnight to 6:00 a.m.
- Government-mandated roadway lighting
- Lighting for theatrical purposes, stages, and video performances
- Hospital emergency department and helipad lighting
- National flag lighting in MLO lighting zones 2, 3, or 4
- Internally illuminated signage (this has its own requirement in the following pages)

If all the exterior luminaires used in the project are classified as "exempt," the project automatically achieves the credit.

Another thing to mention before going into detail is the lighting boundary. Projects will need to define their lighting boundary for the credit calculations and documentation. In LEED, the **lighting boundary** is located at the property lines of the project. However, there are several exceptions through which projects can modify their lighting boundary, and those exceptions are as follows:

- If the property line is adjacent to a public area that is a parking lot, walkway, bikeway, or plaza, the lighting boundary can be moved 5 feet (1.5 meters) beyond the property line.
- When there are adjacent properties owned by the same entity, and those properties are contiguous to the property that the LEED project is within, the lighting boundary may be expanded to include those properties if they have the same or higher MLO lighting zone designation as the LEED projects.
- When a property line is adjacent to a street, alley, or transit corridor, the lighting boundary can be moved to the centerline of the street, alley, or transit corridor.

Let us now take a look at the credit requirements for uplight, light trespass, and internally illuminated signage:

Uplight:

OPTION 1: BUG RATING METHOD

Projects should not exceed the following luminaire uplight ratings, based on the specific light source installed in the luminaire as defined in **IES TM-15-11, Addendum A.**

Maximum uplight ratings for luminaires	
MLO lighting zone	Luminaire uplight rating
LZ0	U0
LZ1	U1
LZ2	U2
LZ3	U3
LZ4	U4

Table 12. Maximum uplight ratings for luminaires

In other words, project teams pursuing this option will identify all the exterior luminaires and their uplight ratings, and they will check to see if all the luminaires used in the project are compatible with the allowed maximum ratings according to the project's lighting zone (according to the previous table). If we say that a project located in an LZ2 lighting zone contains one exterior luminaire with an uplight rating of U1, the project will achieve this requirement since the maximum allowed uplight rating is U2.

If every exterior luminaire used in the project cannot achieve these ratings, the project team may decide to pursue option 2 and check to see if those luminaires can pass the credit requirement when considered together with the remaining luminaires.

OR

OPTION 2: CALCULATION METHOD

Under this option, projects should not exceed the following percentages for total lumens emitted above horizontal. Unlike option 1, in this option project teams will calculate the <u>cumulative</u> (total) maximum allowable uplight percentages based on the lighting zone. (In option 1, <u>each</u> luminaire had to meet the allowable uplight rating individually, not cumulatively.) This is also the reason that projects can pursue option 2 if some of their luminaires can't meet the rating requirements in option 1.

Maximum % of total lumens emitted above horizontal by lighting zone	
MLO lighting zone	Max. allowed % of total luminaire lumens emitted above horizontal
LZ0	0%
LZ1	0%
LZ2	1.5%
LZ3	3%
LZ4	6%

Table 13. Maximum percentage of total lumens emitted above horizontal by lighting zones

AND

Light Trespass:

OPTION 1: BUG RATING METHOD

Projects should not exceed the luminaire backlight and glare ratings as defined in **IES TM-15-11, Addendum A**, based on the mounting location and distance from the lighting boundary (shown in the following table).

Projects should orient all luminaires **less than two mounting heights** from the lighting boundary such that the backlight points toward the nearest lighting boundary line. Mounting height is measured from the ground level to the bottom of the luminaire. Building-mounted luminaires with the backlight oriented toward the building are exempt from the backlight rating requirement.

Luminaire mounting	MLO lighting zone				
	LZ0	LZ1	LZ2	LZ3	LZ4
	Allowed backlight ratings				
> 2 mounting heights from the lighting boundary	B1	B3	B4	B5	B5
1 to 2 mounting heights from the lighting boundary and properly oriented	B1	B2	B3	B4	B4
0.5 to 1 mounting height from the lighting boundary and properly oriented	B0	B1	B2	B3	B3
< 0.5 mounting height from the lighting boundary and properly oriented	B0	B0	B0	B1	B2
	Allowed glare ratings				
Building-mounted > 2 mounting heights from any lighting boundary	G0	G1	G2	G3	G4
Building-mounted 1 to 2 mounting heights from any lighting boundary	G0	G0	G1	G1	G2
Building-mounted 0.5 to 1 mounting heights from any lighting boundary	G0	G0	G0	G1	G1
Building-mounted < 0.5 mounting heights from any lighting boundary	G0	G0	G0	G0	G1
All other luminaires	G0	G1	G2	G3	G4

Table 14. Allowed luminaire backlight and glare ratings

As can be seen from the table, the closer the luminaire is located to the lighting boundary, the lower the allowed backlight and glare rating since the luminaire will have a bigger potential to contribute to light trespass. Another way to reduce the light trespass potential of a luminaire is to select a luminaire with a lower pole height.

To summarize, project teams pursuing this option will identify all the exterior luminaires and their glare/backlight ratings, identify the luminaires' locations, and check to see if all the luminaires used in the project are compatible with the allowed maximum ratings, according to the project's lighting zone in the previous table.

One thing to note for light trespass is that projects need to consider the luminaires' location too, as this is not the case for option 1 of the uplight.

Again, if every exterior luminaire used in the project cannot achieve these ratings, the project team may decide to pursue option 2 and check to see if those luminaires can pass the credit requirement when considered with the remaining luminaires.

OR

OPTION 2: CALCULATION METHOD

Under the calculation method, projects should not exceed the following vertical illuminances at the lighting boundary shown on table 15. Vertical illuminance refers to the illuminance levels that are calculated on a vertical plane. In other words, the vertical illuminances should be calculated on vertical planes running parallel to the lighting boundary, with the normal for each plane oriented toward the property and perpendicular to the lighting boundary.

Project teams will need to use lighting software and develop a photometric site plan to pursue this option (manually measuring it with a light meter may not be possible at all). In the lighting software, project teams will define vertical calculation grids at each segment of the project's lighting boundary and set vertical illuminance calculation points. The vertical illuminance calculation points can be no more than 5 feet (1.5 meters) apart and must extend from the grade level to at least 33 feet (10 meters) above the height of the highest luminaire in the project. Next, the project team will confirm that the allowed vertical illuminances at the lighting boundary shown on the following table are not exceeded.

Maximum vertical illuminance at lighting boundary by lighting zone	
MLO lighting zone	Vertical illuminance
LZ0	0.05 footcandle (0.5 lux)
LZ1	0.05 footcandle (0.5 lux)
LZ2	0.1 footcandle (1 lux)
LZ3	0.2 footcandle (2 lux)
LZ4	0.6 footcandle (6 lux)

Table 15. Maximum vertical illuminance at lighting boundary by lighting zone

AND

<u>**Internally illuminated exterior signage:**</u>

Any internally illuminated exterior signage should not exceed a luminance of **200 cd/m²** (nits) **during nighttime hours** and **2,000 cd/m²** (nits) **during daytime hours**. (Candela per square meter equals one nit.)

- 📄 All projects should submit the site lighting plan with fixture locations, and projects with internally illuminated exterior signage should additionally provide maximum luminance data.
- 📄 Projects pursuing option 1-uplight should submit a luminaire schedule showing uplight ratings.
- 📄 Projects pursuing option 1-light trespass should submit a luminaire schedule showing backlight and glare ratings with the mounting heights.
- 📄 Projects pursuing option 2-uplight should submit calculations for lumen per luminaire and lumens emitted above horizontal.
- 📄 Projects pursuing option 2-light trespass should submit the greatest vertical illuminance value for each vertical calculation plane at the lighting boundary, the calculation grid for one vertical plane with the greatest vertical illuminance, and the highlighting point of greatest illuminance.

EXEMPLARY PERFORMANCE

This credit does not qualify for exemplary performance.

CASE STUDY

To illustrate, let us say that a project team that wants to pursue this credit calculates compliance for the "uplight" portion of the credit under the "Option 2: Calculation method." The project is located in lighting zone LZ3, which means that the allowable percentage of total luminaire lumens emitted above horizontal cannot exceed 3% (from table 13). The project team creates the following table based on the manufacturer's data for the exterior luminaires used in the project.

Luminaire type	Quantity	Lumens per luminaire	Total luminaire lumens	Lumens emitted above horizontal per luminaire	Total luminaire lumens above 90° horizontal
Type A	3	1,000	3,000	50	150
Type B	4	1,500	6,000	100	400
Type C	2	2,000	4,000	0	0
		Total	**13,000**	Total	**550**

Now the project team calculates the percentage of total luminaire lumens emitted above horizontal.

$$550 / 13000 = \textbf{4.23\%} > \textbf{3\%}$$

With this result, the project cannot achieve compliance with the uplight requirements since the allowable percentage of total luminaire lumens emitted above horizontal exceeds 3%.

KEY THINGS TO REMEMBER

■ Backlight is the primary factor of light trespass onto adjacent sites; uplight is the cause of artificial glow; and glare is caused by the high-angle front lights.

■ Model Lighting Ordinance (MLO) lighting zones are prepared by the International Dark-Sky Association (IDA) and the Illuminating Engineering Society of North America (IES).

■ LEED considers the lighting zone of the project property <u>at the time construction starts</u>.

■ Types of lighting that are exempt from the credit requirements.

■ The lighting boundary is located at the property lines of the project.

■ The conditions that projects are allowed to modify their lighting boundary (3 conditions).

■ Building-mounted luminaires with the backlight oriented toward the building are exempt from the backlight rating requirement.

■ The photometric characteristics of each luminaire should be considered in the same orientation and tilt as in the project design.

■ If every exterior luminaire used in the project cannot achieve these allowed ratings in option 1, the project team may decide to pursue option 2 and check to see if those luminaires can pass the credit requirement when considered with the remaining luminaires.

■ Vertical illuminances must be calculated on vertical planes running parallel to the lighting boundary with the normal to each plane oriented toward the property and perpendicular to the lighting boundary, extending from **grade level** to **33 feet (10 meters) above the height of the highest luminaire.**

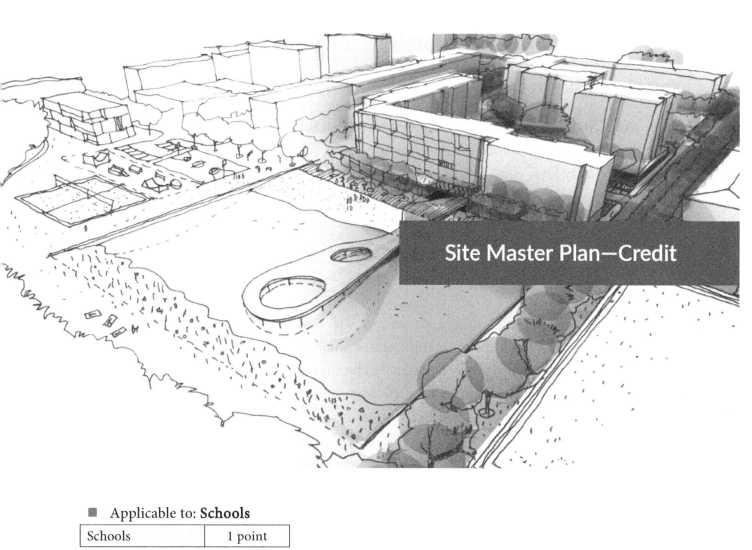

Site Master Plan—Credit

■ Applicable to: **Schools**

Schools	1 point

CREDIT SUMMARY

School projects should continually adapt to expansions and modifications, which can be because of the changes in programs, demographics, and other reasons. This credit encourages projects to create a master plan that will support sustainable development strategies in order to ensure that the site infrastructure can be maintained with future developments. With this approach, any new construction can easily be integrated into existing site infrastructure and facilities.

CREDIT INTENT

To ensure that the sustainable site benefits are achieved regardless of future changes in demographics or programs.

CREDIT REQUIREMENTS

In order to be eligible for this credit, school projects should <u>plan for future developments</u> and additionally achieve **at least four** of the following credits.

- High-Priority Site
- Site Development—Protect or Restore Habitat
- Open Space
- Rainwater Management
- Heat Island Reduction
- Light Pollution Reduction

Under this credit, projects should develop a site master plan in collaboration with the school authorities. With the implementation of sustainable site design measures, existing infrastructure should be retained wherever possible. The master plan should include both the current construction activity and future construction activities within the building's life span. (This also covers parking, paving, and utilities.) It is also essential to include flexibility in the site master plan to allow for future changes in the planned developments.

Next, the project teams will need to recalculate the achieved credits from the previous list, at that point using the future development data from the master plan.

If the project is not planning any future development, this credit cannot be pursued.

> 📄 Project teams should document a site plan that includes current and future phases of development and a description of updates made for future development. Additionally, project teams should document credit forms and documentation for the selected credits, rewritten using the data for the site master plan.

EXEMPLARY PERFORMANCE

This credit does not qualify for exemplary performance.

KEY THINGS TO REMEMBER

- To qualify for this credit, a team's project should achieve at least four of the six credits listed, and the team must plan for future developments.
- The names of the six credits listed should be known.
- The achieved credits must be recalculated to cover the whole master plan.
- This credit is only applicable to school projects.

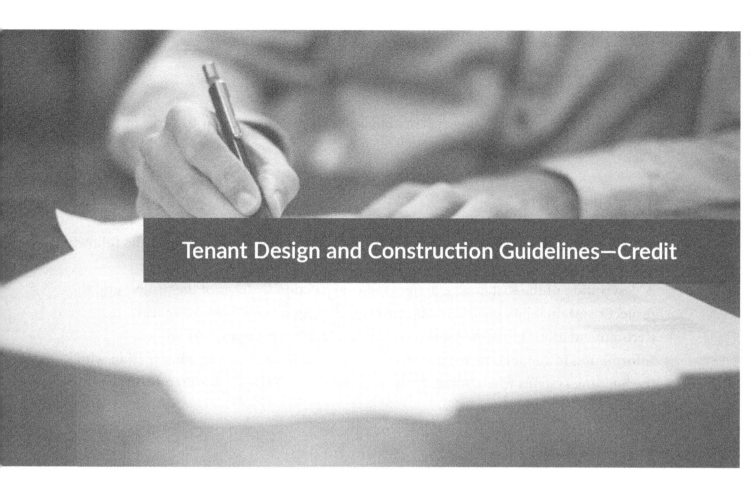

Tenant Design and Construction Guidelines—Credit

■ Applicable to: **Core and Shell**

Core and Shell	1 point

CREDIT SUMMARY

When developing a core and shell building, project owners usually don't have much control over the tenant spaces. However, the way tenant spaces operate is also very important for the overall building performance.

This credit is designed to encourage sustainable principles in the tenant spaces of the core and shell projects. If project teams provide a guideline containing the sustainable design and construction features of the project, the project's sustainability goals, and recommendations for green strategies, tenants are encouraged to employ sustainable principles.

Furthermore, the tenants of a LEED-certified core and shell building will have a big advantage toward achieving a LEED ID+C certification for their office spaces. And if the project teams provide information that enables tenants to coordinate space design and construction with the building, tenants can have a much easier time obtaining a LEED ID+C certification.

It is important to note that this credit requires projects to provide this information to the tenants <u>before signing the lease</u>, and these guidelines will not be binding on lessees.

CREDIT INTENT

To educate tenants in implementing sustainable design and construction features in their tenant improvement fit-out work.

CREDIT REQUIREMENTS

<u>Before a lease is signed</u>, project teams should create an illustrated document with the following content as applicable:

- A description of the sustainable design and construction features of the project and the project's sustainability goals and objectives, including those for tenant spaces
- Recommendations for sustainable products, materials, strategies, and services
- Information to support the tenants to coordinate space, design, and construction with the building systems when pursuing the following LEED ID+C v4 prerequisites and credits:
  - Indoor Water Use Reduction—Prerequisite
  - Indoor Water Use Reduction—Credit
  - Minimum Energy Performance—Prerequisite
  - Fundamental Refrigerant Management—Prerequisite
  - Optimize Energy Performance—Credit
  - Thermal Comfort—Credit
  - Interior Lighting—Credit
  - Advanced Energy Metering—Credit
  - Renewable Energy Production—Credit
  - Enhanced Refrigerant Management—Credit
  - Storage and Collection of Recyclables—Prerequisite
  - Minimum Indoor Air Quality Performance—Prerequisite
  - Environmental Tobacco Smoke Control—Prerequisite
  - Enhanced Indoor Air Quality Strategies—Credit
  - Low-Emitting Materials—Credit
  - Construction Indoor Air Quality Management Plan—Credit
  - Indoor Air Quality Assessment—Credit
  - Daylight—Credit
  - Quality Views—Credit
  - Acoustic Performance—Credit

To illustrate, for the "Thermal Comfort" credit, project teams may describe the HVAC system in the building and its design criteria. If natural ventilation can be incorporated, the project team can provide information about how it can be designed.

Note that these guidelines will not be binding on lessees.

> 📄 Project teams should submit the tenant design and construction guidelines document.

EXEMPLARY PERFORMANCE

This credit does not qualify for exemplary performance.

KEY THINGS TO REMEMBER

- This credit requires project teams to provide the information above to tenants <u>before signing a lease</u>, and these guidelines will not be binding on lessees.
- This credit is only applicable to "LEED BD+C: Core and Shell" projects.

Places of Respite—Credit

■ Applicable to: **Healthcare**

Healthcare	1 point

CREDIT SUMMARY

Fresh air is one of the most important elements that greatly affects human well-being. And if we think about patients in hospitals, fresh air becomes a much more important factor for patient recovery. This credit is designed to award healthcare projects that provide places of respite that are accessible to patients, visitors, and staff, which also contain vegetation and allow opportunities for exercise and movement.

CREDIT INTENT

To provide patients, staff, and visitors with the health benefits of a natural environment by designing outdoor places of respite located at the healthcare facility.

CREDIT REQUIREMENTS

Projects should provide places of respite for <u>patients and visitors</u> equal to **5%** of the **net usable program area of the building**, and they should provide places of respite for <u>staff</u> equal to **2%** of the **net usable program area of the building**. Net usable program area is defined by the sum of all the interior areas in the building that are available to the project's program. Since it's really the area that can be used, it excludes all the areas used for structural components, building equipment, mechanical equipment, etc.

Places of respite should be ideally outdoors. However, maximum **30%** of the respite area can be located in interior atria, solaria, greenhouses, or conditioned spaces. To qualify as a place of respite in an interior space, **90%** of the space should achieve a direct line of sight to unobstructed views of nature.

Both the dedicated <u>indoor</u> and <u>outdoor</u> areas should meet the following requirements:

- The dedicated area should be accessible from within the building or located within **200 feet** (60 meters) of a building entrance or access point.
- No medical care should be delivered in the places of respite.
- Options for shade or indirect sunlight should be provided, and projects should install at least one seating space per 200 square feet (18.5 square meters) of each respite area, with one wheelchair space per five seating spaces.
- Horticulture therapy and other specific clinical or special-use gardens unavailable to all building occupants may not account for more than 50% of the required area.
- Universal-access natural trails, which are available to visitors, staff, or patients, cannot account for more than 30% of the required area.

<u>Outdoor</u> areas should additionally contain a minimum of **25%** vegetation (not turf grass) at the ground plane or have an overhead vegetated canopy, and they should not be within 25 feet (7.6 meters) of smoking areas. Additionally, the outdoor area should be open to fresh air, the sky, and the natural elements while the wayfinding signage of these areas should meet the FGI Guidelines for Design and Construction of Healthcare Facilities.

> 📄 Project teams should document area, patient, staff, shading, and vegetation calculations, and they should submit a site plan showing outdoor and/or indoor places of respite identified by user type that indicates access points, planes of vegetation, shaded seating spaces and proximity to smoking areas. They should also submit the drawings or photographs of the wayfinding signage.

EXEMPLARY PERFORMANCE

To qualify for exemplary performance under this credit, projects need to provide 10% of net usable program area as places of respite for patients and visitors in addition to providing 4% of net usable program area as places of respite for staff (which basically doubles the credit requirements).

KEY THINGS TO REMEMBER

- Projects should provide places of respite for patients and visitors equal to **5%** of the net usable program area of the building, and they should also provide places of respite for staff equal to **2%** of the net usable program area of the building.
- This credit is only applicable to healthcare projects.
- The definition of "net usable program area" should be known.

Direct Exterior Access—Credit

■ Applicable to: **Healthcare**

Healthcare	1 point

CREDIT SUMMARY

Similar to the "Places of Respite" credit, this credit aims to encourage projects to provide direct exterior access to patients and allow those patients to connect with nature. However, this credit does not require vegetation and opportunities for exercise and movement. Instead, the projects should provide exterior access directly from the patients' treatment areas or rooms. For LEED, direct exterior access refers to entering an exterior space without having to leave the floor or pass through a major public space or another patient's room. It may only include shared exterior connections.

CREDIT INTENT

To provide patients and staff with the health benefits related to direct access to the environment.

CREDIT REQUIREMENTS

Under this credit, projects should provide direct access to an exterior courtyard, terrace, garden, or balcony. Remember that in the "Places of Respite" credit, project teams have the option to locate 30% of the places of respite in the interior of a building. However, in this credit, as its name implies, no interior space qualifies, and projects should provide direct <u>exterior</u> access.

The provided space must be at least **5 square feet** (0.5 square meters) per patient for **75%** of all <u>inpatients</u> and **75%** of <u>outpatients whose length of stay exceeds four hours</u>. The only exclusion to this rule is the patients whose length of stay exceeds four hours and whose treatment makes them unable to move. For instance, that could apply to emergency stage 1 surgical recovery and critical care patients.

In order to calculate the minimum required space, project teams should use the peak number of inpatients and outpatients. If there are private balconies in the patient rooms, these spaces will qualify if they are at least 5 square feet (0.5 square meters).

An "outpatient" is a patient who does not need to stay in the hospital for more than 24 hours but visits a hospital or associated healthcare facility for diagnosis or treatment. An "inpatient" is a patient who needs to stay in the hospital for more than 24 hours for surgical or other medical care purposes.

Exterior places of respite—which meet the requirements of the "Places of Respite" credit and that are also adjacent to clinical areas or have direct access from inpatient units—can be included in this credit as well.

Qualifying spaces must be designated as nonsmoking, and all the spaces must meet the requirements for outdoor air contaminant concentrations in option 2 of the "Enhanced Indoor Air Quality Strategies" credit. All the qualifying spaces should be located more than 100 feet (30 meters) from loading docks, building exhaust air locations, and roadways with idling vehicles.

> 🗎 Project teams should submit area and patient calculations, and they should submit a site plan showing the locations of accessible outdoor areas, area takeoffs, air exhausts, exhaust vents, and access points and distances to outdoor areas.

EXEMPLARY PERFORMANCE

This credit does not qualify for exemplary performance.

KEY THINGS TO REMEMBER

■ Under this credit, the space with direct exterior access must be at least **5 square feet** (0.5 square meters) per patient for **75%** of all inpatients and **75%** of qualifying outpatients whose length of stay exceeds four hours.

■ Projects should provide exterior access directly from the patients' treatment areas or rooms. In LEED, direct exterior access refers to entering an exterior space without having to leave the floor or pass through a major public space or another patient's room. It may only include shared exterior connections.

■ For LEED, an "outpatient" is a patient who does not need to stay in the hospital for more than 24 hours but visits a hospital or associated healthcare facility for diagnosis or treatment. An "inpatient" is a patient who needs to stay in the hospital for more than 24 hours for surgical or other medical care purposes.

■ This credit is only applicable to healthcare projects.

Joint Use of Facilities—Credit

■ Applicable to: **Schools**

Schools	1 point

CREDIT SUMMARY

As will be mentioned under the "Materials and Resources" credit category, a very effective way to reduce the environmental impact of a building is to reuse existing buildings since it is not necessary to think about the environmental impacts of producing new materials when existing buildings can be reused. This credit encourages school projects to share their spaces—such as auditoriums, gymnasiums, cafeterias and more—with the general public or specific organizations under options 1 and 2. And in option 3, the credit requires schools to use other facilities outside of their school campus, such as an auditorium, gymnasium, and cafeteria that are accessible by foot with direct pedestrian access.

These strategies will reduce the environmental consequences of a new development and the cost of new construction.

CREDIT INTENT

To integrate the school with the neighborhood by sharing the building and its playing fields for nonschool events and functions.

CREDIT REQUIREMENTS

OPTION 1: MAKE BUILDING SPACE OPEN TO THE GENERAL PUBLIC – (1 Point)

Under this option, with the collaboration of school authorities, project teams should ensure that at least three of the following types of spaces in the school are available to be shared by the general public:

- Auditorium
- Gymnasium
- One or more classrooms
- Cafeteria
- Playing fields and stadiums
- Joint parking

Additionally, in the joint-use areas, access to toilets should be provided after normal school hours.

> 📄 Projects should document floor plans indicating joint-use spaces, restroom facilities, and room names as well as a shared-use policy with all the terms and conditions.

OR

OPTION 2: CONTRACT WITH SPECIFIC ORGANIZATIONS TO SHARE BUILDING SPACE – (1 Point)

Under this option, with the collaboration of school authorities, a contract should be signed with the community or other organizations or businesses to provide at least two of the following types of dedicated-use spaces inside the building:

- Commercial office
- Health clinic
- Community service centers
- Library or media center
- Police office
- Parking lot
- One or more commercial businesses

Additionally, in the joint-use areas, access to toilets should be provided after normal school hours.

📄 Project teams should document floor plans indicating joint-use spaces, restroom facilities, and room names, and they should have a signed agreement between school authorities and occupying organizations.

OR

OPTION 3: USE SHARED SPACE OWNED BY OTHER ORGANIZATIONS — (1 Point)

In this option, the students will use other facilities outside of their school building. With the collaboration of the school authorities, school project teams should ensure that at least two of the following six types of spaces that are owned by other organizations or agencies are accessible to students:

- Auditorium
- Gymnasium
- One or more classrooms
- Cafeteria
- Swimming pool
- Playing fields and stadiums

All the joint-use facilities should be accessible by foot, and there must be <u>direct pedestrian access</u> to these spaces from the school. Joint-use agreements should be signed with the other organizations or agencies that demonstrate how these spaces will be shared.

📄 Project teams should document a signed agreement stipulating how spaces will be shared with students, and they should provide a site plan showing pedestrian access routes and distance from the school building to joint-use spaces.

EXEMPLARY PERFORMANCE

This credit does not qualify for exemplary performance.

KEY THINGS TO REMEMBER

- All the shared facilities that are owned by other organizations should be accessible by foot, and there must be <u>direct pedestrian access</u> to these spaces from the school.
- This credit is only applicable to school projects.

CHAPTER 6

WATER EFFICIENCY (WE)

Seventy percent of the earth's surface is covered by water; however, fresh water only comprises 1% of the total volume and it is the only percentage that is accessible for human use. According to the United Nations Environment Programme, if the current water consumption rates continue, two out of every three people will live in water-stressed conditions by the year 2025.

With the increase of residential, commercial, and industrial development, the use of potable water increases. From flushing toilets to industrial water uses, potable water becomes wastewater, which overwhelms treatment facilities, results in heavy energy use during water treatment, and creates more greenhouse gases.

Green buildings need to address this issue by improving their water efficiency. Please note that "efficiency" does not mean finding an alternative method; rather, it means doing the same thing by using less of the same resource. As a result, water will still be used, but it will be used in a smarter way.

The **water balance** approach, which aims to balance water supply with water consumption, is not achievable for every location.

(An example of the water balance approach would be to use only captured rainwater and/or underground water for the water needs of a building so that no water would be used from municipal lines.) Nonetheless, getting as close as possible to the water balance approach can still bring about considerable change.

This chapter will discuss the LEED requirements for water efficiency. The "Water Efficiency" credit category contains the following prerequisites/credits:

- Outdoor Water Use Reduction—Prerequisite
- Indoor Water Use Reduction—Prerequisite
- Building-Level Water Metering—Prerequisite
- Outdoor Water Use Reduction—Credit
- Indoor Water Use Reduction—Credit
- Cooling Tower Water Use—Credit
- Water Metering—Credit

However, before getting into the prerequisites/credits, the required LEED calculations for indoor water use need to be mentioned.

LEED INDOOR WATER USE CALCULATIONS

When approaching strategies to reduce the water consumption of a project, it is necessary to first calculate a **baseline** water usage and then find innovative ways to establish water use reductions from the baseline during the design phase. In LEED, projects are awarded points under the WE credits in accordance with the percent reduction made from their baseline water usage.

To calculate the baseline water usage of a project, first the baseline rates for flow and flush fixtures and fittings should be determined. In the LEED prerequisite and credit calculations, the baseline flow and flush rates are specified by the **Energy Policy Act of 1992 (EPAct 1992)**.

The occupant usage should then be calculated to find out how much those fixtures and fittings will be used. This calculation is made to demonstrate that the more occupants there and the more time they spend in a building, the more water will be used.

In LEED, the **full-time equivalent (FTE)** value will be used to determine the occupant usage of the fixtures and fittings. And to obtain the FTE of the building, the occupants will first be identified by the following occupant types:

- Full-time staff
- Part-time staff
- Transient occupants (who do not use the facility consistently, such as visitors, customers, students, etc.)
- Residents

The number of FTE occupants is based on a standard 8-hour occupancy period. A full-time staff member who works 8 hours a day will have an FTE of 1, and a part-time staff member who works 4 hours a day will have an FTE of 0.5. FTE calculations also include multiple shifts.

In a building that contains 40 full-time occupants and 20 part-time occupants, the total FTE for only the full-time and part-time staff would be:

$$(40 \text{x} 1) + (20 \text{x} 0.5) = \mathbf{50}$$

In addition to this value, the transient occupants and residents need to be considered and added to 50 in order to reflect the total building users (if applicable).

Once the FTE is calculated and the baseline flow and flush rates for fixtures and fittings are taken from the Energy Policy Act of 1992, the baseline indoor water consumption can be calculated. Next, project teams need to discover innovative strategies for reducing water consumption as much as possible.

Outdoor Water Use Reduction—Prerequisite

■ Applicable to: All the LEED BD+C Rating Systems

PREREQUISITE SUMMARY

In some projects, potable water used for irrigation exceeds the total indoor water consumption of the building. That can be addressed through water-wise landscaping designs, water-efficient irrigation technology, using nonpotable water (such as reclaimed water, using graywater, using harvested rainwater), and installing submeters to track and log irrigation trends.

Careful plant selection will make a great contribution to reducing outdoor water use. The use of native and adapted plants, **xeriscaping** (type of landscaping in which plants do not need any irrigation), and cleaning out any invasive plants can help considerably.

This prerequisite forces the smart use of outdoor water by choosing landscaping that requires no irrigation, or the project will need to reduce its **landscape water requirement (LWR)** by a minimum of **30%** from the calculated baseline. Areas covered with turf or grass will need high amounts of irrigation water and will make it hard to satisfy this prerequisite. Projects without any landscapes will be exempt from this prerequisite.

The baseline landscape water requirement (LWR) is the amount of water that the landscape of the site will require <u>during the site's peak watering month</u>. To calculate the LWR, projects will use the **US Environmental Protection Agency WaterSense Water Budget Tool**.

This is an online calculator that the project team needs to input the project location, types of vegetation, area of each vegetation, water demand of each vegetation (low, medium, or high), and irrigation system type. The online calculator will calculate the total LWR of the project, which will be the baseline value. To classify the water demand of each vegetation as low, medium, or high, the project teams can refer to plant guidelines, state agricultural extension services, or nurseries. Next, project teams will need to discover innovative ways of reducing this value by 30%.

One important thing to note under this prerequisite is that <u>project teams cannot use nonpotable water sources</u> (such as reclaimed water, graywater, or harvested rainwater) to establish the 30% outdoor water reduction. However, this can happen under the "Outdoor Water Use Reduction" credit, which will be discussed in the following pages.

PREREQUISITE INTENT

To reduce outdoor water consumption.

PREREQUISITE REQUIREMENTS

Projects should reduce outdoor water use through one of the options below. Nonvegetated surfaces (such as pavements) must be excluded from landscape area calculations. <u>Athletic fields</u> and <u>playgrounds</u>, if vegetated, and <u>food gardens</u> may be included or excluded in the prerequisite calculations at the project teams' discretion.

OPTION 1: NO IRRIGATION REQUIRED

As the name of the option implies, if a project has a landscape that does not need any irrigation beyond a maximum of a <u>two-year establishment period</u>, documenting it will fulfill the prerequisite.

> 📄 Project teams should document a site plan showing the vegetated areas, and they should submit a narrative about the plant species and their water requirements.

OR

OPTION 2: REDUCED IRRIGATION

Under this option, projects need to reduce the project's landscape water consumption by **at least 30%** from the calculated baseline for the <u>site's peak watering month</u>.

This reduction should be established by careful selection of the plant species and the irrigation systems according to their efficiency. For the landscape water requirement calculation, the EPA WaterSense Water Budget Tool will be used.

For projects in the United States, the WaterSense Water Budget Tool will automatically derive rainfall/precipitation and evapotranspiration data from the project's zip code. However, projects outside the United States will need to manually enter this data and can also use the Excel version of the WaterSense Water Budget Tool. The World Meteorological Organization website can be helpful in figuring out the precipitation data, and the Food and Agriculture Organization of the United Nations can be beneficial in determining the evapotranspiration data.

Please remember that if a project has large areas of turf or grass, it will be harder to satisfy the prerequisite since their water consumption will be much higher than other vegetation types. Projects should mainly use native and adapted plants.

Once more, nonvegetated areas, such as pavements, should be excluded from the calculations. Athletic fields, vegetated playgrounds, and food gardens may be included or excluded from these calculations according to the project team's decision. And project teams cannot use nonpotable water sources (such as reclaimed water, graywater, or harvested rainwater) to establish the 30% outdoor water reduction. However, this can happen under the "Outdoor Water Use Reduction" credit.

> 🗎 Project teams should document a site plan indicating the location and size of each landscaping zone, and they should submit the WaterSense Water Budget Tool report.

CASE STUDY

To illustrate, let us assume that project teams are working on this prerequisite for a project located in San Francisco, and the teams calculate the LWR and find the following results:

		STEP 1 Location and Area	STEP 2 Plants and Irrigation	STEP 3 The Results			

Fill out the chart below with all the appropriate information to calculate your landscape's water needs.

	Zone	Area (sq. ft.)	Plant Type / Landscape Feature	Water Demand	Irrigation Type	Impact on Water Use	Required Water (gal/month)
×	1	20000	Trees	Low	Drip (Standard)	💧💧💧	23579
×	2	10000	Shrubs	Low	Drip (Standard)	💧💧💧	11789
×	3	20000	Trees	Medium	Drip (Press Comp)	💧💧💧💧💧💧	45847
×	4						
×	5						
×	6						

Total: 50000

+ add zone

0	144,419	81,215	63,204	
Remaining Area (sq. ft.)	Water Allowance (gal/month)	Total Water Requirement for the Site (gal/month)	Below Allowance (gal/month)	NEXT STEP >

The **water allowance**, which is 144,419 gal./month, represents 30% below the baseline value. (The baseline value is 206,312 gal./month for this project). And the LWR of the project is 81,215 gal./month. Since the LWR corresponds to the 39.36% of the baseline value, the project earns the prerequisite with a 60.64% reduction from the baseline. Note that the first four columns of the water budget tool will be inputted by the project team. The rest will be automatically calculated by the WaterSense Water Budget Tool.

KEY THINGS TO REMEMBER

- Projects should reduce the baseline outdoor water usage **30%** from the calculated baseline for the site's peak watering month.
- Nonvegetated surfaces (such as pavement), should be excluded from landscape area calculations. Athletic fields and playgrounds, if vegetated, and food gardens may be included or excluded at the project teams' discretion.
- Project teams cannot use nonpotable water sources (such as reclaimed water, graywater, or harvested rainwater) to establish the 30% outdoor water reduction.
- The US Environmental Protection Agency WaterSense Water Budget Tool is an online calculator that the project teams need to input the project location, types of vegetation, area of each vegetation, water demand of each vegetation (low, medium or high), and irrigation system type.
- Landscapes that do not need any irrigation beyond a maximum **two-year establishment period** will satisfy option 1.

Indoor Water Use Reduction—Prerequisite

- Applicable to: All the LEED BD+C Rating Systems

PREREQUISITE SUMMARY

In order to save potable water, all green buildings must address indoor water use and find creative ways to increase their water efficiency. Use of water for urinals, toilets, showers, kitchens, and other applications all contribute to indoor water use. Indoor potable water consumption can be seriously reduced by using water-efficient fixtures and fittings and/or using nonpotable water sources where appropriate.

The use of WaterSense-labeled products can be another good strategy that will contribute to reducing indoor water usage. WaterSense is a program developed by the US Environmental Protection Agency to identify high-performance, water-efficient fixtures, and fittings. In other words, a fixture or a fitting that has a WaterSense label will guarantee high water-efficiency.

This prerequisite aims to reduce projects' indoor potable water usage by encouraging the use of water-efficient fixtures and fittings. Project teams will need to calculate indoor water consumption and reduce the water usage **20%** by utilizing more efficient fixtures and fittings. The baseline calculations for determining the indoor potable water usage will be according to the flush or flow rates in table 16, and calculating the FTE value of the project will be essential to figuring out the indoor potable water usage. (The calculations will be conducted with the USGBC's indoor water use calculator.)

Furthermore, projects must use WaterSense-labeled products for all the newly installed toilets, urinals, private lavatory faucets, and showerheads that are eligible for WaterSense labeling.

If all the installed fixtures and fittings do not exceed WaterSense maximum levels, projects can earn the prerequisite by only documenting their fixtures and applicable appliances with **"product cutsheets"** or **"fixture schedules"** and manufacturers' information. This time there will be no need to calculate the indoor water consumption of the building if the project does not intend to pursue the credit of this prerequisite: the "Indoor Water Use Reduction" credit.

The credit awards points for further reduction of indoor water consumption, but to calculate the established percent of water reduction, projects need to calculate the indoor water consumption in this prerequisite. Using solely WaterSense-labeled products will not be sufficient to determine the exact percentage reduction.

Appliance and process water are also addressed inside this credit. They can consume more water than all the other water-consuming items in the building. For projects under the LEED BD+C: Healthcare, Retail, Schools, and Hospitality rating systems, there are even further requirements for the appliances and processes used.

Process water is the type of water used by the mechanical or other types of systems in buildings such as cooling towers or for medical equipment in hospitals. If the projects choose to install **closed-loop** systems, which use and circulate the same process water inside, instead of using **open-loop** systems, then even more potable water can be saved. Open-loop systems require outside water, which is called the **makeup water**, to support the system.

Another important thing to note under this prerequisite is that project teams cannot use nonpotable water sources (such as reclaimed water, graywater, or harvested rainwater) to establish the 20% indoor water reduction. However, this can happen under the "Indoor Water Use Reduction" credit, which will be discussed in the following pages. (This rule is similar with the "Outdoor Water Use Reduction" prerequisite and credit).

PREREQUISITE INTENT

To reduce indoor water consumption.

PREREQUISITE REQUIREMENTS

For Building Water Use:

For all the following fixtures and fittings shown in table 16, projects should reduce aggregate water consumption by **20%** from their baseline number of units. The baseline flow and flush rates are specified by the **Energy Policy Act of 1992 (EPAct 1992)**.

For all newly installed toilets, urinals, private lavatory faucets, and showerheads (that are eligible), projects should use WaterSense-labeled products, or an equivalent labeling can be used for projects that are located outside the United States.

Fixture or Fitting	Baseline Water Consumption Values (IP units)	Baseline Water Consumption Values (SI units)
Toilet (water closet)*	1.6 gpf	6 lpf
Urinal*	1.0 gpf	3.8 lpf
Public lavatory faucet	0.5 gpm at 60 psi	1.9 lpm at 415 kPa
Private lavatory faucet*	2.2 gpm at 60 psi	8.3 lpm at 415 kPa
Kitchen faucet	2.2 gpm at 60 psi	8.3 lpm at 415 kPa
Showerhead*	2.5 gpm at 80 psi per shower stall	9.5 lpm at 550 kPa per shower stall

*WaterSense label is available for this type of product

Table 16. Baseline water consumption values

❓ Please note that the baseline water consumption of toilets and urinals are specified in gallons per flush (gpf), and others are specified in gallons per minute (gpm).

For Appliance and Process Water Use:
All the installed appliances and processes must meet the following standards:

Appliance	Requirement
Residential clothes washer	ENERGY STAR or performance equivalent
Commercial clothes washer	CEE Tier 3A
Residential dishwasher	ENERGY STAR or performance equivalent
Pre-rinse spray valves	Less than or equal to 1.3 gpm (4.9 lpm)
Ice machine	ENERGY STAR or performance equivalent that uses air-cooled or closed-loop cooling

Table 17. Requirements for appliances

Projects outside the United States can use appliances without the ENERGY STAR label, but project teams should still ensure that they meet ENERGY STAR specifications available on the ENERGY STAR website.

Process	Requirement
Heat rejection and cooling	No once-through cooling with potable water for any equipment, or appliances that reject heat
Cooling towers and evaporative coolers	Must contain; makeup water meters, conductivity controllers, overflow alarms, and efficient drift eliminators

Table 18. Requirements for processes

Projects under the **LEED BD+C: Healthcare, Retail, Schools, and Hospitality** rating systems should additionally meet LEED's baseline water usage requirements for the following appliances and processes:

For appliances;

- Dishwasher: Undercounter, stationary, single tank, multiple tank, flight machine
- Food steamer: Batch or cook to order
- Combination oven: Countertop, stand, or roll-in

For process;

- Discharge water temperature tempering: If the local requirements limit discharging high- temperature fluids into the drainage systems, projects should only use tempering devices that run water only when the equipment discharges hot water. Or projects should provide thermal heat exchangers to cool the drained discharge below local code minimums. Or if the fluid is steam condensate, it should be returned to the boiler.
- Venturi-type flow-through vacuum generators or aspirators: No vacuum-generating device by means of water flowing through the device into a drain can be used.

To better understand the prerequisite, let us list the steps on how to achieve it:

As there are two paths to achieve this prerequisite (**Path 1: Prescriptive Achievement** and **Path 2: Usage-Based Calculations**), the project teams should first decide if they will pursue the "Indoor Water Use Reduction" credit or not since path 2 must be chosen in order to earn the mentioned credit. Next, the project team should also make sure that the water usage of every fixture in the project is 20% below the baseline rates defined in the prerequisite in order to avoid path 2.

Path 1 – Prescriptive Achievement: If the project teams will not pursue the above-mentioned credit, they will need to use WaterSense-labeled products for all newly installed fixtures that are eligible for labeling. For the fixture types that are not eligible for labeling, the project teams will need to make sure the installed products' water usage rates are **20%** below the baseline minimums defined in the prerequisite. Additionally, the project teams will need to fulfill the mentioned requirements for appliances and processes. (LEED BD+C: Healthcare, Retail, Schools, and Hospitality projects should address even further requirements.) Finally, project teams will document the product cutsheets and manufacturers' information or fixture schedule.

OR

Path 2 – Usage-Based Calculations: In this path, the project teams will again need to use WaterSense-labeled products, as applicable, and will calculate their baseline water usage to establish a 20% water use reduction. The calculations will be made on the indoor water usage calculator provided by USGBC. Furthermore, the project teams should comply with the additional requirements for processes and appliances. Again, the LEED BD+C: Healthcare, Retail, Schools, and Hospitality projects will need to address the extra requirements set forth for the appliances and processes.

In order to calculate the baseline water usage, the project teams should determine **project occupancy**, **gender ratio**, **days of building operation**, and **fixture types used** in the project.

For project occupancy, project teams should identify the daily average number of building users by type, such as employees, residents, students, or visitors (as discussed under the "LEED Indoor Water Use Calculations" section). With this information, the full-time-equivalent (FTE) value of the project will be calculated. Please note that this information will also be needed for other prerequisites and credits, and the occupant calculations should be consistent throughout all of them.

The default gender ratio in the calculator is half male and half female, and if the project teams use a different gender ratio, they should provide a narrative explaining the reasons.

Lavatory faucets will need to be classified as public or private since their baseline usage will change according to their classification.

Next, the project teams should input the **fixture type**, **flush** or **flow rate** (which should also match the values in the product cutsheets), and the **percentage of occupants using each fixture**. The USGBC's indoor water use calculator will determine the project's water usage according to the following equation:

$$\text{Daily water use for each fixture type} = \text{Fixture flush or flow rate} \times \text{Duration of use} \times \text{Users} \times \text{Use per person per day}$$

Equation 10. Daily water use for each fixture type

In the product cutsheets, if the flow rate of a fixture is measured in gallons (liters) per cycle (gpc, lpc), this should be converted to flow rate in gallons (liters) per minute (gpm, lpm) with the following formula:

$$\text{Flow rate (gpm)} = \frac{\text{Gallons per cycle (gpc)} \times 60 \text{ seconds}}{\text{Cycle duration (sec)}}$$

Equation 11. Faucet flow rate conversion

After the calculation is complete, the calculator will provide the <u>annual baseline volume</u> and <u>annual design case volume</u>, which will be used to determine the percentage of indoor water use reduction, with the formula below. (In the "Indoor Water Use Reduction" <u>credit</u>, the same formula will be used to calculate the percentage water use reduction, but in this case the annual nonpotable water supply will be subtracted from the annual design case volume if nonpotable water is used.)

$$\text{\% Water use reduction} = \frac{(\text{Annual baseline water use volume}) - (\text{Annual design case volume})}{\text{Annual baseline water use volume}} \times 100$$

Equation 12. Percentage indoor water use reduction

Once 20% water use reduction is established, the project will earn the prerequisite.

- 📄 Projects with fixtures and fittings that do not exceed WaterSense maximum levels, documenting the product cutsheets and manufacturers' information will be sufficient.
- 📄 Project teams calculating baseline indoor water usage need to document their indoor water use calculations in addition to product cutsheets and manufacturers' information.
- 📄 For projects using appliance or process water, project teams will additionally need to document their product cutsheets and manufacturers' information.

📄 Project teams of the "LEED BD+C: Core and Shell" projects should additionally document the tenant lease agreement and tenant scope-of-work narrative. This is to prove that all the fixtures, except the ones in the incomplete tenant spaces, were considered in the baseline indoor water usage calculations.

KEY THINGS TO REMEMBER

- Projects aiming to pursue the "Indoor Water Use Reduction" credit should calculate the baseline indoor water consumption in this prerequisite and avoid earning this prerequisite through path 1.
- Projects should reduce the baseline indoor water usage **20%** by utilizing more efficient fixtures and fittings.
- The logic of how LEED calculates the indoor water use reduction with the mentioned equations.
- In the prerequisite calculations, the baseline flow and flush rates are specified by the **Energy Policy Act of 1992** (EPAct 1992).
- Names of items that fall under appliances, processes, or fixture/fittings.
- Project teams cannot use nonpotable water sources (such as reclaimed water, graywater, or harvested rainwater) to establish the 20% indoor water reduction; that will only happen under the "Indoor Water Use Reduction" credit.
- Know the requirements for the "appliances" and "processes" shown on table 17 and 18.

Building-Level Water Metering—Prerequisite

- Applicable to: All the LEED BD+C Rating Systems

PREREQUISITE SUMMARY

With this prerequisite, USGBC aims to compare every project's designed water usage data with the actual water usage data by tracking potable water use with the installation of water meters for all the potable water sources. All projects should commit to sharing their potable water data for 5 years or until the building changes ownership or lessee. The 5 years starts from the typical occupancy or date of LEED certification, whichever comes first.

Since disparities can occur between the designs of buildings compared with their actual performance, USGBC will collect and analyze data in order to identify the common traits among high and low performers, and it will also share its findings with the project teams so that they can improve their performance.

PREREQUISITE INTENT

To support project water management and identify opportunities for additional water savings by tracking the project's water consumption.

PREREQUISITE REQUIREMENTS

Projects should install permanent water meters that can measure the **total potable water use** for the <u>building</u> and <u>associated grounds</u>. Metered data should be collected in <u>monthly</u> and <u>annual</u> summaries. (The meter readings can be automated or manual.)

For a <u>5-year period</u>, the project should commit to sharing the whole-project water use data with USGBC, beginning on the date that the project accepts <u>LEED certification</u> or <u>typical occupancy</u>, whichever comes first. (The only exception to data sharing is a change of building ownership or lessee during the first 5 years of data sharing).

Projects should first determine all end uses of potable water in the building and the associated grounds, which can include the public water supply, on-site well, on-site potable water treatment system, and more. If all potable water comes from the public water supply and the water meter provides monthly usage data, the prerequisite can be earned without the need of installing an additional water meter. Even if the public water supplier uses a remote reporting technology, the project can still track water through the monthly billing. However, for additional sources of potable water supply, if applicable, projects should install additional meters to measure the total potable water use.

> 📄 Project teams should document a meter declaration (including a narrative describing the location of all the building-level water meters) and the sharing commitment.

KEY THINGS TO REMEMBER

- Why USGBC collects potable water usage data; USGBC will collect and analyze data in order to identify common traits among high and low performers and will also share its findings with the project teams so that they can improve their performance.
- For a 5-year period, the whole-project water use data should be shared with USGBC on the date that the project accepts LEED certification or typical occupancy, whichever comes first.
- Metered data should be collected in monthly and annual summaries.

Outdoor Water Use Reduction—Credit

■ Applicable to: All the LEED BD+C Rating Systems

New Construction	1 - 2 points	Retail	1 - 2 points	Hospitality	1 - 2 points
Core and Shell	1 - 2 points	Data Centers	1 - 2 points	Healthcare	1 point
Schools	1 - 2 points	Warehouses & Dist. Centers	1 - 2 points		

CREDIT SUMMARY

This is the credit of the "Outdoor Water Use Reduction" prerequisite, and it awards points for further reductions in outdoor water use.

In the prerequisite, the projects needed to reduce their irrigation water by 30% from the calculated baseline for the site's peak watering month. And in this credit, projects will be awarded points if they can make a **50%** or **100%** reduction from the baseline, again for the site's peak watering month. If the project has a landscape that does not need any irrigation beyond the 2-year establishment period, the credit will be automatically earned by the project.

The landscape water requirement (LWR) will again be calculated by the **US Environmental Protection Agency's WaterSense Water Budget Tool**, and nonvegetated surfaces such as pavements will be excluded from the calculations while the athletic fields and playgrounds (if vegetated) and food gardens may be included or excluded at the project team's discretion, just like in the "Outdoor Water Use Reduction" prerequisite.

One important thing to note for this credit is that alternative water sources, such as graywater, can be used here to make a reduction in the outdoor water above the 30% threshold.

To reinforce knowledge, it may be helpful to give an overview about the nonpotable water sources. Graywater is the untreated household water that did not come into contact with toilet waste. Used water from bathtubs, showers, bathroom washbasins, and water from clothes washers and laundry tubs are examples of graywater, and that graywater may be used as flush water in toilets or urinals or as irrigation water.

By installing graywater treatment systems, the used water can be filtered and then sent back to the building for reuse. The definition of graywater changes from state to state, and there are some states that do not allow the use of graywater as toilet flush water. Because of this, it is advised that the project team first check with the local code requirements before deciding on using graywater.

It is also important to mention **blackwater** and **reclaimed water**. Blackwater is the term to describe the used water that has come into contact with waste. Thus the water collected from urinals and toilets can be classified as blackwater. Reclaimed water is the former blackwater that has been treated and purified for reuse, and it can even be used for irrigation. However, projects need to be verified according to local code requirements, as some codes may classify some types of graywater as blackwater and may not allow its use.

CREDIT INTENT

To reduce outdoor water consumption.

CREDIT REQUIREMENTS

Projects should reduce outdoor water consumption through one of the following options:

OPTION 1: NO IRRIGATION REQUIRED – (2 Points)

As the name implies, if the project contains a landscape that does not need any irrigation beyond a maximum two-year establishment period, it will automatically fulfill this option.

> 🗎 No documentation is necessary for this option, as the required documents will be submitted under the "Outdoor Water Use Reduction" prerequisite.

OR

OPTION 2: REDUCED IRRIGATION — (2 Points)

Under this option, project teams should reduce the project's landscape water consumption by at least **50%** (1 point) or **100%** (2 points) from the calculated baseline for the site's <u>peak watering month</u>. This reduction should be established by careful selection of the plant species and by increasing the efficiency of the irrigation systems. The **US Environmental Protection Agency WaterSense Water Budget Tool** will be used for water budget calculations.

> 💡 This calculation will basically be conducted once and be used for both this credit and the "Outdoor Water Use Reduction" prerequisite. Project teams will not perform two separate calculations for the prerequisite and this credit.

<u>Nonvegetated surfaces</u>, such as pavements, are excluded from landscape calculations. <u>Athletic fields</u>, <u>vegetated playgrounds</u>, and <u>food gardens</u> may be included or excluded from these calculations according to the project teams' decision.

Additional reductions beyond the prerequisite level of **30%** may be achieved with the use of any combination of efficiency, <u>alternative water sources</u>, and smart scheduling technologies. Alternative water sources can include graywater, reclaimed wastewater, swimming pool backwash water, captured rainwater, refrigeration system condensate, fluid cooler discharge, food steamer discharge, fire pump test water, industrial process water, municipally supplied treated wastewater, stormwater and foundation drain water, and ice machine condensate.

It is always recommended to test the alternative water sources for irrigation use and calculate the necessary storage volume before deciding on using an alternative water source. Projects using captured rainwater as an alternative water source should estimate the amount of captured rainwater that will be available for irrigation use and the size of the rainwater system, and the project teams should show those values in the credit calculations. (See the case study of this credit.)

% of water reduction from the baseline	Points (except Healthcare)	Points LEED BD+C: Healthcare
50%	1	1
100%	2	—

Table 19. Points awarded according to the percent reduction from the baseline

📄 Teams for projects using alternative water sources should submit their alternative water sources and controls calculations. Since establishing water use reductions by using alternative water sources is not permitted under the "Outdoor Water Use Reduction" prerequisite, the project teams should document and submit the alternative water source calculations under this credit. No other documentation is necessary under this credit since the site plans showing the landscaping zones, as well as the WaterSense Water Budget Tool report, will be submitted under the "Outdoor Water Use Reduction" prerequisite.

EXEMPLARY PERFORMANCE

This credit does not qualify for exemplary performance.

CASE STUDY

To illustrate, let us continue the case study under the "Outdoor Water Use Reduction" prerequisite and assume that the project teams want to use captured rainwater from the roof as an alternative water source to establish a 100% water use reduction and earn 2 points.

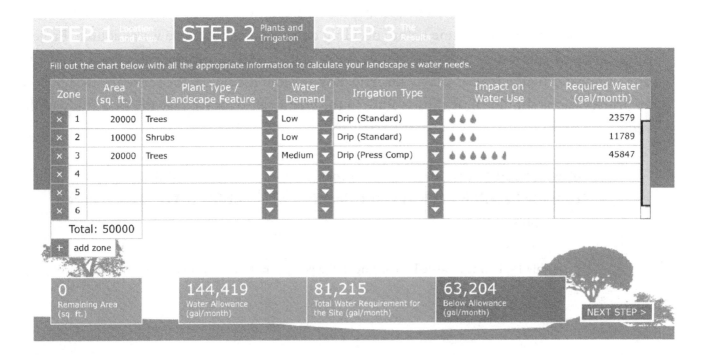

The water allowance is 144,419 gal./month (represents 30% below the baseline value), and the LWR of the project is 81,215 gal./month (which corresponds to 39.36% of the baseline value), which means that the project earns only one point since it has a 60.64% reduction from the baseline.

In order to earn 2 points, the project team would need to install a rainwater harvesting system that could account for 81,215 gal./month during the site's peak watering month. According to the monthly rainfall data in the project's location and taking into account the project's roof area, the project team calculates the amount of captured rainwater available, which would be 98,000 gal./month. With this result, the project team now confirms that enough irrigation water can be captured to establish a 100% reduction from the baseline. Lastly, the project team proceeds with installing a cistern capable of holding a minimum of 81,215 gal./month of rainwater.

KEY THINGS TO REMEMBER

- Landscapes that do not need any irrigation beyond a maximum **2-year establishment period** will satisfy option 1 and earn 2 points.
- In option 2, 50% water use reduction will lead to an award of 1 point, and a 100% water use reduction will lead to an award of 2 points (except with healthcare).
- Nonvegetated surfaces, such as pavements, will be excluded from the calculations, and athletic fields and playgrounds (if vegetated) and food gardens may be included or excluded at the project team's discretion, just as in the "Outdoor Water Use" prerequisite.
- Additional reductions beyond the prerequisite level of **30%** may be achieved with the use of any combination of efficiency, alternative water sources, and smart-scheduling technologies.
- Projects using alternative water sources should estimate the amount that can be generated through those sources and the size of storage.
- Alternative water sources can include graywater, reclaimed wastewater, swimming pool backwash water, captured rainwater, refrigeration system condensate, fluid cooler discharge, food steamer discharge, fire pump test water, industrial process water, municipally supplied treated wastewater, stormwater and foundation drain water, and ice machine condensate.

■ Applicable to: All the LEED BD+C Rating Systems

New Construction	1 - 6 points	Retail	1 - 7 points	Hospitality	1 - 6 points
Core and Shell	1 - 6 points	Data Centers	1 - 6 points	Healthcare	1 - 7 points
Schools	1 - 7 points	Warehouses & Dist. Centers	1 - 6 points		

CREDIT SUMMARY

This is the credit of the "Indoor Water Use Reduction" prerequisite, which aims for further indoor water use reduction.

In the prerequisite, the projects need to reduce their building water use by 20% from the calculated baseline, and in this credit, projects will be awarded points if they can make further reductions from the same baseline. Alternative water sources can this time be used to reduce potable water use. Those alternative water sources include on-site surface sources, subsurface natural freshwater sources, graywater, on-site reclaimed water, collected rainwater, captured condensate, and nonpotable water from entities other than public utilities.

Another addition from the prerequisite is that this credit requires further standards for appliances and processes.

CREDIT INTENT

To reduce indoor water consumption.

CREDIT REQUIREMENTS

<u>For Building Water Use</u>:

Projects should further reduce indoor water consumption from the calculated baseline in the "Indoor Water Use Reduction" prerequisite. Additional potable water savings above the prerequisite level (20%) can be established by using alternative water sources. Points will be awarded according to the level of reduction shown on the following table:

% of water reduction from the baseline	Points (BD+C)	Points (Schools, Retail, Hospitality and Healthcare)
25%	1	1
30%	2	2
35%	3	3
40%	4	4
45%	5	5
50%	6	—

Table 20. Points awarded according to the percent reduction from the baseline

Even though some of the fixtures and fittings that are needed to meet the needs of the occupants may be outside the project boundary, they still should be included in these calculations.

In this type of prerequisites and credits, "LEED BD+C: Core and Shell" projects should always consider the installed fixtures and appliances under their scope of work and exclude the scope of the tenant spaces in credit calculations.

AND

<u>For Appliances and Process Water Use</u>:

Projects should install equipment fulfilling the minimum LEED requirements of any of the following categories. One point will be awarded for projects that fulfill any of the following categories, while "LEED BD+C: Schools", "LEED BD+C: Retail", and "LEED BD+C: Healthcare" projects can earn an additional point for fulfilling the requirement of a second category.

<u>Category 1</u>: Commercial Washing Machines

▪ This category applies to projects processing 120,000 lbs (57,606 kg) of laundry per year.

<u>Category 2</u>: Commercial Kitchen Equipment

▪ This category applies to projects serving at least 100 meals per day.

▪ All types of dishwashers should contain an ENERGY STAR label or meet the ENERGY STAR specifications for projects outside the United States.

<u>Category 3</u>: Laboratory and Medical Equipment

▪ This category applies to medical or laboratory facilities.

<u>Category 4</u>: Municipal Steam Systems

▪ This category applies to projects in which the project must be connected to a municipal or district steam system that does not allow the return of steam condensate.

Projects using nonpotable water sources should calculate their percent reduction by using the equation below. (Note that this equation is similar to the equation in the "Indoor Water Use Reduction" prerequisite, with the exception of the nonpotable water volume being subtracted.)

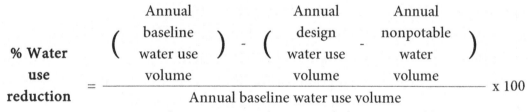

Equation 13. Percentage indoor water use reduction, including non-potable water sources

Furthermore, when using any nonpotable water sources, project teams must always address any seasonal change in demand, supply, and storage capacity, also considering the monthly demand of irrigation if nonpotable water sources are also used for irrigation.

🖹 Project teams using alternative water sources should submit their alternative water source calculations and narrative, if applicable, plumbing system design drawings, cutsheets, manufacturers' information, and indoor water use calculator. Since establishing water use reductions from the baseline water usage by using alternative water sources is not permitted under the "Indoor Water Use Reduction" prerequisite, the alternative water source calculations are submitted under this credit.

🖹 Retail, healthcare, and school projects can earn an additional point for meeting the requirements of two categories under appliances and process water, and in this case, project teams will need to document cutsheets and manufacturers' information for appliances and process water.

EXEMPLARY PERFORMANCE

To qualify for exemplary performance under this credit, projects need to achieve **55%** water use reduction.

KEY THINGS TO REMEMBER

■ Alternative water sources can include on-site surface sources, subsurface natural freshwater sources, graywater, on-site reclaimed water, collected rainwater, captured condensate, and nonpotable water from entities other than public utilities.

■ One point will be awarded for projects that fulfill any of the appliance and process categories, while "LEED BD+C: Schools", "LEED BD+C: Retail", and "LEED BD+C: Healthcare" projects can earn an additional point for fulfilling the requirement of a second category.

■ Names of the categories under appliances and process water use.

Cooling Tower Water Use Reduction—Credit

■ Applicable to: All the LEED BD+C Rating Systems

All the LEED BD+C Rating Systems	1 - 2 points

CREDIT SUMMARY

This credit aims to reduce the water usage of cooling towers and evaporative condensers. When cooling the building, the HVAC system needs to take heat away from the building, and cooling towers are needed to release this heat into the atmosphere.

In order to release the building's heat, cooling towers evaporate water using the building's heat. As the cooling tower water evaporates, the remaining water becomes more concentrated and starts to deposit scale, thereby reducing the cooling tower's efficiency. To minimize the deposit of scales, some of the cooling tower's water is replaced by fresh potable water. (The removal of water is called **blowdown**.) **Makeup water** is used to replace both the lost water from evaporation and the blowdown.

With this credit, projects will need to chemically analyze cooling tower water (condenser water) to evaluate its concentration levels and to calculate how many cycles the cooling tower can make using the same condenser water without going beyond the targeted concentration levels defined in the credit.

To gain an additional point, projects can use a minimum of **20%** of recycled nonpotable water in their cooling towers or can instead increase the cooling tower cycles beyond **10** by increasing the level of treatment in the condenser or makeup water.

CREDIT INTENT

To reduce the water used for cooling tower makeup and to control corrosion, microbes, and scale in the condenser water system.

CREDIT REQUIREMENTS

Projects should conduct a one-time potable water analysis for cooling towers and evaporative condensers to find the actual values of the parameters in table 21.

Project teams can find the number of cooling tower cycles by dividing the "maximum allowed concentration level" of each parameter by the "actual concentration" level of each parameter found in the testing potable makeup water. Next, projects should limit the cooling tower cycles to avoid exceeding the maximum values for any of these parameters. A higher number of cycles a cooling tower can make, will indicate a higher water efficiency and potable water savings because of the reduction in the makeup water usage.

$$\text{Cycles of concentration} = \frac{\text{Maximum parameter concentrations in condenser water}}{\text{Actual parameter concentrations in makeup water}}$$

Equation 14. Cycles of concentration

Parameter	Maximum Level
Ca	1,000 ppm
Total alkalinity	1,000 ppm
SiO₂	100 ppm
CI⁻	250ppm
Conductivity	2,000 MS/cm

Table 21. Maximum parameter concentrations

Projects that meet the requirements up to this point will earn one point under this credit. To gain an additional point, projects can use a minimum of **20%** of recycled nonpotable water in their cooling towers or can instead increase the cooling tower cycles beyond **10** by increasing the level of treatment in the condenser or makeup water.

Cooling tower cycles	Points
Maximum number of cycles achieved without exceeding maximum values (up to 10 cycles maximum)	1 point
Achieve a minimum of 10 cycles by increasing the level of treatment in condenser or make-up water **OR** Meet the minimum number of cycles to earn one point and use a minimum of 20% recycled non-potable water	2 points

Table 22. Points awarded according to cooling tower cycles

EXEMPLARY PERFORMANCE

This credit does not qualify for exemplary performance.

CASE STUDY

To illustrate, let's assume that a project aiming for this credit conducted a potable water analysis and found the following results:

Ca: 400 ppm
Total alkalinity: 500 ppm
SiO_2: 20 ppm
CI: 50 ppm
Conductivity: 400 MS/cm

In this case, the cycles of concentration according to the credit's formula would be as follows:

Ca: 1,000 / 400 = 2.5 cycles
Total alkalinity: 1,000 / 500 = **2 cycles**
SiO_2: 100 / 20 = 5 cycles
CI: 250 / 50 = 5 cycles
Conductivity: 2,000 / 400 = 5 cycles

According to these results, the lowest cycle of concentration will determine the cycles of concentration for the makeup water, which is "2 cycles" from the total alkalinity parameter.

As a result, the project team will need to adjust the cooling tower or evaporative condenser settings for maximum of 2 cycles in order not to exceed the allowable concentration levels and will earn one point from this credit.

If the project team wants to aim for 2 points, this time the system performance should be increased, and the project team will have two options to choose from. In the first option, the project team can choose to treat the water and achieve a minimum of 10 cycles. Or the project team can choose to meet the minimum number of cycles and use a minimum of 20% recycled nonpotable water. Good nonpotable water sources with low mineral content can include air-conditioner condensate, rainwater, steam system condensate, fire pump test water, food steamer discharge water, and ice machine condensate.

> 📄 Project teams earning 1 point under this credit should document potable water analysis results and narrative, and they should document cycles of concentration calculations.
>
> 📄 Project teams earning 2 points under this credit should additionally document nonpotable water calculations, water treatment calculations, and nonpotable water analysis (if using 100% nonpotable water).

KEY THINGS TO REMEMBER

- The purpose of makeup water
- Definition of blowdown and why it is needed
- Paths to earn 1 and 2 points
- This credit will not be awarded if a project does not use a cooling tower

Water Metering—Credit

■ Applicable to: All the LEED BD+C Rating Systems

All the LEED BD+C Rating Systems	1 point

CREDIT SUMMARY

This is the credit of the "Building Level Water Metering" prerequisite, which requires projects to track the water use of different subsystems. By submetering different building systems, a facility manager can identify major water uses and look for ways to reduce water use.

CREDIT INTENT

To support water management and find opportunities for additional water savings by tracking a building's water consumption.

CREDIT REQUIREMENTS

Project teams should install permanent water meters to **at least two** or more of the following water subsystems that are applicable:

- Irrigation: Meter water systems that serve at least **80%** of the irrigated landscape area. Landscaping that requires no irrigation are exempt. However, if reclaimed water is used for irrigation, then 100% of the reclaimed water should be metered.

- Indoor plumbing fixtures and fittings: Meter water systems that serve at least **80%** of the total number of fixtures and fittings described in the "Indoor Water Use Reduction" prerequisite. If not directly metered, project teams can deduct other water uses from the total water consumption and find the water consumption of indoor plumbing fixtures and fittings.

- Domestic hot water: Meter at least **80%** of the installed domestic hot water heating capacity, including tanks and on-demand heaters.

- Boilers with aggregate projected annual water use of 100,000 gallons (378,541 liters) or more, or boilers with more than 500,000 Btu/hr (150 kW): For multiple boilers, a single makeup meter can record the total flow.

- Reclaimed water: Meter all the reclaimed water. If the reclaimed water contains a makeup water connection, that should be metered as well.

- Other process water: Meter at least **80%** of process end uses, which can include humidification systems, clothes washers, dishwashers, pools, and more.

> ♀ Note that metering of cooling towers is not addressed under this credit.

The submetering equipment to be used can be read manually, or it can be connected to the building automation system. Projects can also choose to install wet meters, which are the types of meters that are installed inside a water pipe to record the volume of passing water.

In addition to the requirements above, "LEED BD+C: Healthcare" projects should install water meters in any five of the following: purified water systems, filter backwash water, water use in laundry, water use in a laboratory, water use in a dietary department, water use in a central sterile and processing department, water use in physiotherapy/hydrotherapy treatment areas, water use in a surgical suite, cold water makeup for domestic hot water systems, and closed-loop hydronic system makeup water.

> 📄 Project teams should document a narrative about their water metering strategy.

EXEMPLARY PERFORMANCE

This credit does not qualify for exemplary performance.

KEY THINGS TO REMEMBER

- The names of the six subsystems—mentioned under the credit requirements—that LEED has a requirement for metering under this credit
- "LEED BD+C: Healthcare" projects should additionally meter five of the mentioned water-consuming items

CHAPTER 7

ENERGY AND ATMOSPHERE (EA)

This credit category contains the highest total points among credit categories in LEED because energy use and the burning of fossil fuels are the biggest contributors to global warming. Green buildings need to use less energy and preferably use energy from sustainable energy sources.

Similar to the "Water Efficiency" credit category, in which the projects calculate baseline water usage and establish reductions by employing water-efficient strategies, this credit category provides for the calculation of the baseline energy usage of the whole building and allows for the discovery of innovative ways to reduce building energy usage.

According to a study by the New Buildings Institute, LEED-certified projects use 24% less energy than regular buildings. Almost half of the green buildings in the study achieved an **ENERGY STAR Portfolio Manager**™ score of 75 or above, with an overall average score of 68.[1]

The ENERGY STAR Portfolio Manager is an interactive, online management tool that enables the tracking and assessment of energy and water consumption. It was set up by the EPA as a part of the ENERGY STAR program. With the ENERGY STAR Portfolio Manager, a score of 50 represents an average building performance.

In addition to the Portfolio Manager, there is another program called **ENERGY STAR Target Finder**™, which allows projects to set target goals for a building design's energy demands. According to their changes in the design, project teams can see the savings in energy demand.

The New Buildings Institute study also found that a significant percentage of buildings underperformed their benchmarks. This is why commissioning building systems and monitoring their performance is very important to ensure that the set benchmarks turn into actual performances.

This chapter will discuss the LEED requirements for the "Energy and Atmosphere" credit category. The credit category contains the following prerequisites/credits:

- Fundamental Commissioning and Verification—Prerequisite
- Minimum Energy Performance—Prerequisite
- Building-Level Energy Metering—Prerequisite
- Fundamental Refrigerant Management—Prerequisite
- Enhanced Commissioning—Credit
- Optimize Energy Performance—Credit
- Advanced Energy Metering—Credit
- Demand Response—Credit
- Renewable Energy Production—Credit
- Enhanced Refrigerant Management—Credit
- Green Power and Carbon Offsets—Credit

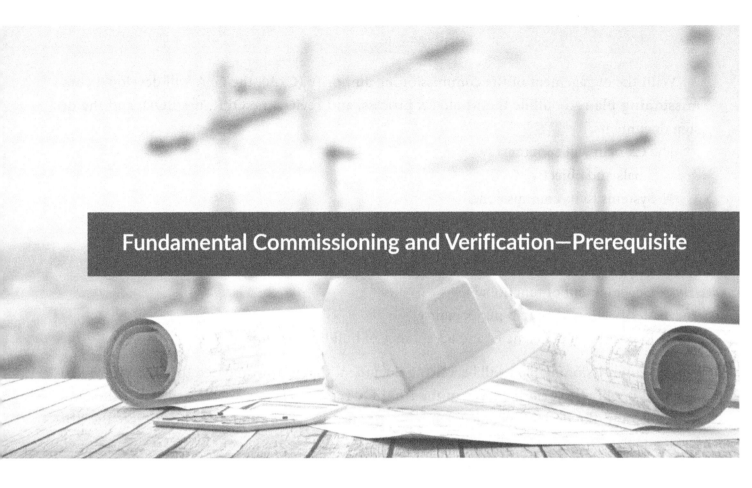

Fundamental Commissioning and Verification—Prerequisite

■ Applicable to: All the LEED BD+C Rating Systems

PREREQUISITE SUMMARY

As a major part of the integrated process, building commissioning ensures that the projects are designed and built as really intended. A well-oriented commissioning (Cx) process will always lead to fewer change orders, will avoid project delays and cost overruns, and will increase the durability of the whole project.

This prerequisite encourages projects to implement a fundamental commissioning and verification process to ensure that the project design and construction meets the **owner's project requirements (OPR)** and **basis of design (BOD)**. Project teams will additionally create a **current facility requirements (CFR)** and **operations and maintenance (O&M) plan** that will contain all the necessary information to operate the building efficiently.

The whole process will start with the development of the OPR in the predesign stage, which will really establish the owner's goals and the building's intended function. Next, the BOD will be prepared during the schematic design phase to provide technical guidance to the whole project, and it will be updated through the design and construction phases. The BOD will contain all the systems to be commissioned.

With the engagement of the commissioning authority (CxA), the CxA will develop a **commissioning plan** to outline the whole Cx process, and review the OPR, the BOD, and the design documents.

The Cx plan will contain:

- Goals and objectives
- Systems to be commissioned
- Team member roles/responsibilities
- OPR reviews
- BOD reviews
- Development of functional tests
- Verification of system performance
- Reporting of deficiencies and acceptance of building systems

The commissioning plan will be a living document that will be updated throughout the project, and it will also form the basis of the **final Cx report**. The CxA will ensure that the OPR, the BOD, and the design documents are consistent throughout and that they reflect the project's intent.

Next, based on the systems to be commissioned, the CxA will develop the Cx requirements and incorporate them into the construction documents. If any revisions to the project are made, the owner will update the OPR, the design team will update the BOD, and the CxA will update the Cx plan.

The process will continue with the Cx kickoff meeting to introduce the project team to the Cx activities. The CxA, the design team, or the contractor will prepare construction checklists and functional test scripts to be used during construction.

During the construction phase, the CxA will regularly conduct site visits, inspect installations, and verify that the contractor is working according to the design. Once all the building systems to be commissioned are installed and energized, the CxA will perform functional performance testing in accordance with the functional test scripts.

The CxA will continuously document findings and track any discovered deficiencies for the owner throughout the whole process. At the end, all the data used during the design and construction phase will be compiled by the CxA as a **final Cx report**. The final Cx report will contain the Cx process overview, a summary of the commissioning process and results, the OPR, the BOD, submittals, the design review log, Cx specifications, installation verifications, functional performance tests, and the issues log.

Finally, in order to assist the building operations phase, the project teams will prepare the **current facility requirements (CFR)** and **operations and maintenance (O&M) plan,** which will contain all the information to operate the building efficiently.

The O&M plan will include equipment run-time schedules, building occupancy schedules, lighting levels of the building, minimum outside air requirements, sequences of operations for the building, and more.

Systems that will be a part of the fundamental commissioning process are:

- Mechanical, including HVAC&R (heating, ventilating, air-conditioning and refrigeration)
- Plumbing (including domestic hot water systems, pumps, and controls)
- Electrical (including service, distribution, lighting, and controls, including daylighting controls)
- Renewable energy systems

Systems that are not required to be commissioned under this prerequisite but may be added to the Cx scope at the request of the owner include the following:

- Building envelope
- Life safety systems
- Communications and data systems
- Fire protection and fire alarm systems
- Process equipment

The OPR and the BOD should cover the building envelope, which means that the design of the building envelope should be reviewed even if the project teams choose not to perform an envelope commissioning during the construction phase. Project teams may also choose to pursue the "Enhanced Commissioning" credit, which awards points for building envelope commissioning during the construction phase.

PREREQUISITE INTENT

To support the design, construction, and building operations that meet the owner's project requirements for energy, water, durability, and indoor environmental quality.

PREREQUISITE REQUIREMENTS

Scope of the commissioning process:

Project teams should complete the following commissioning activities for the mechanical, electrical, plumbing, and renewable energy systems and assemblies according to **ASHRAE Guideline 0-2005** and **ASHRAE Guideline 1.1-2007 for HVAC&R systems**, as related to energy, water, indoor environmental quality, and durability.

For the building envelope, the requirements are limited including the envelope in the OPR and the BOD and review of the OPR, the BOD, and the project design. **NIBS Guideline 3-2012 for Exterior Enclosures** can provide additional guidance on building envelope commissioning.

The project teams should first develop the **OPR** and the **BOD**. Next, the project teams should assign the commissioning authority. The CxA is the person who will manage the whole commissioning process. The CxA will complete the following tasks:

- Review the OPR, the BOD, and the project design
- Develop and implement the Cx plan
- Ensure that the Cx requirements are integrated into the construction documents
- Prepare construction checklists and system test procedures
- Confirm system test execution
- Maintain an issues and benefits log throughout the Cx process
- Prepare a final Cx report
- Report all the findings **directly to the owner** throughout the whole process

The review of the design of the building envelope can be performed by a qualified member of the design or construction team (or an employee of that firm) who is not responsible for the design of the building envelope.

Qualifications of the Commissioning Authority (CxA):

By the end of the design development phase, the project teams should engage a commissioning authority.

The qualified CxA should have completed commissioning for at least two similar projects from the early design phase to a minimum of ten months of occupancy.

The CxA can be

- A qualified employee of the owner;
- An independent consultant;
- An employee of the design or construction firm who is not a part of the project design or construction team (except that for projects smaller than 20,000 square feet, the CxA can be a qualified member of the design or construction team as well);
- A disinterested subcontractor of the design or construction team; and
- For small projects with computer room peak cooling loads less than 2,000,000 Btu/h (600 kW) or a total computer room peak cooling load less than 600,000 Btu/h (175 kW), the CxA may be a qualified member of the design or construction team.

In all the cases, the CxA should report directly to the owner.

💡 Project teams that want to pursue the "Enhanced Commissioning" credit should choose the CxA according to that credit's requirements. In the "Enhanced Commissioning" credit, the CxA cannot be an employee of the design or construction firm and cannot be a disinterested subcontractor of the construction team. (However, the CxA can still be a disinterested subcontractor of the design team.) And for projects smaller than 20,000 square feet, the CxA can be a member of the design or construction team.

Current Facilities Requirements (CFR) and Operations and Maintenance (O&M) plan:
Projects should prepare a **CFR** and **O&M plan**, which should contain all the information necessary to operate the building efficiently. The plan must include the following:

- A schedule for building occupancy
- A run-time schedule for equipment
- A sequence of operations for the building
- Setpoints for all the HVAC equipment
- Building lighting levels
- Any changes in schedules or setpoints for different seasons, days of the week, and times of day
- Minimum requirements for outside air
- A preventive maintenance plan for building equipment that is described in the systems
- A commissioning program to include periodic commissioning requirements, ongoing commissioning tasks, and continuous tasks for critical facilities

📄 Projects should document the;
- Previous experience of the CxA
- List of systems to be commissioned
- Confirmation of OPR and BOD
- Verification of CxA activities and reviews
- Cx plan, CFR, O&M plan, and Cx report
- Documentation of testing and verification

KEY THINGS TO REMEMBER

- Project teams should complete the commissioning activities for the mechanical, electrical, plumbing, and renewable energy systems and assemblies according to **ASHRAE Guideline 0-2005** and **ASHRAE Guideline 1.1-2007 for HVAC&R systems**, as related to energy, water, indoor environmental quality, and durability.
- In all cases, the CxA must report directly to the owner.
- The qualifications of the CxA, both for this prerequisite and the Enhanced Commissioning credit.
- For the building envelope, the requirements are limited to inclusion in the OPR and the BOD in addition to the review of the OPR, the BOD, and the project design.
- The purpose and elements of the Cx plan, final Cx report, and CFR and O&M plan.

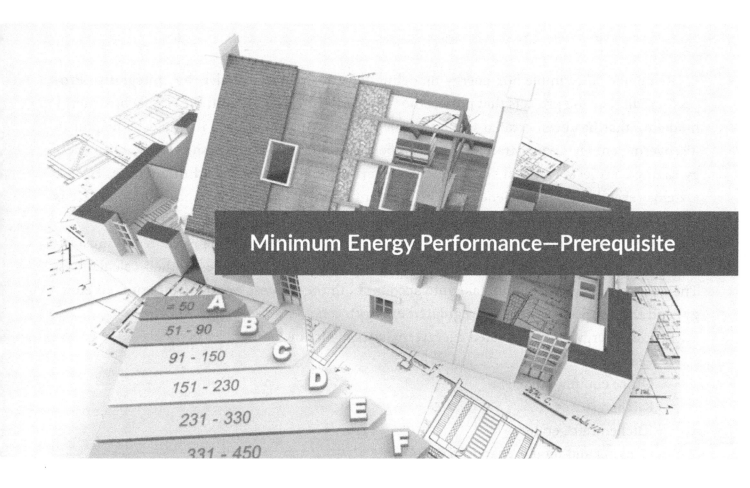

Minimum Energy Performance—Prerequisite

■ Applicable to: All the LEED BD+C Rating Systems

PREREQUISITE SUMMARY

Just like the "Water Use Reduction" prerequisite aims to decrease potable water usage of a building, this prerequisite aims to establish minimum energy performance.

In this prerequisite's option 1, project teams can perform a whole-building energy simulation in accordance with **ANSI/ASHRAE/IESNA Standard 90.1-2010, Appendix G, with errata**. This allows work to start on the model, and by applying different strategies, project teams will need to establish a minimum of **5%** reduction in energy costs. (The 5% requirement is applicable for new construction projects.) Additionally, projects pursuing option 1 will need to comply with the <u>mandatory provisions</u> of the **ANSI/ASHRAE/IESNA Standard 90.1-2010, with errata**.

Instead of performing a whole-building energy simulation and establishing a 5% reduction in energy costs, the project team can choose to achieve prescriptive compliance with the **ASHRAE 50% Advanced Energy Design Guide** in option 2, or with the **Advanced Buildings™ Core Performance Guide™** in option 3 by additionally complying with the <u>mandatory</u> and <u>prescriptive</u> provisions of **ANSI /ASHRAE/ IESNA Standard 90.1-2010, with errata** for both options 2 and 3.

Remember the simple box energy modeling that was required under the "Integrative Process" credit. For the projects that pursue the "Integrative Process" credit, the simple box energy modeling that has been created will also be a good starting point, and it would be helpful in discovering energy saving strategies that can be used under this prerequisite. To establish energy savings, projects can evaluate different scenarios for the massing and orientation, HVAC systems (evaluating the efficiencies of the different HVAC systems and optimizing their size is very important), natural ventilation, daylighting, lighting, building envelope, and more.

When doing a whole-building energy simulation under option 1, the project teams must establish reduced energy costs without including renewable energy sources in their calculations. The energy calculations should take into account both the **process energy (unregulated energy)** and the **nonprocess energy (regulated energy)**.

Process energy, or unregulated energy, includes the following:

- Computers
- Office equipment
- Kitchen stoves
- Kitchen refrigerators
- Cooking and food preparation equipment
- Washers and dryers
- Elevators and escalators

Note that most of the items above work by being connected to a plug, with the exception of elevators and escalators.

The term "process load" is synonymously used with **plug load** (receptacle load), which represents the electrical use by all the equipment that is connected to the electrical system via electrical receptacle. Therefore, the energy consumed while charging the battery of a cell phone would be considered a plug load as well as a process load.

Nonprocess, or regulated energy, includes items that are used to condition spaces and maintain comfort and amenities for building occupants:

- Interior and exterior lighting (parking garage, security, landscape, architectural)
- HVAC (heating, cooling, fans, pumps)
- Hot water heating
- Toilet exhaust
- Parking garage ventilation

With the consumption of process energy in the building, **building process loads** occur; with the consumption of nonprocess energy, **building nonprocess loads** occur.

This prerequisite also has an "Optimize Energy Performance" credit that will be discussed in the following pages; it awards points for making further reductions in the energy costs, and the number of points is tied to the percentage of the reductions.

The credit has two options: the first option is the "Whole Building Energy Simulation", and the second option is "Prescriptive Compliance with the ASHRAE Advanced Energy Design Guide." <u>Project teams that will pursue option 1 of the credit should pursue option 1 of this prerequisite and create an energy model to be used for both this prerequisite and the "Optimize Energy Performance" credit</u>. To pursue the maximum number of points in the "Optimize Energy Performance" credit, the project teams will need to choose option 1 since it contains the most points (18 points) while option 2 contains 6 points.

In this prerequisite, the "LEED BD+C: Data Center" projects only have one option and should implement a whole-building energy simulation.

PREREQUISITE INTENT

Reducing the economic and environmental harms resulting from excessive energy use by implementing a minimum level of energy efficiency for a building and its systems.

PREREQUISITE REQUIREMENTS

<u>For all LEED BD+C Rating Systems, except "LEED BD+C: Data Centers"</u>:
For all the options, project teams should first determine the climate zone of the project according to **ASHRAE 90.1-2010, Appendix B** since the energy consumption of the building will be heavily linked to the climate. Projects outside the United States can refer to **ANSI/ASHRAE/IESNA Standard 90.1–2010, Appendixes B and D** and determine the appropriate climate zone for their project.

Project teams should set energy performance targets no later than the schematic design phase. Projects pursuing option 3 must use the EPA's ENERY STAR Target Finder to establish the energy performance target and achieve a score greater than **90**.

Before going into further details, it is important to mention the rules of each option under this prerequisite. All project teams can pursue option 1 of this prerequisite. However, to pursue option 2 and option 3, projects should meet their eligibility requirements.

Option 2 is for projects that basically do not contain unique designs and systems beyond simple improvements to the MEP (mechanical, electrical, and plumbing) systems. Office buildings less than 100,000 square feet (9,290 square meters), retail buildings between 20,000 and 100,000 square feet (1,860–9,290 square meters), school buildings of any size, and hospitals larger than 100,000 square feet (9,290 square meters) are eligible to pursue this option.

In order to pursue option 3 of this prerequisite, projects should be less than 100,000 square feet (9,290 square meters), and the project should not be a school, healthcare facility, warehouse, or laboratory.

However, one important thing to note is that projects pursuing option 3 will not be eligible to pursue the "Optimize Energy Performance" credit. That credit is basically a continuation of this prerequisite and it does not contain an option 3.

OPTION 1: WHOLE-BUILDING ENERGY SIMULATION

Under this option, project teams should create a building energy model and simulate the whole-building energy use. Projects should demonstrate a percentage improvement in the baseline building performance by implementing a new design. New construction projects should demonstrate a minimum **5%** improvement, major renovation projects should demonstrate a minimum **3%** improvement, and core and shell projects should demonstrate a minimum **2%** improvement. (Since new construction projects will have greater control over the project design, these projects should establish more energy savings than major renovations and core and shell projects). All these percentage improvement calculations will be based on energy costs, not energy usage.

In addition to the energy modeling requirements, projects' designs should meet the mandatory provisions of **ANSI/ASHRAE/IESNA Standard 90.1-2010, with errata** (or a USGBC-approved equivalent for projects outside the United States). While meeting this prerequisite's requirements, project teams should make sure that all the energy consumption and costs associated with the project are taken into account. (That covers the unregulated loads as well as the regulated loads.)

The percent improvement in the baseline building performance must be established without considering the on-site renewable energy sources, if any. However, on-site renewable energy sources can be counted toward energy savings under the "Optimize Energy Performance" credit. Therefore, project teams that want to earn points with the project's on-site renewable energy systems should pursue option 1 of this prerequisite so that they can also pursue option 1 of the "Optimize Energy Performance" credit and earn extra points. In the credit's option 2, the on-site renewable energy generation sources will not lead to an award of additional points.

> 💡 As mentioned above, the percent improvement in the baseline building performance must be established without considering the on-site renewable energy sources, if any. This is similar to the "Outdoor Water Use Reduction" prerequisite and credit. In that prerequisite, projects need to establish a minimum of 30% potable water savings and cannot include the alternative on-site water sources in their calculations. However, projects can include the alternative water sources under the "Outdoor Water Use Reduction" credit.

Going back to this prerequisite, project teams should calculate the baseline building performance according to **ANSI/ASHRAE/IESNA Standard 90.1-2010, <u>Appendix G</u> with errata** (or a USGBC-approved equivalent for projects outside the United States using a simulation model).

Projects should document the assumptions used to model the unregulated loads, and the unregulated loads should be identical in the baseline and in the proposed design. If the unregulated loads are not identical and the simulation program cannot model the energy savings, project teams should then follow the **exceptional calculation method (ANSI/ASHRAE/IESNA Standard 90.1-2010, G2.5)**. The exceptional calculation method (ECM) is used when the modeling software cannot accurately model a design, material, or device.

Project teams may also use the <u>COMNET Modeling Guidelines and Procedures</u> for documenting the measures for reducing unregulated loads.

> 📄 Projects should document the energy modeling inputs, input and output reports from the energy modeling software, energy consumption and demand rates for each building end use and its fuel types and fuel rates. If applicable, projects should also submit the exceptional calculations and retail process energy calculations.

OR

OPTION 2: PRESCRIPTIVE COMPLIANCE: ASHRAE 50% ADVANCED ENERGY DESIGN GUIDE

Under this option, projects should comply with the <u>mandatory</u> and <u>prescriptive</u> provisions of **ANSI/ASHRAE/IESNA Standard 90.1-2010, with errata** (or a local equivalent for projects located outside the United States). Next, projects should comply with the <u>HVAC and service water heating requirements</u>, <u>equipment efficiencies</u>, <u>economizers</u>, <u>ventilation</u>, and <u>duct-and-damper</u> requirements in "Chapter 4, Design Strategies and Recommendations by Climate Zone" of the corresponding **ASHRAE 50% Advanced Energy Design Guide.** Below are the ASHRAE 50% Advanced Energy Design Guides for different project types:

- "ASHRAE 50% Advanced Energy Design Guide for Small to Medium Office Buildings"—for office buildings smaller than 100,000 square feet (9,290 square meters)
- "ASHRAE 50% Advanced Energy Design Guide for Medium to Large Box Retail Buildings"—for retail buildings between 20,000 and 100,000 square feet (1,860 to 9,290 square meters)
- "ASHRAE 50% Advanced Energy Design Guide for K–12 School Buildings"
- "ASHRAE 50% Advanced Energy Design Guide for Large Hospitals"—the project should be over 100,000 square feet (9,290 square meters) to pursue this option.

Projects that want to pursue option 2 of the "Optimize Energy Performance" credit, should also consider the additional Advanced Energy Design Guide requirements under the credit beforehand and design the building appropriately.

> 📄 Project teams should document the Advanced Energy Design Guide compliance tables.

OR

OPTION 3: PRESCRIPTIVE COMPLIANCE: ADVANCED BUILDINGS™ CORE PERFORMANCE™ GUIDE

(Once more, only the projects of **less than 100,000 square feet** can pursue this option. School, healthcare, warehouse, and laboratory projects are ineligible to pursue this option, regardless of their size.)

Under this option, projects should comply with the <u>mandatory</u> and <u>prescriptive</u> provisions of **ANSI/ASHRAE/IESNA Standard 90.1-2010, with errata** (or a local equivalent for projects outside the United States). Next, the projects should comply with the **Advanced Buildings™ Core Performance™ Guide (CPG)**. If these standards conflict with each other, project teams should implement the more stringent code.

Projects should meet the following section of the CPG as applicable:

- Section 1: Design Process Strategies
- Section 2: Core Performance Requirements
- Section 3: Enhanced Performance Strategies
    - 3.5 Supply Air Temperature Reset
    - 3.9 Premium Economizer Performance
    - 3.10 Variable Speed Control

In this option, the energy performance target should be established using the EPA's **ENERGY STAR Target Finder,** and projects should achieve a minimum score of **90**.

Again, projects pursuing option 3 will not be eligible to pursue the "Optimize Energy Performance" credit.

> 📄 Project teams should document the Target Finder results and summary, building configuration analysis, building loads and mechanical system design capacity, building envelope details, confirmation stating that all aspects of CPG sections 1 and 2 are met, and a narrative or calculations about the CPG enhanced-performance strategies.

For "LEED BD+C: Data Centers":

"LEED BD+C: Data Center" projects should comply with the mandatory provisions of **ANSI/ASHRAE/IESNA Standard 90.1-2010, with errata** (or a local equivalent for projects outside the United States). Next, project teams need to create a whole-building energy simulation in accordance with **ANSI/ASHRAE/IESNA Standard 90.1–2010, Appendix G, with errata** (or a USGBC-approved equivalent standard for projects outside the United States), and they should demonstrate a **5%** improvement in the proposed performance rating over the baseline performance rating. All energy consumption and costs associated with the project should be considered in the whole-building energy model.

As is the case for the other rating systems, projects must meet the minimum percentage savings before counting the on-site renewable energy systems. Again, the reductions will be based on energy costs, not energy usage.

So far, all the requirements have been the same as in option 1 of the other rating systems. From this point on, the requirements for the "LEED BD+C: Data Center" projects will differ.

To determine the total energy cost savings, project teams should create two separate models, one for building energy cost and the other for IT equipment energy cost. Two IT load models should be developed by using two scenarios, one for the maximum estimated IT load rating and the second for the startup IT rating expected at the time of commissioning.

For data centers, cooling units for computer and data rooms, critical power conditioning equipment, critical distribution equipment, heat rejection plants, and mechanical and electrical support rooms all contribute to regulated energy.

If the unregulated loads are not identical and the simulation program cannot model the savings, project teams should follow the **exceptional calculation method** (ANSI/ASHRAE/ IESNA Standard 90.1-2010, G2.5) and document measures that reduce the unregulated loads.

Data center project teams should also determine the **power utilization effectiveness (PUE) value** of the proposed design. A PUE value is a measure of effectiveness that demonstrates how efficiently a data center uses power, and compares the power used by the computing equipment against for cooling and overhead.

At last, for data center projects a minimum of **2%** of the **5% energy savings** must come from building power and cooling infrastructure.

> 📄 Data center project teams should document the energy modeling inputs, input and output reports from the energy modeling software, energy consumption, demand rates for each building end use and its fuel types and fuel rates. Additionally, project teams should submit the data center calculator.

KEY THINGS TO REMEMBER

- **ASHRAE 90.1-2010, Appendix B** is used to determine the climate zone of the project.
- Under option 1, new construction projects should demonstrate a minimum **5%** improvement, major renovation projects should demonstrate a minimum **3%** improvement, and core and shell projects should demonstrate a minimum **2%** improvement.
- Whole-building energy simulation should be created in accordance with **ANSI/ASHRAE/ IESNA Standard 90.1–2010, Appendix G, with errata.**
- The percent improvement in baseline building performance must be established without considering the on-site renewable energy sources, if any.
- The ASHRAE 50% Advanced Energy Design Guide.
- The Advanced Buildings™ Core Performance™ Guide.
- COMNET Modeling Guidelines and Procedures.
- The exceptional calculation method (ECM) is used when the modeling software cannot accurately model a design, material, or device.
- Definitions and examples of process energy (unregulated energy), nonprocess energy (regulated energy), process loads, nonprocess loads, and plug loads.
- To determine the total energy cost savings, data center project teams should create two separate models, one for <u>building energy cost</u> and the other for <u>IT equipment energy cost</u>. Two IT load models should be developed by using two scenarios, one for the <u>maximum estimated IT load rating</u> and the second for the <u>startup IT rating</u> expected at the time of commissioning.
- For data center projects, a minimum of **2%** of the **5%** energy savings must come from building power and cooling infrastructure.

Building-Level Energy Metering—Prerequisite

■ Applicable to: All the LEED BD+C Rating Systems

PREREQUISITE SUMMARY

Similar to the "Building-Level Water Metering" prerequisite, this prerequisite requires the tracking of the total building energy consumption by installing energy meters or submeters for all the energy sources that serve the building.

All projects should commit to sharing their energy consumption and electrical demand data for **5 years**, starting from the <u>LEED certification date</u> or <u>typical occupancy</u>, whichever comes first. USGBC will then collect and analyze data in order to identify common traits among high and low performers, and it will share its findings with the project teams so that they can improve their performance.

PREREQUISITE INTENT

To support energy management and find opportunities for additional energy savings by tracking the building's energy use.

PREREQUISITE REQUIREMENTS

Projects should install new building-level energy meters/submeters, or use existing ones, that can be aggregated to provide **total building energy consumption,** including <u>electricity</u>, <u>natural gas</u>, <u>chilled water</u>, <u>steam</u>, <u>fuel oil</u>, <u>propane</u> and <u>biomass</u> energy sources. Utility-owned meters capable of aggregating total building energy consumption are also acceptable.

The total building energy consumption and the electrical demand data (if metered) should be shared with USGBC **at a minimum of one month intervals for a five year period or until the building changes ownership or lessee.** Data sharing should start on the date the project accepts LEED certification or typical occupancy, whichever comes first.

"LEED BD+C: Core and Shell" projects should install **base building-level energy meters/submeters** that can be aggregated to provide base building-level data to represent total building energy consumption, including electricity, natural gas, chilled water, steam, fuel oil, propane, and biomass energy sources. (Base building represents the core and shell scope of the work.) The rest of the requirements are the same as with the other LEED BD+C rating systems' requirements discussed, which the projects are obligated to share their resulting energy consumption and electrical demand data (if metered) with USGBC, at a minimum of one month intervals for a 5-year period or until the building changes ownership or lessee. Data sharing should start on the date the project accepts LEED certification or typical occupancy, whichever comes first.

For all the LEED BD+C rating systems, this prerequisite <u>does not require metering of the locally generated sources</u> dedicated to the project building, such as photovoltaic (PV) panels or wind-generated electricity.

> 🖹 Project teams should document a confirmation of the permanently installed meters, letter of commitment, and confirmation of data-sharing source.

KEY THINGS TO REMEMBER

- The reasons why USGBC collects the water usage data: USGBC will collect and analyze data in order to identify common traits among high and low performers and will also share its findings with the project teams so that they can improve their performance.
- Project teams should share their total energy usage for a **5-year period** or until the building changes ownership or lessee at a minimum of **one-month intervals**, starting from the **LEED certification date** or **typical occupancy**, whichever comes first.
- Electricity, natural gas, chilled water, steam, fuel oil, propane, and biomass energy sources all need to be included in the energy metering.
- This prerequisite <u>does not require metering of the locally generated sources</u> dedicated to the project building, such as PV panels or wind-generated electricity.
- "LEED BD+C: Core and Shell" projects should install **base building-level energy meters/submeters**, which can be aggregated to provide base building-level data to represent total building energy consumption.

Fundamental Refrigerant Management—Prerequisite

■ Applicable to: All the LEED BD+C Rating Systems

PREREQUISITE SUMMARY

Chlorofluorocarbons (CFCs) are one of the primary causes of ozone depletion, and ozone depletion is primarily addressed by a building's energy use and the types of refrigerants used.

This prerequisite aims to reduce ozone depletion by prohibiting CFC-based HVAC&R systems. If the project is reusing existing HVAC&R systems, then the project team should complete a **CFC phase-out conversion before the completion of the project**. HVAC&R equipment, as well as other equipment such as refrigerators and small water coolers that contain less than 0.5 pound (225 grams) of refrigerant are exempt from the prerequisite requirements. Even though **CFCs, HCFCs** (hydrochlorofluorocarbons), and **halons** (chemicals used in fire suppression systems) all contribute to ozone depletion, this prerequisite only addresses CFCs.

In 1987, the Montreal Protocol was established in order to phase out the use of most harmful ozone-depleting substances, including CFCs. Through the Montreal Protocol, CFC production was phased out before 1995 in the countries that had signed the protocol. Before 2010, CFC production was phased out in most other countries. Even so, many CFCs still remain in a large amount of existing products. With the CFC phase-out requirement, this prerequisite aims to support the Montreal Protocol.

PREREQUISITE INTENT

To reduce stratospheric ozone depletion.

PREREQUISITE REQUIREMENTS

Projects should not use chlorofluorocarbon-based refrigerants in their HVAC&R systems. When reusing existing HVAC&R equipment, project teams should complete a **comprehensive CFC phase-out conversion** before the project completion. Phase-out plans going beyond the project completion date will be considered on their merits.

Existing small HVAC&R or other equipment, such as standard refrigerators and small water cooler units containing less than **0.5 pound** (225 grams) of refrigerant, are exempt from the prerequisite requirements.

> 💡 Under special conditions, if all the CFC-containing equipment cannot be replaced or retrofitted before the project completion, project teams can develop a narrative stating the reasons preventing the CFC phase-out before the project completion and present that with a CFC phase-out plan and schedule. Note that this exception is only for special conditions. In the exam, if a question asks the requirements of this prerequisite without mentioning any special conditions, do not consider this option, and choose the answer that restricts any CFC phase-out after project completion.

> 📄 Projects that do not use any equipment containing CFCs should document a confirmation that no new or existing equipment contains CFCs.
>
> 📄 Projects that need to complete a CFC phase-out should document the equipment type, refrigerant type, CFC conversion or replacement plan, refrigerant leakage rate and quantity, and phase-out completion date.

KEY THINGS TO REMEMBER

- Expect to see several questions relating to refrigerants. In the exam, refrigerant questions are the most favorite.
- When using existing HVAC&R units, comprehensive CFC phase-out conversion should be completed before project completion.
- Existing small HVAC&R or other equipment, such as standard refrigerators and small water cooler units containing less than **0.5 pound** (225 grams) of refrigerant, are exempt from LEED requirements.

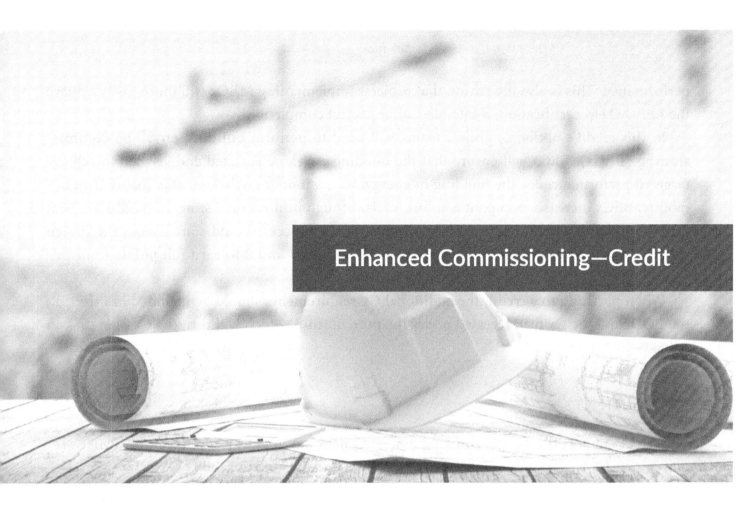

Enhanced Commissioning—Credit

■ Applicable to: All the LEED BD+C Rating Systems

All the LEED BD+C Rating Systems	2 - 6 points

CREDIT SUMMARY

This is the credit of the "Fundamental Commissioning and Verification" prerequisite, which has additional requirements.

In this credit, the CxA will additionally review the contractor submittals, verify operator and occupant training requirements, review the building operations ten months after substantial completion, provide an ongoing commissioning plan and perform other tasks.

In credit's option 1 - path 1, project teams can choose to implement enhanced systems commissioning.

In addition to implementing the enhanced systems commissioning, projects can also choose to implement **monitor-based commissioning (MBCx)** to gain additional points under option 1 by choosing path 2. MBCx is the process of utilizing software that will monitor real-time data from the building automation system and building meters. The automated system should be able to detect faulty equipment and discover unusual energy usage as they occur. In other words, MBCx is also a component of ongoing commissioning that continuously tracks building performance. This is also the reason that projects implementing MBCx will more easily achieve the LEED O+M certification, if intended, after project completion.

In this credit's option 2, project teams will need to perform **building envelope commissioning (BECx)**. BECx will ensure that the building envelope is tested and verified to achieve targeted performance for the building in energy, water, indoor environmental quality, and durability. BECx increases occupant comfort levels through infiltration testing, reduced solar heat gain, and glare control. The envelope commissioning process should start during the design phase. Project teams may choose to pursue both options 1 and 2 to earn full points from this credit.

When pursuing this credit, the additional Cx requirements should be included in the OPR, the BOD, and the Cx plan (created under the prerequisite), which will turn the Cx plan into an enhanced Cx plan.

CREDIT INTENT

To further support the design, construction, and operation of a project to meet the owner's requirements for energy, water, indoor environmental quality, and durability.

CREDIT REQUIREMENTS

Qualifications of the Commissioning Authority (CxA):
As with the "Fundamental Commissioning and Verification" prerequisite, the qualified CxA should have completed commissioning for **at least two similar projects from the early design phase to the minimum ten months of occupancy**. But with this credit the CxA can only be an independent consultant, owner's employee, or a disinterested subcontractor of the design team. Note that in the prerequisite, the CxA can also be a disinterested subcontractor of the design and construction team, but in this credit, the CxA can only be a disinterested subcontractor of the design team.

It is also important to mention that in a project there may be more than one CxA. For example, the project teams may decide to employ two commissioning authorities, one responsible for the building envelope and the other for the electrical, mechanical, and renewable energy systems. Or one commissioning authority can oversee the "Fundamental Commissioning and Verification" prerequisite while the other one can oversee this credit. The most critical point when employing more than one commissioning authority is that one of them should be in a position to coordinate the whole commissioning scope by also managing the other commissioning authorities.

OPTION 1: ENHANCED SYSTEMS COMMISSIONING – (3-4 Points)

PATH 1: ENHANCED COMMISSIONING – (3 Points)

As with the "Fundamental Commissioning and Verification" prerequisite, project teams should complete the commissioning process in accordance with **ASHRAE Guideline 0-2005** and **ASHRAE guideline 1.1-2007 for HVAC&R systems** with respect to the electrical, mechanical, plumbing, and renewable energy systems as they relate to energy, water, indoor environmental quality, and durability.

The Cx plan created under the prerequisite will eventually become the **enhanced Cx plan** under this credit since the Cx plan created will need to cover the scope of this credit as well. (This applies for all the options and paths of this credit.)

Under this credit, the CxA will **review the contractor submittals** and additionally do the following:

➤ Verify inclusion of **systems manual requirements** in construction documents to be issued for bid. (The CxA will outline the requirements of the systems manual to include all the necessary information.)

➤ Verify inclusion of **operator and building user training requirements** in construction documents to be issued for bid.

➤ Verify the **systems manual updates and delivery** and also verify that the necessary **operating documents** are delivered to the owner before building occupancy.

➤ Verify **operator and occupant trainings delivery and effectiveness.**

➤ Verify **seasonal testings.**

➤ Review the **building operations ten months after the project's substantial completion** (which is also called postconstruction verification). This can include interviews with the O&M personnel and occupants, follow-up functional performance testings when necessary, and more.

➤ **Develop an ongoing commissioning plan** (which should provide all the procedures and schedules of the ongoing commissioning activities).

Furthermore, all the tasks of the enhanced commissioning process should be included in the OPR and the BOD.

The ongoing Cx is to ensure that all building systems continue to perform as intended. Just like the functional testings that project teams conduct during the construction phase, ongoing performance tests can continue to be conducted, preferably twice a year to evaluate the building's ongoing performance.

OR

PATH 2: ENHANCED AND MONITORING BASED COMMISSIONING — (4 points)

<u>In addition</u> to all the requirements in "Path 1: Enhanced commissioning," project teams should develop monitoring-based procedures and identify points to be measured in order to assess the performance of energy and water-consuming items.

The enhanced Cx plan should be updated to cover the MBCx requirements (procedures and measurement points). Project teams should address the following:

- Roles and responsibilities
- Measurement requirements, such as points, metering systems, or data access
- Points to be tracked
- Limits of acceptable values for the points tracked
- Elements used to evaluate performance
- Action plan for identifying and correcting errors
- Planning for repairs
- Training to prevent errors
- The analyses frequency in the first year of occupancy, which should be analyzed at least quarterly

The systems manual should be updated with any modifications or new settings.

<u>Only for the "LEED BD+C: Data Center" projects</u>:

For projects choosing option 1 (either path) and have peak cooling loads <u>less than</u> 2,000,000 Btu/h (600 kW), or a total computer room peak cooling load less than 600,000 Btu/h (175 kW), the CxA must additionally:

- Perform at least one commissioning verification review of the OPR, the BOD, and the design documents before the development of mid-construction documents
- Evaluate and confirm the review comments in all the design submissions
- Conduct an additional full verification review with 95% completion of the design documents and the BOD.

For projects with peak cooling loads of <u>more than</u> 2,000,000 Btu/hr (600kW) or a total computer room peak cooling load of more than 600,000 Btu/hr (175 kW), the CxA should conduct **at least three verification reviews** of the <u>basis of design</u>. The first one should be before the start of design development, one should be before the midconstruction documents, and one final verification of the completed design documents should ensure that the owner's project requirements are met.

AND/OR

OPTION 2: ENVELOPE COMMISSIONING— (2 Points)

In the "Fundamental Commissioning and Verification" prerequisite, the building envelope should have been a part of the OPR and the BOD, while the OPR, the BOD, and the project design should have been reviewed with the inclusion of the building envelope. In this option, the project teams should complete the prerequisite's requirements as they apply to the building envelope (which also means that the Cx plan created under the prerequisite should also cover the building envelope) and additionally commission the building envelope in accordance with **ASHRAE Guideline 0-2005** and the **National Institute of Building Sciences (NIBS) Guideline 3-2012, Exterior Enclosure Technical Requirements for the Commissioning Process** as they relate to energy, water, indoor environmental quality, and durability.

The CxA should **review the contractor submittals** and additionally do the following:

- Verify inclusion of systems manual requirements in the construction documents
- Verify inclusion of operator and building user training requirements in the construction documents
- Verify systems manual updates and delivery
- Verify operator and occupant training delivery and effectiveness
- Verify seasonal testings
- Review the building operations ten months after the project completion
- Develop an ongoing commissioning plan

Some examples of the building envelope testing can be conducted for water infiltration, air infiltration, thermal performance, glare control, building envelope pressure, and air leakage.

Only for the LEED BD+C: Healthcare" projects:

"LEED BD+C: Healthcare" projects may have additional testing procedures and requirements for the life safety equipment under this credit.

> 🖹 All project teams pursuing option 1 and/or option 2 should document a list of all the tasks completed as part of Cx activities, the training outline and participation list, confirmation of systems manual delivery, and an ongoing Cx plan.
> 🖹 Project teams pursuing option 1-path 2 should additionally document the inclusion of monitoring and tracking in the Cx plan. Projects pursuing option 2 should additionally document the inclusion of the envelope in the Cx plan.

EXEMPLARY PERFORMANCE

This credit does not qualify for exemplary performance.

KEY THINGS TO REMEMBER

- The CxA can only be an independent consultant, owner's employee, or disinterested subcontractor of the design team.
- When pursuing this credit, the additional Cx requirements should also be included in the OPR, the BOD, and the Cx plan, which will become the enhanced Cx plan.
- For enhanced commissioning, the CxA will review the contractor submittals, verify the inclusion of systems manual and operator and occupant training requirements in construction documents, verify the operator and occupant trainings' delivery and effectiveness, verify seasonal testings, conduct a postconstruction verification ten months after the project completion, and develop an ongoing commissioning plan.
- Projects can get full points by selecting both of the options.
- ASHRAE Guideline 0-2005 and ASHRAE guideline 1.1-2007 (for HVAC&R Systems).
- National Institute of Building Sciences (NIBS) Guideline 3-2012.

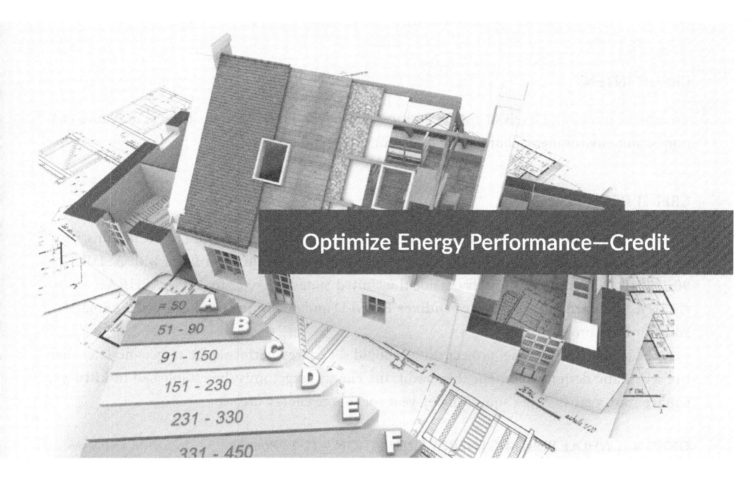

Optimize Energy Performance—Credit

- Applicable to: All the LEED BD+C Rating Systems

(**This is the credit that contains the most points**)

New Construction	1 - 18 points	Retail		1 - 18 points	Hospitality	1 - 18 points
Core and Shell	1 - 18 points	Data Centers		1 - 18 points	Healthcare	1 - 20 points
Schools	1 - 16 points	Warehouses & Dist. Centers	1 - 18 points			

CREDIT SUMMARY

This is the credit of the "Minimum Energy Performance" prerequisite, which aims for further energy reductions.

In this credit's option 1, new construction projects can use their whole building energy simulations (if they choose to create it by pursuing option 1 of the prerequisite) and make further reductions from their baseline energy use from **6%** to **50%**.

In this credit's option 2, project teams need to achieve prescriptive compliance to the **ASHRAE Advanced Energy Design Guide**.

In order to pursue option 1 of this credit, project teams need to pursue option 1 of the "Minimum Energy Performance" prerequisite. To pursue option 2 of this credit, the prerequisite's option 2 should be pursued. Projects pursuing option 3 of the "Minimum Energy Performance" prerequisite are ineligible to pursue this credit.

CREDIT INTENT

To achieve increasing levels of energy performance beyond the prerequisite level to reduce economic and environmental harms that arise from excessive energy use.

CREDIT REQUIREMENTS

As is the case in the "Minimum Energy Performance" prerequisite for both of the options, project teams should first determine the climate zone of the project in accordance with **ASHRAE 90.1-2010, Appendix B**. Projects outside the United States can refer to **ANSI/ASHRAE /IESNA Standard 90.1–2010, Appendixes B and D** and determine the appropriate climate zone for their project.

As with the prerequisite, project teams should set energy performance targets no later than the schematic design phase. For this credit, the energy target must be established in **kBtu per square foot-year** (kW per square meter-year) of source energy use.

OPTION 1: WHOLE BUILDING ENERGY SIMULATION – (1-18 Points)

Under this option, projects should follow the criteria in option 1 of the "Minimum Energy Performance" prerequisite to further improve the building's energy performance. Projects will be awarded points according to their percentage of annual <u>energy cost savings</u>. A new construction project that makes a reduction of 6% will get 1 point, and a project that makes a reduction of 50% will get the full 18 points. What follows is a table that shows the points awarded according to the savings in energy costs.

New Construction	Major Renovation	Core and Shell	Points (except School and Healthcare)	Points for Healthcare	Points for School
6%	4%	3%	1	3	1
8%	6%	5%	2	4	2
10%	8%	7%	3	5	3
12%	10%	9%	4	6	4
14%	12%	11%	5	7	5
16%	14%	13%	6	8	6
18%	16%	15%	7	9	7
20%	18%	17%	8	10	8
22%	20%	19%	9	11	9
24%	22%	21%	10	12	10
26%	24%	23%	11	13	11
29%	27%	26%	12	14	12
32%	30%	29%	13	15	13
35%	33%	32%	14	16	14
38%	36%	35%	15	17	15
42%	40%	39%	16	18	16
46%	44%	43%	17	19	-
50%	48%	47%	18	20	-

Table 23. Points awarded for percentage improvement in energy performance

Unlike in the "Minimum Energy Performance" prerequisite, under this option, projects using renewable energy sources can count the on-site renewable energy generated in the credit calculations. Project teams should calculate the total amount of renewable energy generated and then convert this value to the equivalent cost of energy. Next, in the credit calculations they can either include this energy in the building energy model, or can directly subtract this number from the building's total annual energy cost and recalculate their percentage of annual energy cost savings.

🗎 Projects should document the energy modeling inputs, input and output reports from the energy modeling software, energy consumption and demand for each building end use and their fuel type, fuel rates, and the renewable energy and exceptional calculations if applicable.

OR

OPTION 2: PRESCRIPTIVE COMPLIANCE: ASHRAE ADVANCED ENERGY DESIGN GUIDE —
(1-6 Points)

Projects pursuing this option should comply with applicable recommendations and standards in "Chapter 4, Design Strategies and Recommendations by Climate Zone," for the appropriate **ASHRAE 50% Advanced Energy Design Guide** and climate zone. The points will be awarded according to the project type and the standard complied with, as follows:

- ASHRAE 50% Advanced Energy Design Guide for Small to Medium Office Buildings:
  - Building envelope: roofs, walls, floors, slabs, doors, and air barriers—1 point
  - Building envelope, glazing: vertical fenestration—1 point
  - Interior lighting—1 point
  - Exterior lighting—1 point
  - Plug loads—1 point
- ASHRAE 50% Advanced Energy Design Guide for Medium to Large Box Retail Buildings:
  - Building envelope: roofs, walls, floors, slabs, doors, and vestibules—1 point
  - Building envelope, glazing: fenestration—1 point
  - Interior lighting, excluding lighting power density for the sales floor—1 point
  - Additional interior lighting for the sales floor—1 point
  - Exterior lighting—1 point
  - Plug loads—1 point
- ASHRAE 50% Advanced Energy Design Guide for K–12 School Buildings:
  - Building envelope: roofs, walls, floors, slabs, and doors—1 point
  - Building envelope, glazing: vertical fenestration—1 point
  - Interior lighting—1 point
  - Exterior lighting—1 point
  - Plug loads—1 point
- ASHRAE 50% Advanced Energy Design Guide for Large Hospitals:
  - Building envelope: roofs, walls, floors, slabs, doors, vestibules, and air barriers—1 point
  - Building envelope, glazing: vertical fenestration—1 point
  - Interior lighting and interior finishes—1 point
  - Exterior lighting—1 point
  - Plug loads—1 point

📄 Project teams should submit the Advanced Energy Design Guide compliance tables and the Target Finder results and summary. Teams for retail projects should also submit the list of process equipment efficiencies.

EXEMPLARY PERFORMANCE

To qualify for exemplary performance under this credit, new construction, major renovation, and core and shell projects should have at least **54%** energy savings under option 1. Option 2 does not qualify for exemplary performance.

KEY THINGS TO REMEMBER

- In the whole-building simulation, newly constructed projects need to establish **6%** to **50%** of energy use reduction from their baselines. A new construction project that makes a reduction of **6%** will get **1 point**, and a project that makes a reduction of **50%** will get the full **18 points**.
- As with the prerequisite, project teams should set energy performance targets no later than the schematic design phase. The energy target must be established in **kBtu per square foot-year** (kW per square meter-year) of source energy use.
- In option 2, this credit refers to ASHRAE 50% Advanced Energy Design Guide.
- The percentage improvement in energy performance is calculated by using the energy cost savings, not energy use.
- In option 1, projects using on-site renewable energy generating sources can count the renewable energy generated on-site in the credit calculations.

Advanced Energy Metering—Credit

■ Applicable to: All the LEED BD+C Rating Systems

All the LEED BD+C Rating Systems	1 point

CREDIT SUMMARY

This is the credit of the "Building-Level Energy Metering" prerequisite, which requires projects to provide energy metering to whole-building energy sources and also to any individual energy end use that consumes more than **10%** of the total annual energy. When metering the whole-building energy sources, projects should also count the locally generated sources, such as on-site renewable energy sources like PV panels or on-site nonrenewable energy sources, if any. (In the prerequisite, metering of the on-site generated energy sources was exempt, even if those sources were part of the whole-building energy sources.)

CREDIT INTENT

To support energy management and discover opportunities for extra energy savings by tracking building-level and system-level energy use.

CREDIT REQUIREMENTS

Project teams should install advanced energy metering for the following:
- All whole-building energy sources used by the building
- Any individual energy end uses that consume **10% or more of the total annual consumption of the building**

The advanced energy metering should meet the following characteristics:
- Meters should be permanently installed and be able to record at intervals of one hour or less and transmit data to a remote location. The metering data should be remotely accessible, and all meters should be capable of reporting hourly, daily, monthly, and annual energy use.
- Electricity meters should record both the energy consumption and the energy demand. If appropriate, the whole-building electricity meters should record the power factor.
- The data collection system should be connected to a local area network, building automation system, wireless network, or comparable communication infrastructure.
- The system must be able to store all meter data for at least thirty-six months.

Project teams should also install and calibrate meters according to the manufacturers' recommendations.

In order to determine which individual end uses represent 10% or more of the building's total annual energy, project teams can use their energy analysis calculated under option 1 of the "Minimum Energy Performance" prerequisite. If project teams did not pursue option 1 of that prerequisite and instead followed option 2 or 3, they could use historical end-use data from similar types of buildings and could reference the Commercial Building Energy Consumption Survey (CBECS). Some examples of end use that can require advanced metering can be space heating, space cooling, interior lighting, exterior lighting, receptacle equipment, and more.

Only for "LEED BD+C: Core and Shell" projects:
Project teams should install meters for future tenant spaces and allow tenants to independently meter their energy consumption in addition to providing advanced energy metering for all the base-building energy sources used by the building. A base-building energy consumption will include the building equipment and systems in the core and shell scope of the project, which typically include elevators, central plants, HVAC equipment serving the core spaces, and more. A minimum of one meter per energy source per floor should be provided, and the meters should be able to capture the total tenant energy use of the tenant. Again, the installed meters should meet the previously defined advanced meter requirements.

📄 Project teams should provide a list of all advanced meters installed in the project, indicating their type and metered energy source, and they should submit the manufacturers' cutsheets.

EXEMPLARY PERFORMANCE

This credit does not qualify for exemplary performance.

KEY THINGS TO REMEMBER

■ In LEED, any individual energy end uses that consume **10%** or more of the total annual consumption of the building should be tracked <u>separately</u> for advanced energy metering.

■ The use of the Commercial Building Energy Consumption Survey (CBECS).

■ When metering whole-building energy sources, project teams should also count the locally generated sources, including on-site renewable energy sources like PV panels or on-site nonrenewable energy sources.

■ <u>For "LEED BD+C: Core an Shell" projects</u>, project teams should install meters for future tenant spaces and allow tenants to independently meter their energy consumption in addition to providing advanced energy metering for all the <u>base-building</u> energy sources used by the building. <u>A minimum of one meter per energy source per floor</u> should be provided, and the meters should be able to capture the total tenant energy use of the tenant.

■ Applicable to: All the LEED BD+C Rating Systems

All the LEED BD+C Rating Systems	1 – 2 points

CREDIT SUMMARY

Think about a power plant that serves the whole city and imagine that the weather gets extremely hot beyond the normal average. As a consequence, everyone simultaneously turns on his or her air conditioner, thus creating a sudden increase in electricity demand.

If the power plant's energy is not enough to handle that peak demand, then the utility company would think about constructing an additional plant or would need to find additional generation sources, including nonrenewable energy sources.

Demand response is a technology that aims to overcome these types of conflicts by reducing energy demand, especially during peak times. The utility company sends an alert, which is called a **DR event,** or a **curtailment event**, to the commercial customers who agree to change their usage patterns at peak demands. In turn, the commercial consumers reduce their demand with the alert. Consumers are rewarded for their participation in the demand-response programs, and the construction of additional power plants is avoided. In some cities, utility companies may charge extra during peak times in order to reduce energy demand.

On top of this, demand-response programs are helpful in balancing the supply of renewable energy sources.

For example, a solar energy source will not be able to generate power at nights, which will therefore lower the power availability; a demand response program can offset this effect.

Projects that participate in demand-response programs will earn this credit. However, if there isn't any available demand-response program in the project's location, the credit can still be earned by providing infrastructure for future demand-response programs.

CREDIT INTENT

To increase participation in demand-response technologies and programs, which enable efficient energy generation and distribution systems, increase grid reliability, and thereby reduce greenhouse gas emissions.

CREDIT REQUIREMENTS

The intent of this credit is to encourage project teams to design the building and equipment to allow participation in demand-response programs through **load shedding** or **load shifting**. On-site electricity generation will not meet the intent of this credit. Projects should pursue one of the cases below in accordance with the demand-response program availability in the project's location.

Load shedding is the intentional action by the power utility to reduce the load in the power system in order to prevent a total failure of the system. Load shifting is storing the energy generated during off peak-hours to use it during peak demand hours. Usually, battery systems are used to store the energy during load shifting.

CASE 1: DEMAND RESPONSE PROGRAM AVAILABLE — (2 Points)

If a demand-response program is available in the project's location, project teams should participate in a demand-response (DR) program and complete the following activities:

- Design a real-time, "**fully automated**" DR system based on external initiation by a DR program provider. "**Semiautomated**" DR—in which the DR coordinator initiates the control strategy programmed in the building automation system and the decision to participate is made by a person—may also be utilized in practice. However, a "**manual**" demand-response system will not satisfy the credit (which basically requires the building operator and occupants to manually turn off their end-use systems).
- With the intention of multiyear renewal, enroll in a **minimum one-year** DR program for at least **10% of the estimated peak electricity demand**. In order to determine which individual end uses represent 10% or more of the building's total annual energy, project teams can use their energy analysis calculated under option 1 of the "Minimum Energy

Performance" prerequisite. If project teams did not pursue option 1 of that prerequisite and instead followed option 2 or 3, they can use the **space peak load calculations** to estimate the overall building peak demand.

➤ Develop a plan for meeting the DR commitment during the DR event. The plan should clearly demonstrate the identified demand-reduction strategies, responsible parties, and anticipated reduction for each measure.

➤ Include the DR processes in the CxA's scope of work, including participation in at least one full test of the DR plan.

OR

CASE 2: DEMAND RESPONSE PROGRAM NOT AVAILABLE — (1 Point)

If a demand-response program is not available in the project's location, projects should provide infrastructure for **future demand-response programs** or **dynamic, real-time pricing programs** and complete the following activities:

➤ Install interval recording meters with communications and ability for the building automation system to accept an external price or control signal.

➤ Develop a comprehensive plan for shedding at least **10% of estimated peak electricity demand**. (Again, in order to determine which individual end uses represent 10% or more of the building's total annual energy, project teams can use their energy analysis calculated in option 1 of the "Minimum Energy Performance" prerequisite. If projects did not pursue option 1 of the mentioned prerequisite and instead followed option 2 or 3, projects can use **space peak load calculations** to estimate overall building peak demand.)

➤ Include the CxA in the DR processes, including participation in at least one full DR testing.

➤ Contact the local utility to discuss participation in future DR programs.

> 🗎 For both case 1 and case 2, project teams need to document a proof of ability to shed 10% of peak demand, with the proof showing that the DR system is capable of receiving and acting on an external signal. The teams also need to document an action plan that meets the reduction requirements during the DR event and an inclusion of DR in the CxA systems testing plan.
>
> 🗎 If a demand-response program is available in the project's location (case 1), projects need to additionally document a declaration of enrollment in the DR program.

EXEMPLARY PERFORMANCE

This credit does not qualify for exemplary performance.

KEY THINGS TO REMEMBER

- Projects need to design the building and equipment to allow participation in demand-response programs through **load shedding** or **shifting**.
- Projects should install a **"fully automated"** DR system based on external initiation by a DR program provider. A **"semiautomated"** DR system may also be utilized in practice. However, a **"manual"** demand-response system will not satisfy the credit.
- Projects pursuing this credit should also include the CxA in the DR processes, including participation in at least one full DR testing.
- In order to determine which individual end uses represent 10% or more of the building's total annual energy, projects can use their energy analysis calculated in option 1 of the "Minimum Energy Performance" prerequisite. If projects did not pursue option 1 of that prerequisite and instead followed option 2 or 3, projects can use **space peak load calculations** to estimate overall building peak demand.

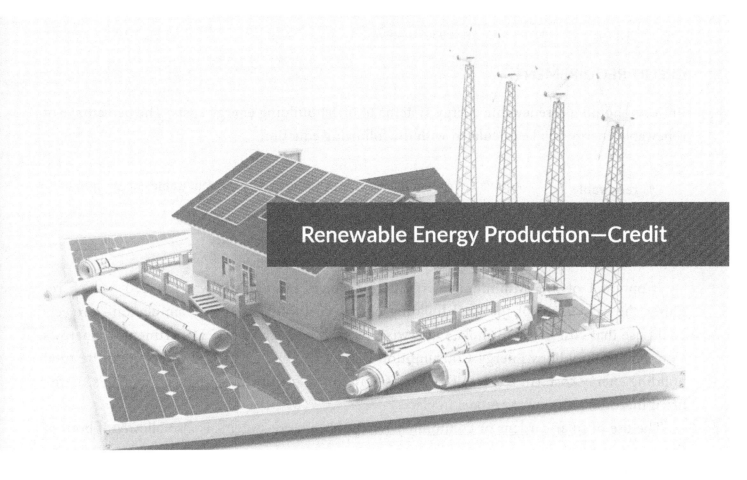

Renewable Energy Production—Credit

- ■ Applicable to: All the LEED BD+C Rating Systems

All the LEED BD+C Rating Systems	1 – 3 points

CREDIT SUMMARY

Using energy from renewable energy sources saves both the environment and human health by reducing carbon emissions as well as other air pollution. This credit aims to award the projects that produce renewable energy on-site or the projects that sign an energy-use agreement with a renewable energy provider in the <u>same utility service area</u>. Producing renewable energy on-site will also aid in eliminating the waste that occurs during electricity transmission.

Green power will be discussed later in this chapter under the "Green Power and Carbon Offsets" credit, which will address the renewable energy produced <u>off-site</u>. The only exception to this credit is that projects can still earn the credit as long as the renewable energy provider that sells green power is in the same utility service area.

CREDIT INTENT

To reduce the environmental and economic harms related to the usage of fossil fuel-generated energy by increasing the use of self-supply of renewable energy.

CREDIT REQUIREMENTS

Projects should use renewable energy systems to offset building energy costs. The percentage of renewable energy will be calculated with the following equation:

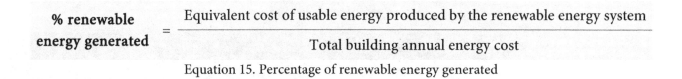

$$\text{\% renewable energy generated} = \frac{\text{Equivalent cost of usable energy produced by the renewable energy system}}{\text{Total building annual energy cost}}$$

Equation 15. Percentage of renewable energy generated

If option 1 of the "Minimum Energy Performance" prerequisite was pursued—which requires the calculation of the total building energy cost with an energy simulation—projects could use that cost in the formula. Otherwise, projects can use the US Department of Energy's Commercial Buildings Energy Consumption Survey (CBECS) database to estimate the total building energy cost. (In LEED, CBECS is used in lots of credits to estimate a building's energy use if there isn't any energy model in place.)

The use of solar gardens or community renewable energy systems is also allowed if both of the requirements below are met:

- The project owns the system or leased the system for a period of at least **10 years**
- The system is located within the **same utility service area**

Points will be awarded according to the project's percentage of renewable energy use as shown on the following table:

Percentage of renewable energy	Points (except Core and Shell)	Points (Core and Shell)
1%	1	1
3%	—	2
5%	2	3
10%	3	—

Table 24. Points awarded according to the percentage of renewable energy used versus the building's total energy

Eligible renewable energy sources contain photovoltaic, solar thermal, wind, biofuel, low-impact hydroelectricity, wave and tidal, and geothermal energy.

If the project is served by a district energy system (DES) that uses renewable energy, the project can also receive points under this credit. Project teams should calculate the cost of renewable energy that is delivered to the project with the following equation (which uses basically the same logic as the previous equation):

$$\textbf{\% Renewable energy} = \frac{\text{Cost of renewable energy used from DES } \times \text{ \% of DES delivered to building}}{\text{Total estimated building energy cost}}$$

Equation 16. Percentage of renewable energy generated for the building by a DES

The last requirement of this credit is that the project must retain the environmental benefits associated with the generated renewable energy. If the environmental benefits are sold, then the project team must purchase an equivalent amount of renewable energy certificates (RECs) and carbon offsets.

RECs represent a tradable, nontangible commodity associated with the qualities of renewable energy generation. An REC is a proof that, when purchased, an amount of energy was created using renewable energy sources.

And carbon offsets allow projects to fund companies or organizations that reduce or remove carbon emissions. An example organization or company may work on reforestation with those funds, or it might perform any other activity that would support the environment and the atmosphere.

> 💡 Remember that project teams installing renewable energy systems and also pursuing the "Enhanced Commissioning" credit should commission their renewable energy systems under that credit as well.

> 📄 All project teams should document the rated capacity for the project's used renewable energy systems, calculations of generated renewable energy, equivalent cost of renewable energy generated (since the credit calculations are based on energy costs, not usage), and annual energy costs.
>
> 📄 If the project is using third-party, system-owned renewable energy sources instead of an on-site system, then the project teams should additionally document the contract that indicates the duration of the agreement.
>
> 📄 If the project is using a community system's renewable energy sources instead of an on-site system, then the project teams should document the contract that indicates the duration of the agreement and shows the percentage of the community energy system owned or leased.

EXEMPLARY PERFORMANCE

To qualify for exemplary performance under this credit, a project's renewable energy sources should make up **15%** of the total energy. For "LEED BD+C: Core and Shell" projects, renewable energy sources should make up **10%** of the total energy.

CASE STUDY

To illustrate, let's imagine that a project team aiming for this credit want to calculate the project's percentage of renewable energy generated in order to estimate the points the project will earn under this credit. The project energy model shows that the project will annually use 400,000 kWh of electricity with a rate of $0.05 per kWh and 10,000 therms of natural gas with a rate of $0.4 per therm. Now let's calculate the annual energy consumption of the building:

Annual cost of electricity = 400,000 x $0.05 = $20,000

Annual cost of natural gas = 10,000 x $0.4 = $4,000

Total building annual energy cost = $20,000 + $4,000 = $24,000

The project team decides to install a photovoltaic energy system that will generate 70,000 kWh of renewable energy annually. Now the project team calculates the equivalent cost of the energy generated:

Equivalent cost of renewable energy generated = 70,000 x $0.05 = $3,500

Note that when calculating the equivalent cost of renewable energy, the electricity rate is used since the PV panels will provide electricity and not natural gas.

Now the project team can calculate the percentage of renewable energy:

% renewable energy = $3,500 / $24,000 = **14,58%**

With this percentage, the project team earns **3 points** under this credit.

If the project did not have an energy model, the project teams would need to use the CBECS to estimate the project's annual total energy cost. From the CBECS tables, the project team was going to find the corresponding estimated energy consumption of the project type and multiply it with the project area to determine the total annual energy use. By multiplying this value with the energy rate, project team would be able to calculate the project's total annual energy cost.

KEY THINGS TO REMEMBER

- In this credit, renewable energy calculations are based on <u>energy costs</u>, not energy usage.
- The projects must retain the environmental benefits associated with the generated renewable energy.
- If the project teams use solar gardens or community renewable energy systems to earn this credit, the project should own or lease the system for a minimum of 10 years, and the system should be located in the same utility service area.
- The use of the US Department of Energy's Commercial Buildings Energy Consumption Survey (CBECS).
- Projects installing renewable energy systems and also pursuing the "Enhanced Commissioning" credit should commission their renewable energy systems under that credit as well.

Enhanced Refrigerant Management—Credit

■ Applicable to: All the LEED BD+C Rating Systems

All the LEED BD+C Rating Systems	1 point

CREDIT SUMMARY

This is the credit of the "Fundamental Refrigerant Management" prerequisite. Remember that the prerequisite only addressees CFCs; however, there are additional refrigerants that harm the environment, such as HCFCs.

Ozone depletion and global warming are heavily linked with a building's energy use and choice of refrigerants. This credit evaluates the refrigerants used in the project according to their ozone depletion potentials (ODP) and global warming potentials (GWP). (The prerequisite only addresses ODPs and not GWPs.) Refrigerants like CFCs and HCFCs deplete the ozone layer and increase global warming rates.

To earn the credit, the projects should either use no refrigerants or only those that have a **0** ozone depletion potential and a global warming potential of less than **50**. If some of the refrigerants exceed those limits, then projects can pursue option 2 and perform a weighted-average calculation of all the refrigerants used in order to see if the weighted average satisfies the credit requirements.

If the project is located in an appropriate climate, it is always best to employ <u>natural ventilation</u> to reduce the amount of refrigerants used.

Through building orientation, massing, shading, insulation, glazing properties, window-to-wall ratios and any other strategies, projects can both reduce the amount of refrigerants used and their energy usage. Or the project teams can look for ways to use <u>natural refrigerants</u> like carbon dioxide, ammonia, or water in their HVAC&R systems to meet the cooling needs of the building. Absorption chillers can be compatible with natural refrigerants. Incorporating direct and indirect <u>evaporative cooling</u> would minimize the refrigerant charge and would be another strategy to earn this credit.

"LEED BD+C: Retail" projects should meet additional requirements after complying with option 1 or option 2.

CREDIT INTENT

To reduce ozone depletion and support early compliance with the Montreal Protocol while minimizing contributions to global climate change.

CREDIT REQUIREMENTS

<u>For all LEED BD+C projects, except "LEED BD+C: Retail"</u>:
Project teams have two options: Option 1 is for projects that do not contain any refrigerants or contain refrigerants that have an ODP of **0**, and a GWP of less than **50**. Option 2 is for projects whose refrigerants exceed the limits in option 1.

Remember that in the "Fundamental Refrigerant Management" prerequisite, only for special conditions, if all the CFC-containing equipment cannot be replaced or retrofitted before the project completion, project teams can develop a narrative stating the causes preventing the CFC phase-out before the project completion, and they can develop a CFC phase-out plan with a schedule. However, those projects that retain CFCs past the initial occupancy, even if using a phase-out plan to meet the "Fundamental Refrigerant Management" prerequisite, are ineligible to pursue this credit.

> ♀ Again, note that this exception is only for special conditions. In the exam, if a question asks for the requirements of the "Fundamental Refrigerant Management" prerequisite without mentioning any special conditions, do not consider this option and choose the answer that restricts any CFC phase-out after the project completion.

OPTION 1: NO REFRIGERANTS OR LOW-IMPACT REFRIGERANTS — (1 Point)

Under this option, projects should not use any refrigerants or only use naturally occurring or synthetic refrigerants that have an <u>ODP</u> of **0** and a <u>GWP</u> of less than **50**.

As with the "Fundamental Refrigerant Management" prerequisite, existing HVAC&R equipment and other equipment such as refrigerators and small water coolers that contain less than 0.5 pound (225 grams) of refrigerant will be exempt from the credit calculations.

OR

OPTION 2: CALCULATION OF REFRIGERANT IMPACT — (1 Point)

Under this option, project teams should select refrigerants to be used in the HVAC&R equipment to minimize or eliminate the emission of compounds that contribute to ozone depletion and climate change by performing weighted average calculations for all the refrigerants used. The combination of the new and existing <u>base building</u> and <u>tenant</u> HVAC&R equipment serving the project must comply with the following equation:

$$\text{LCGWP} + \text{LCODP} \times 10^5 \le 100$$

Equation 17. Calculation of refrigerant impact

In this equation, LCGWP is the life-cycle direct global warming potential, while the LCODP is the life-cycle ozone depletion potential. To calculate the LCGWP and LCODP, the following equations should be used:

$$\text{LCODP} = [\text{ODPr} \times (\text{Lr} \times \text{Life} + \text{Mr}) \times \text{Rc}] / \text{Life}$$

Equation 18. Calculation of LCODP

$$\text{LCGWP} = [\text{GWPr} \times (\text{Lr} \times \text{Life} + \text{Mr}) \times \text{Rc}] / \text{Life}$$

Equation 19. Calculation of LCGWP

Let's take a closer look at the variables used in the previous equations:

- "**ODPr**" indicates the ozone depletion potential of the refrigerant.
- "**Lr**" indicates the refrigerant leakage rate, which is assumed to be **2%,** and no alternative value can be used.
- "**Life**" basically indicates the equipment life, which is <u>10 years</u> as a default unless otherwise demonstrated. It can change according to the equipment used.
- "**Mr**" indicates the end-of-life refrigerant loss, which is assumed to be **10%,** and no alternative value can be used.
- "**Rc**" indicates the refrigerant charge, which is 0.5 to 5.0 lbs of refrigerant per ton of gross rated cooling capacity under standards from the Air Conditioning, Heating, and Refrigeration Institute. The AHRI is an institute that develops standards for HVAC&R equipment. The "Rc" is basically the ratio of the total refrigerant used in a piece of equipment to the total cooling capacity of that equipment. In other words, if an air-conditioning unit uses 10 pounds of refrigerant and its cooling capacity is 10 tons, the "Rc" will be 1. If projects avoid using equipment with high refrigerant charge (such as split air-conditioning systems or small packaged units) and instead use central plants and chillers, they will be more likely to meet this credit's requirements.
- "**GWPr**" indicates the global warming potential of the refrigerant.

For projects using existing equipment, project teams can check LEED's default equipment life table and use the corresponding values according to their equipment type.

If the project is using multiple pieces of HVAC&R equipment, project teams should calculate a weighted average of all base building HVAC&R equipment with the following equation:

$$\frac{\Sigma \ [\ (\ LCGWP + LCODP \times 10^5 \ ) \ \times \ Q_{unit} \ ]}{Q_{total}} \leq 100$$

Equation 20. Weighted calculation for the refrigerant impact for multiple pieces of HVAC&R equipment

This equation is pretty much the same as the first equation introduced in the credit, but this one calculates a weighted average of multiple pieces of HVAC&R equipment. In this equation, "Q_{unit}" indicates the gross AHRI-rated cooling capacity of the individual HVAC or refrigeration unit, and "Q_{total}" indicates the total gross AHRI-rated cooling capacity of all HVAC or refrigeration units.

Following is the table to be used in the credit calculations, which shows the ODPr and GWPr values of the common refrigerants:

Ozone Depletion and Global Warming Potentials of Common Refrigerants			
Refrigerant	ODPr	GWPr	Common building application
Chlorofluorocarbons			
CFC-11	1.0	4,680	Centrifugal chiller
CFC-12	1.0	10,720	Refrigerators, chiller
CFC-114	0.94	9,800	Centrifugal chiller
CFC-500	0.605	7,900	Centrifugal chiller, humidifier
CFC-502	0.221	4,600	Low-temp refrigeration
Hydrochlorofluorocarbons			
HCFC-22	0.04	1,780	Air conditioning, chiller
HCFC-123	0.02	76	CFC-11 replacement
Hydrofluorocarbons			
HFC-23	~0	12,240	Ultra-low-temperature refrigeration
HFC-134a	~0	1,320	CFC-12 or HCFC-22 replacement
HFC-245fa	~0	1,020	Insulation agent, centrifugal chiller
HFC-404A	~0	3,900	Low-temperature refrigeration
HFC-407C	~0	1,700	HFC-22 replacement
HFC-410A	~0	1,890	Air-conditioning
HFC-507A	~0	3,900	Low-temperature refrigeration
Natural refrigerants			
Carbon dioxide (CO2)	0	1	
Ammonia (NH3)	0	0	
Propane	0	3	

Table 25. Ozone Depletion and Global Warming Potentials of Common Refrigerants

This table is one of the most important tables to know for the exam. Knowing the <u>types</u>, <u>names,</u> and <u>common building applications</u> of these refrigerants is essential. It is even possible to get a question asking the replacement for HCFC-123. Note that natural refrigerants do not have any ozone depletion potential, and the ozone depletion potentials for HFCs are very close to zero.

If project teams for "LEED BD+C: Core and Shell" projects like to include the HVAC systems associated with the anticipated work by the tenant, they can do so by submitting supporting documentation, such as the tenant sales agreement or the lease agreement.

Projects that are using a district energy system (DES)—which is basically a central energy conversion plant that distributes thermal energy to a group of buildings—should find the corresponding weighted average of the refrigerant impact value of the DES and consider it in the credit calculations.

<u>For "LEED BD+C: Retail":</u>

"LEED BD+C: Retail" projects should also meet either "Option 1" or "Option 2" for all their HVAC&R systems. However, stores that contain commercial refrigeration systems must also comply with the following requirements:

- Use only non-ozone depleting refrigerants.
- Use equipment with an average HFC refrigerant charge of no more than 1.75 pounds of refrigerant per 1,000 Btu/h total evaporator cooling load.
- Establish a predicted store wide annual refrigerant emissions rate of no more than 15%. Projects should conduct leak testing using the procedures in the **EPA GreenChill**'s best practices guideline for leak tightness at installation.

Alternatively, for the newly constructed stores, projects with commercial refrigeration systems can provide proof of attainment of EPA GreenChill's <u>silver-level store certification</u>, instead of following the mentioned prescriptive criteria.

> 📄 Project teams whose projects use no refrigerants or low-impact refrigerants (option 1) should document a confirmation stating that only no-impact or low-impact refrigerants are used.
>
> 📄 Project teams calculating their refrigerant impacts (option 2) should document their equipment types, refrigerant charge calculations (VRF systems only), equipment quantities, equipment cooling capacities, refrigerant charge, equipment life, and leak test results, and they should submit their refrigerant equipment schedule of GreenChill certification for the commercial refrigeration systems.

EXEMPLARY PERFORMANCE

This credit does not qualify for exemplary performance.

KEY THINGS TO REMEMBER

- Table 25.
- In LEED, enhanced refrigerant management addresses both the ODP and the GWP.
- The equations mentioned in the credit.
- "**Lr**" indicates the refrigerant leakage rate, which is assumed to be **2%,** and no alternative value can be used.
- "**Mr**" indicates the end-of-life refrigerant loss, which is assumed to be **10%,** and no alternative value can be used.
- AHRI is an institute that develops standards for HVAC&R equipment, and LEED addresses AHRI standards for enhanced-refrigerant management.
- Projects that retain CFCs past the initial occupancy, even if using a phase-out plan to meet the "Fundamental Refrigerant Management" prerequisite, are ineligible to pursue this credit.
- Newly constructed "LEED BD+C: Retail" stores with commercial refrigeration systems can provide proof of attainment of EPA GreenChill's <u>silver-level store certification</u> instead of following the mentioned prescriptive criteria.

Green Power and Carbon Offsets—Credit

■ Applicable to: All the LEED BD+C Rating Systems

| All the LEED BD+C Rating Systems | 1 – 2 points |

CREDIT SUMMARY

This credit encourages projects to buy green power, carbon offsets, and/or renewable energy certificates that correspond to either **50%** or **100%** of the project's energy use.

As mentioned, renewable energy certificates represent a tradable, nontangible commodity associated with the qualities of renewable energy generation. An REC is a proof that, when purchased, an amount of energy was created using renewable energy sources.

If the local utility in a project team's location does not sell green power, then the project team can offset the building's energy use by purchasing green power from renewable energy projects around the country.

Green-e is the leading certification program for green power generation in the United States. And under this credit, LEED requires projects to use **Green-e Energy-certified**, or equivalent, green power.

Again, **carbon offsets** allow projects to fund companies or organizations that reduce or remove carbon emissions. An example organization or company may work on reforestation or any other activity that would support both the environment and the atmosphere.

A carbon offset is a reduction of carbon dioxide made in order to compensate for, or offset, an equivalent carbon dioxide emission made elsewhere. Since energy use of the green building will result in carbon emissions, green buildings can calculate their carbon emissions from their energy use and purchase the same amount of carbon offsets to compensate for their emissions. For a carbon offset to qualify in this credit, it needs to be **Green-e Climate-certified** or equivalent.

In the credit, different types of energy uses are categorized under different scopes. The following table shows the types of energies and their corresponding scopes.

Common Sources of Federal Greenhouse Gas Emissions	
Category	**Sources**
Scope 1 Energy	Vehicles and equipment
	Stationary sources
	On-site landfills and wastewater treatment
	Fugitive emissions
Scope 2 Energy	Purchased electricity
	Purchased heating/cooling
	Purchased steam
Scope 3 Energy	Transmission and distribution losses from purchased electricity
	Business travel
	Employee commuting
	Contracted solid waste disposal
	Contracted wastewater treatment

Table 26. Common sources of greenhouse gas emissions from federal facilities as required out by Executive Order 13514

A scope 1 energy source relates to direct energy from <u>owned or controlled sources</u>, a scope 2 energy source relates to <u>purchased energy</u>, and a scope 3 energy source relates to energy sources <u>that are not owned or directly controlled</u>. To illustrate, the energy generated on-site through burning fossil fuels will fall under scope 1 energy sources, and the resulting greenhouse gas emissions will be classified as scope 1 emissions. The electricity bought from a utility company will be classified as a scope 2 energy source, and the resulting greenhouse gas emission will be scope 2 emissions.

CREDIT INTENT

To encourage the reduction of greenhouse gas emissions with the use of grid source, renewable energy technologies, and carbon-reduction projects.

CREDIT REQUIREMENTS

Projects should engage in a contract for a **minimum of 5 years,** to be delivered **at least annually**, from the qualified resources that have come online since January 1, 2005. The contract should specify the provision of at least **50%** or **100%** of the project's energy from green power, carbon offsets, and/or renewable energy certificates (RECs).

Green power and RECs should be **Green-e Energy-certified** or the equivalent. RECs can only be used to mitigate the effects of **scope 2** electricity use only. And carbon offsets may be used to mitigate **scope 1** or **scope 2** emissions on a **metric ton of carbon dioxide-equivalent** basis, and they can be used for both electricity and nonelectricity energy sources, such as natural gas. All the purchased carbon offsets should be **Green-e Climate-certified** or equivalent.

For projects located in the United States, the carbon offsets should be from greenhouse gas emission reduction projects within the United States, while for the projects outside the United States, purchasing carbon offsets from the country that the project is located in is not mandatory.

Projects should determine the percentage of green power or offsets based on the **quantity** of energy consumed. Note that calculating the energy based on energy quantity is not the case for some other LEED prerequisites/credits like the "Renewable Energy Production" credit or the "Minimum Energy Performance" prerequisite, which require energy calculations based on energy costs, not quantities.

Points are awarded according to the following table:

Percentage of building's total energy addressed by green power, RECs, and/or carbon offsets	Points
50%	1
100%	2

Table 27. Points awarded according to the percentage of a building's total energy addressed by green power, RECs, and/or carbon offsets

To illustrate, let's assume that teams for project A want to address 50% of the building's total energy through green power, RECs, and/or carbon offsets.

In this scenario, if the project is only using both grid source electricity and natural gas, the project team can choose to address both the electricity and natural gas by only buying carbon offsets for 50% of total energy use. Or the project team may decide to buy RECs for 50% of the electricity use, and carbon offsets for 50% of the natural gas use. (RECs cannot be used to mitigate the effects of natural gas, and therefore can only address scope 2 electricity use.) Or the project team may decide to buy RECs for 70% of the electricity use and buy carbon offsets for 35% of the natural gas use, which works if their total adds up to 50% of the building's total energy.

If option 1 of the "Minimum Energy Performance" prerequisite was pursued, the energy model could be used to calculate the amount of green power, RECs, and/or carbon offsets required under this credit. Otherwise, projects can use the US Department of Energy's Commercial Buildings Energy Consumption Survey (CBECS) database to estimate the total building energy cost. (Similar to the other LEED credits requiring energy calculation, CBECS is used to determine energy usage of the building if the project does not have an energy model.)

For "LEED BD+C: Core and Shell" projects **only**, the energy usage for the core and shell floor area will be defined by Building Owners and Managers Association (BOMA) standards, and the core and shell area should not be less than 15% of the project's floor area. If the core and shell area of the project is less than 15% of the project's floor area, then the project should address 15% of the total building area in the credit calculations.

Remember that in the "Renewable Energy Production" credit, projects had to retain the environmental benefits associated with the generated renewable energy on-site, if generated. And if the environmental benefits were sold, the project teams had to purchase an equivalent amount of renewable energy certificates (RECs) and carbon offsets. Selling RECs for the renewable energy created on-site really means that the environmental benefits of the generated energy do not belong to the project anymore. But if the project retains the environmental benefits associated with the generated renewable energy on-site, this will mean that under this credit, the project team will not need to buy RECs or carbon offsets for the renewable energy generated on-site. Therefore, project teams would exclude any renewable energy quantity serving the project from their calculations. If a project is a net-zero energy project, which means that the project only uses its own generated renewable energy, the project will automatically receive full points under this credit.

All other types of nonrenewable energy used by the building should be included in the calculations, such as nonelectric energy, steam purchased from the utility, fuel purchased for on-site energy generation, or anything similar.

📄 Because the credit's calculations are based on energy usage, not cost, project teams need to document their annual electricity and nonelectricity energy use calculations and the calculations showing their required REC, green power, or carbon offsets according to their target points. Additionally, project teams need to document their purchase contract or letter of commitment showing the corresponding REC, green power, and/or carbon offset amounts. If Green-e certified products are not available, project teams that wish to use a local benchmark (for projects located outside the United States) should additionally document Green-e equivalency.

EXEMPLARY PERFORMANCE

This credit does not qualify for exemplary performance.

CASE STUDY

To illustrate, let's assume that a project aiming for this credit wants to address 50% of the project's total energy consumption by purchasing RECs and carbon offsets and earn 1 point under this credit. The building's annual energy consumption is as follows:

Annual electricity use: 4,200,000 kWh

Annual natural gas use: 6,200,000 kBtu

Annual use of renewable energy generated on-site: 1,200 MWh

There is more than necessary information here, which is the annual use of renewable energy generated on-site (assuming that the project retains the environmental benefits). This energy is already clean energy and therefore will not be included in the credit calculations. And the project teams will only need to address the following:

Annual electricity use: 4,200,000 kWh

Annual natural gas use: 6,200,000 kBtu

~~**Annual use of renewable energy generated on-site**: 1,200 MWh~~

If the project team decides to buy RECs for 50% of the annual electricity use, and 50% of the carbon offsets are bought for the annual natural gas use, then the following numbers apply:

4,200,000 kWh/yr **x** 50% = **2,100,000 kWh/yr** (The project team will need to buy this amount of RECs annually)

6,200,000 kBtu/yr **x** (5.32×10^{-5} mtCO$_2$e/kBtu) **x** 50% = **164.92 mtCO$_2$e/yr** (The project team will need to buy this amount of carbon offsets annually)

Note that the 5.32×10^{-5} mtCO$_2$e/kBtu value in this equation is the direct greenhouse gas (GHG) emission factor for natural gas, which is defined by ENERGY STAR.

If the project team decides to buy only carbon offsets for 50% of the total energy use and again earns 1 point under this credit, then the numbers below would apply:

4,200,000 kWh/yr **x** (5.90×10^{-4} mtCO$_2$e/kBtu) **x** 50% = **1,239 mtCO$_2$e/yr**

Note that the 5.90×10^{-4} mtCO$_2$e/kBtu value in the above equation is the direct greenhouse gas emission factor for electricity, which is defined by ENERGY STAR.

6,200,000 kBtu/yr **x** (5.32×10^{-5} mtCO$_2$e/kBtu) **x** 50% = **164.92 mtCO$_2$e/yr**

And their total would be as follows:

1,239 mtCO$_2$e/yr + 164.92 mtCO$_2$e/yr = **1403.92 mtCO$_2$e/yr** (The project team would need to buy this amount of carbon offsets annually)

Also note that the values are per year, and this credit requires the commitment to continue at least for 5 years, to be delivered at least annually.

Following are the equations of this credit, which were also used in the case study. (It is recommended that you not memorize the formulas but rather know the logic of the formulas by just going through this case study.)

$$\text{Total qualifying annual energy use} = \left(\begin{array}{c} \text{Total annual grid base electricity used} \end{array} - \begin{array}{c} \text{Total annual site generated renewable electricity} \end{array} \right) + \left(\begin{array}{c} \text{Total annual fossil use} \end{array} - \begin{array}{c} \text{Total annual renewable fossil use} \end{array} \right)$$

Equation 21. Total qualifying energy use

(This equation basically excludes the on-site generated renewable energy sources, as it was excluded in this case study)

$$\text{\% Energy purchased or offset} = \left(\frac{\text{Quantity of RECs in kWh}}{\text{Annual building energy use in kWh}} \right) + \left(\frac{\text{Purchased green power}}{\text{Annual building energy use in kWh}} \right) + \left(\frac{\text{Purchased carbon offsets}}{\text{GHG emissions associated with project's annual energy use}} \right)$$

Equation 22. Weighted calculation for the refrigerant impact for multiple HVAC&R equipment

(This equation calculates the percentage of energy purchased or offset, or can show how much RECs, green power or carbon offsets are needed when aiming for a specific percentage, which was the case in this case study.)

$$\text{Metric tons of } CO_2 \text{ equivalent, Fuel X} = \text{Annual use of Fuel X (kBtu)} \quad \text{x} \quad \text{Direct GHG emissions factor for Fuel X } (mtCO_2e/kBtu)$$

Equation 23. Metric tons of CO_2 equivalent fuel type

(This equation calculates the metric tons of CO_2 equivalency, as the annual natural gas use was multiplied with the direct greenhouse gas emissions factor in this case study.)

KEY THINGS TO REMEMBER

- Credit calculations are based on energy usage, not cost.
- RECs and green power are measured in MWh or KWh, while the carbon offsets are measured in metric tons of CO_2 equivalent.
- Electricity usage can be addressed by RECs, green power, and/or carbon offsets.
- Carbon offsets may be used to mitigate **scope 1** or **scope 2** emissions on a **metric ton of carbon dioxide** equivalent basis, and they can be used for both <u>electricity</u> and <u>nonelectricity</u> energy sources.
- Green-e Energy certification is required for green power and RECs, while Green-e Climate certification is required for carbon offsets.
- The usage of the US Department of Energy's Commercial Buildings Energy Consumption Survey (CBECS).
- Sources of scope 1, 2 and 3 emissions.

CHAPTER 8

MATERIALS AND RESOURCES (MR)

Construction and demolition waste constitutes about 40% of the total solid waste stream in the United States.[1] However, there are much better alternatives than classifying items as waste, and there are many ways to reduce the environmental harm associated with materials. Using fewer materials, choosing environmentally preferable materials, using locally harvested materials, and eliminating waste all provide great benefits.

The conservation of materials starts by eliminating the need for materials during the planning and design phases. Rightsizing the project is the first step toward conservation of materials. An example of rightsizing includes designing buildings that are not larger than really needed and will therefore require fewer materials and resources. The same logic also applies to neighborhoods, as denser and more compact mixed-use neighborhoods will require fewer miles of roads and less infrastructure.

Reusing existing materials, salvaged materials, and especially existing buildings results in tremendous material savings.

According to the EPA, the best way to eliminate waste is through source reduction. Source reduction refers to the exact sizing of the materials to be produced through prefabrication, modular construction, or similar methods so that no waste is generated on-site.

Since it's about decreasing the unnecessary materials brought into a building, it also covers the use of products with less packaging.

A systems-based, life-cycle perspective and an integrative process will help projects achieve their goals when addressing the use of materials and resources. Life-cycle assessment (LCA) will also serve as a great tool to evaluate materials and resources according to their environmental performances.

Life-cycle assessment, which examines all the environmental effects of a product (or even a building) quantitatively during an entire life cycle, can allow project teams to see the background of the building products. A cradle-to-grave approach, and even further, a cradle-to-cradle approach, is used in LCA, allowing both the total energy use and other environmental consequences resulting from the creation of that material to be calculated.

The benefits of conducting an LCA can be to see the trade-offs between different materials and to select the materials that would be the best fit for the project and the environment. The project teams may decide not to use some materials and reduce the total amount of materials in the building, which is also called dematerialization.

A cradle-to-cradle approach analyzes a product's life cycle from the first resource extraction/harvesting of the product to its new life as another product or as a part of another product. Thus, cradle-to-cradle products are waste-free products that can be recycled—with their high recyclable content—and reused.

On the other hand, a cradle-to-grave approach analyzes a product's life cycle from the first resource extraction/harvesting of the product to the end of its life, resulting in a form of waste.

All green buildings need to evaluate the effects of a particular product on the environment. During their life cycles, all buildings and building materials have different impacts on the environment. The building materials are harvested/extracted, manufactured in factories, and then installed in buildings to be used. After that, they either get demolished, disposed of, or recycled. Energy is also consumed during each of these stages.

In addition, the way that manufacturers, contractors, or individuals manage each of these steps will vary for each manufacturer, contractor, or consumer. Materials that get extracted or harvested in a sourceful manner, get manufactured in environmentally friendly facilities, and get recycled to be a part of another product should be less harmful to the environment than regular products. On the other hand, a product that requires lots of energy consumption for extraction and is also not very durable cannot be considered environmentally friendly.

Using locally produced materials is another plus. An environmentally friendly recyclable material that was extracted in China, manufactured in Germany, and brought to the United

States cannot be considered environmentally friendly because of all the greenhouse gas emissions that occurred during transportation.

Several credits under this credit category provide a location valuation factor, which means that if the purchased products or materials are extracted, manufactured, and purchased within 100 miles (160 kilometers) of the project, LEED will award the project in the credit calculations by valuing those products at 200% of their cost.

This chapter will discuss the LEED requirements for the "Materials and Resources" credit category. The "Materials and Resources" credit category contains the following prerequisites/credits:

- Storage and Collection of Recyclables—Prerequisite
- Construction and Demolition Waste Management Planning—Prerequisite
- PBT Source Reduction—Mercury—Prerequisite
- Building Life-Cycle Impact Reduction—Credit
- Building Product Disclosure and Optimization (BPDO)—Environmental Product Declarations—Credit
- Building Product Disclosure and Optimization (BPDO)—Sourcing of Raw Materials—Credit
- Building Product Disclosure and Optimization (BPDO)—Material Ingredients—Credit
- PBT Source Reduction—Mercury—Credit
- PBT Source Reduction—Lead, Cadmium, and Copper—Credit
- Furniture and Medical Furnishings—Credit
- Design for Flexibility—Credit
- Construction and Demolition Waste Management—Credit

Storage and Collection of Recyclables—Prerequisite

■ Applicable to: All the LEED BD+C Rating Systems

PREREQUISITE SUMMARY

Waste is one of the primary burdens on the environment. In the United States, metals, paper, food, glass, and plastics comprise approximately 69% of the total amount of municipal solid waste[2]. Furthermore, all the mentioned products can be recycled, which not only reduces the need for virgin materials but also reduces landfills.

In addition to solid waste, electronic waste (e-waste) is a major problem in today's world, as the disposal of these materials can cause more harm to the environment, and handling electronic waste requires different procedures.

This prerequisite aims to reduce the waste that is generated by <u>building occupants.</u> (Waste produced during the construction phase will be addressed by the next prerequisite; this prerequisite <u>only</u> addresses waste produced by the building users.) In turn, this prerequisite encourages the project teams to have spaces dedicated to the collection and storage of recyclables, at least for <u>mixed paper</u>, <u>corrugated cardboard</u>, <u>glass</u>, <u>plastics</u>, and <u>metals</u>, which can be accessed by waste haulers and building occupants in the entire building.

Such projects should also be able to have an infrastructure in place to collect, store, and dispose of **at least two** of the following e-wastes: <u>batteries</u>, <u>lamps containing mercury</u>, and <u>elec-</u>

tronic waste. Note that these materials are not considered recyclable items under this prerequisite, as they will be only collected, stored, and disposed.

For "LEED BD+C: Retail" projects, the prerequisite requirements are completely different. Retail projects must conduct a waste stream analysis to determine the project's top **five** recyclable waste streams (by weight or volume) using consistent metrics. And according to the waste stream analysis, projects should list at least the top **four** waste streams and provide collection and storage areas for handling them.

PREREQUISITE INTENT

To reduce waste generated by building users and hauled to and disposed of in landfills.

PREREQUISITE REQUIREMENTS

For all the LEED BD+C rating systems, except LEED BD+C: Retail, projects should provide dedicated areas that can be accessible by the waste haulers and building occupants for the collection and storage of recyclable materials for the entire building. Collection and storage areas can be located separately as well. Recyclable materials must include **mixed paper, corrugated cardboard, glass, plastics,** and **metals**. Additionally, projects should take the necessary actions for safe collection, storage, and disposal of two of the following: **batteries, mercury-containing lamps,** and **electronic waste.**

"LEED BD+C: Retail" projects only:
Retail projects should conduct a waste stream analysis and identify a project's top **five** recyclable waste streams (by weight or volume) using consistent metrics throughout. (The waste stream study period should be a minimum of 24 hours.) If the project teams cannot find any information regarding the waste streams, data from similar operations can be used to make projections. Or retailers with other stores of similar size and function can use their historical data from their other stores.

Once the waste stream study is completed, project teams should list the top **four** recyclable waste streams and provide dedicated areas for separation, collection, and storage of the recyclables, which should also be accessible to the waste haulers and the building occupants. If project teams identify batteries, lamps containing mercury, or electronic waste as one the four waste streams, all necessary measures should be taken for safe collection, storage, and disposal (not recycling) of those items.

For all projects, even if there isn't any recycling program available at the project's location, dedicated storage should be available for any future services, and dedicated areas should always be easily accessible by the building occupants, visitors, and waste haulers.

For the "LEED BD+C: Core and Shell" projects, the project teams can estimate the tenants' recycling needs based on historical data and should consider incorporating the recycling policy of the building into tenant guidelines.

> 🖹 All projects, including retail, should document a description of the recycling storage and collection strategies and verification of recycled material types, and they should submit floor plans showing the recycling, collection, and storage areas.
>
> 🖹 Retail projects should document their methodology and the results of their waste stream study.

KEY THINGS TO REMEMBER

■ Batteries, mercury-containing lamps, and electronic waste are not recyclable materials under this prerequisite, and they are thus classified as hazardous materials. They should be collected, stored, and disposed of.

■ By this prerequisite, every LEED BD+C project, except retail, should recycle at least <u>mixed paper</u>, <u>corrugated cardboard</u>, <u>glass</u>, <u>plastics</u>, and <u>metals</u>.

■ This prerequisite is only for the building operations phase and not for the construction phase. The next credit will be only for the construction phase and not for the building operations phase.

■ <u>Teams for retail projects</u> should conduct a waste stream analysis and identify a project's top **five** recyclable waste streams (by weight or volume), using consistent metrics throughout, and they should identify the top **four** recyclable waste streams and provide dedicated areas for <u>separation</u>, <u>collection</u>, and <u>storage</u> of the recyclables, which are also supposed to be accessible to waste haulers and building occupants.

Construction and Demolition Waste Management Planning—Prerequisite

■ Applicable to: All the LEED BD+C Rating Systems

PREREQUISITE SUMMARY

Construction waste is another waste category that makes up a significant portion of the total waste produced in the world. This prerequisite encourages the project teams to create a **construction and demolition waste management plan** to identify potential strategies for reducing the generation of construction waste.

To achieve this prerequisite, the project teams should set goals for waste diversion by choosing at least five suitable materials to be diverted. At the end of construction, the project teams should prepare a final report showing the total construction waste generated and the portion of waste disposed of or diverted. Typically, materials to be diverted would include wood, scrap metals, drywall, brick, metals, concrete, ceiling tiles, and more. These materials can also be named "clean waste," which is another name for nonhazardous materials left over from construction. Hazardous materials, such as asbestos, cannot be diverted under the LEED requirements and are therefore exempt from these calculations.

This prerequisite also has a credit called "Construction and Demolition Waste Management" that will be discussed at the end of this chapter. If the project teams choose to implement the construction and demolition waste management plan by meeting the target diversion rates

<u>defined in the credit</u>, then the credit can be earned according to the diversion rates that have been met. In fact, this prerequisite does not force implementation of a developed waste management plan with the target diversion rates set forth by USGBC; rather, it only asks the project teams to create a plan, which includes their targets, and a final report showing the total waste versus amount of diverted and disposed of waste. In other words, there is no minimum threshold for diversion in this prerequisite. However, if the project teams aim for the "Construction and Demolition Waste Management" credit, their CWM plan created under this prerequisite should also address the mentioned credit's threshold levels.

The best technique to eliminate project waste is source reduction, which is to plan the materials to be produced at exact sizes through prefabrication, modular construction, or a similar method so that no waste is generated on-site at all. The other waste reduction strategies can include reuse, recycling, donation, and salvage. And for the generated waste, <u>source separation</u> can be accomplished by sorting the waste materials into recycling streams, which can be done either on-site or off-site. If reuse and recycling methods are not available, incineration may be considered diversion, and waste can be converted to energy as long as it complies with additional LEED requirements. (Wood-based products are exempt from the additional LEED requirements for incineration and are considered diversion.) But the project teams should document the reasons for choosing incineration rather than proceeding with reuse and recycling.

It is important to note that this prerequisite only addresses waste management during the <u>construction phase</u>, and therefore it does not cover the waste from the building occupants, unlike the previous prerequisite. In order not to confuse these prerequisites and credits, simply look at the title and see whether or not it contains the word "construction."

PREREQUISITE INTENT

To reduce construction and demolition waste disposed of in landfills and incineration facilities by reusing, recycling, and recovering materials.

PREREQUISITE REQUIREMENTS

Projects should develop and implement a **construction and demolition waste management plan** by meeting the following:

- Establish waste diversion goals by identifying **at least 5 materials** (both structural and nonstructural) targeted for diversion. Make an approximate calculation to show the percentage of these materials compared to the total construction waste. Units may be by weight or volume but must be consistent throughout the calculations.

⮞ Specify whether the materials be separated or commingled and explain the diversion strategies planned. Describe how these materials will be transported to the recycling facilities and describe the recycling process.

Project teams should write down a final report showing all major waste streams generated, including their disposal and diversion rates. Below is the formula to be used for disposal and diversion-rate calculations:

Diversion rate = (Total waste diverted from landfill / Total waste produced by the project) x 100

Equation 24. Diversion rate

It's important to note that **alternative daily cover (ADC)** does not qualify as a material diverted from disposal in LEED calculations. (Even though ADC will not count as a diversion, it should still be included as a portion of the total construction waste generated.) And **land-cleaning debris**, which is created by the removal of rock, soil, stone, and vegetation, is not considered waste since the ingredients are all natural products. However, the handling of both alternative daily cover and land-cleaning debris, as well as all the other materials not contributing to diversion, should still be addressed in the construction and demolition waste management plan.

For this prerequisite and its credit, "Construction and Demolition Waste Management," projects that cannot implement reuse and recycling methods can consider waste-to-energy systems if the **European Commission Waste Framework Directive 2008/98/EC** and **Waste Incineration Directive 2000/76/EC** are followed. Waste-to-energy facilities must meet the applicable **European Committee for Standardization (CEN) EN 303** standards. Wood-based products will be exempt from this additional requirement for incineration and will be directly considered diversion.

📄 Project teams should document their construction waste management plan and their total construction waste.

KEY THINGS TO REMEMBER

- The diversion rate formula (units may be by weight or volume, but must be consistent throughout the calculations).
- This prerequisite is only for the construction phase, not for the building operations phase.
- Land cleaning debris, alternative daily cover (ADC), excavated soil, and hazardous materials do not qualify as materials diverted.
- If reuse and recycling methods are not available, incineration may be considered diversion, and waste can be converted to energy as long as it complies with additional LEED requirements. (Wood-based products are exempt from the additional LEED requirements for incineration and will be considered diversion.)
- If the project team aims for the "Construction and Demolition Waste Management" credit, their CWM plan created under this prerequisite should also address the credit's threshold levels.

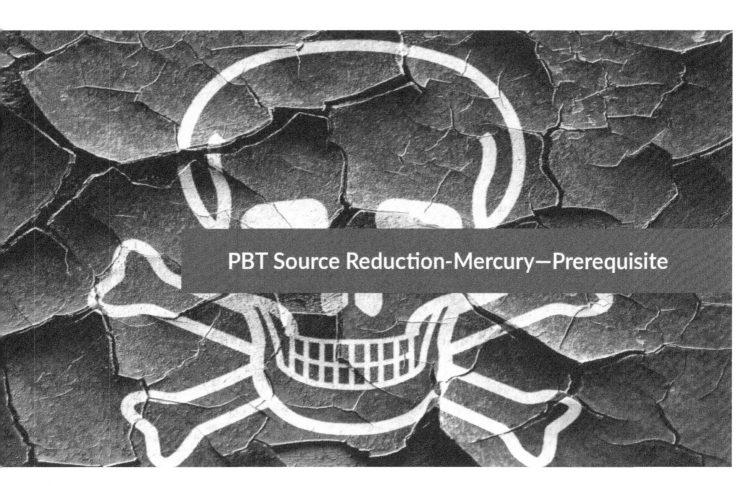

PBT Source Reduction-Mercury—Prerequisite

■ Applicable to: Healthcare

PREREQUISITE SUMMARY

Mercury, which is a persistent, bioaccumulative, and toxic (PBT) chemical, can present a great deal of harm to both human health and the environment, and unfortunately, we come across plenty of products and equipment that contain mercury in our everyday lives, homes, offices, or even hospitals without really knowing the long-term effects of this element. That being said, for healthcare projects, which are the most critical facilities for improving human health, setting strict requirements on mercury use should not be a choice; it should be mandatory.

This prerequisite encourages healthcare projects to either use products free of mercury, or lower the mercury content in the products used. All new construction project teams should incorporate mercury limits into project specifications, they should track purchased products during construction, and they should create a plan for collecting and recycling mercury-containing equipment. On the other hand, renovation projects should identify existing inventory that contains mercury (such as equipment and lamps), and develop phase-out and upgrade plans to replace noncompliant items with compliant items.

PREREQUISITE INTENT

To reduce products and devices with mercury content and reduce mercury by product substitution, capture, and recycling.

PREREQUISITE REQUIREMENTS

In the project's recycling collection system, project teams should identify <u>the types of mercury-containing products and devices to be collected,</u> <u>identify the criteria for their handling by a recycling program,</u> and <u>identify the disposal methods for captured mercury.</u> Applicable mercury-containing devices include lamps (linear, circular fluorescent, HIDs, etc.), dental wastes, and more. For dental care facilities, projects should specify and install amalgam separation devices that meet the ISO 11143 standard.

Additionally, all healthcare projects should comply with **2010 FGI Guidelines for Design and Construction of Health Care Facilities, Section A1.3-4b, Mercury Elimination**, as outlined in the following section:

- <u>New construction projects</u>: Healthcare facilities cannot use mercury-containing equipment, including switching devices, thermostats, and other building system sources, with the exclusion of lamps.
- <u>Renovation projects</u>: Healthcare facilities should develop a **phase-out plan** to eliminate mercury-containing products and upgrade current mercury-containing lamps to high-efficiency, mercury-free or low-mercury lamp technology.

Renovation projects using existing items with mercury content can work with the building maintenance department to identify and collect mercury-containing equipment and lamps beyond the LEED thresholds and replace noncompliant equipment and lamps with low-mercury or no-mercury products. It is recommended that project teams completely eliminate mercury in the building, which would avoid the need for recycling and disposal of these items.

New construction projects, as well as renovation projects, should incorporate mercury limits into the project specifications, specify compliant amalgam separation for dental facilities (if applicable), track the specified products during construction, and create a plan to collect and recycle any mercury-containing equipment even below the LEED thresholds.

All projects are required not to use any T-9, T-10, or T-12 fluorescent lights, mercury vapor high-intensity discharge lamps (HID) lamps, probe start metal halide lamps, and any exit signs with mercury or that use more than 5 watts of electricity. For the other types of lamps, projects should meet the allowed mercury content according to each lamp type.

📄 Project teams should document their recycling plan for mercury-containing lamps, lighting schedules (including the lamp type and mercury content), and USGBC's PBT source reduction calculator (or equivalent). Renovation projects also need to document their existing inventory and their phase-out plan.

KEY THINGS TO REMEMBER

■ This credit is only applicable to healthcare projects.

■ PBTs are substances that poses high long-term risks to humans and the environment, can remain in the environment for long periods, and can travel far from their original source.

■ For their recycling collection system, project teams should identify <u>the types of mercury-containing products and devices to be collected</u>, <u>criteria for their handling by a recycling program</u>, and <u>disposal methods for captured mercury</u>.

■ Renovation projects should phase out products above the LEED thresholds.

■ All healthcare projects should meet the requirements of the 2010 FGI Guidelines for Design and Construction of Healthcare Facilities, Section A1.3-4b.

Building Life-Cycle Impact Reduction—Credit

■ Applicable to: All the LEED BD+C Rating Systems

New Construction	2 - 5 points	Retail	2 - 5 points	Hospitality	2 - 5 points
Core and Shell	2 - 6 points	Data Centers	2 - 5 points	Healthcare	2 - 5 points
Schools	2 - 5 points	Warehouses & Dist. Centers	2 - 5 points		

CREDIT SUMMARY

This credit is about reducing the environmental impact that is created throughout the building's life cycle. Life-cycle assessment (LCA) comes as a great tool and is featured in option 4 of the credit, and the project teams that implement a whole-building life-cycle assessment will earn points under option 4.

LCA, which examines all the environmental effects of a product, or even a building, quantitatively during an entire life cycle, can allow project teams to see the background of the building products and materials. A **cradle-to-grave** approach will be used in LCA, allowing both the total energy use and other environmental consequences resulting from the extraction or harvest, manufacture, on-site construction, maintenance, deconstruction or demolition and disposal of that material to be calculated over the assumed 60-year service life.

The LCA conducted will consider the following effects:

- Global warming potential
- Depletion of the stratospheric ozone layer
- Acidification of land and water sources
- Eutrophication
- Formation of tropospheric ozone
- Depletion of non-renewable energy resources

The benefits of conducting an LCA can be to see the trade-offs between different materials and, with that information, selecting the materials that would best fit the project and the environment. The project teams may decide not to use some materials and reduce the total amount of materials in the building, which is also called **dematerialization**.

Nevertheless, there is even a more effective way to reduce the environmental impact of a building, which is to reuse existing buildings/materials. That's because it is not necessary to think about the environmental impacts of producing new materials when the existing material can be reused. A report by the National Trust for Historic Preservation states that building reuse almost always offers environmental savings over demolition and new construction. A new, energy-efficient building will not compensate for the climate change effects of its construction for at best 10 years and perhaps 80 years, according to preservationnation.org.[3]

This credit's options 1, 2, and 3 each award more points than option 4, with the reuse of historic buildings, renovation of abandoned/blighted buildings, or building and material reuse.

CREDIT INTENT

Encouraging adaptive reuse strategies and to optimize the environmental performance of products and materials.

CREDIT REQUIREMENTS

In this credit, project teams should demonstrate reduced environmental effects by reusing existing building resources or demonstrating a reduction in materials used through life-cycle assessment. Options 1, 2, and 3 require the projects to reuse all or part of an <u>existing building</u>, and option 4 is for <u>newly constructed buildings</u>. Project teams should choose one of the following options.

OPTION 1: HISTORIC BUILDING REUSE — (5 Points)

Under this option, in order to avoid new construction, projects should be reusing a historic building with a "historic" designation, or the existing building should be inside a historic district. To qualify as a historic building, the building or the historic district must be listed or eligible for listing in the <u>local</u>, <u>state</u>, or <u>national register</u> of <u>historic places</u>. If the building does not have a "historic" designation but is located inside a historic district, it may qualify under this credit if it meets one of the four **US National Register of Historic Places** criteria or the **state** or **local historic criteria**. Below are the four criteria of the US National Register of Historic Places used to define a building as "historic":[4]

- It is associated with events that have made a significant contribution to the broad patterns of our history.
- It is associated with the lives of significant persons in the past.
- It embodies the distinctive characteristics of a type, period, or method of construction; represents the work of a master; possesses high artistic values; or represents a significant and distinguishable entity whose components may lack individual distinction.
- It has yielded, or may be likely to yield, information important in history or prehistory.

Projects outside the United States can use local equivalent agencies for credit compliance. If there isn't any process for determining the historic status of the building in the country where the project is located, project teams can consult the UNESCO website to determine historic significance.

Once the status of the building is confirmed, project teams should maintain the existing building <u>structure</u>, <u>envelope</u>, and <u>interior nonstructural elements</u> of the historic building or the contributing building inside a historic district. Project teams should not demolish any part of the historic building or the contributing building in a historic district unless it has structural problems or contains hazardous materials.

For buildings listed <u>locally</u>, the approval for any demolition should be granted by the <u>local historic preservation review board</u>. For the buildings listed in a state register or the US National Register of Historic Places, the approval for any demolition should be in a programmatic agreement with the state historic preservation office or National Park Service. Again, projects outside the United States can use the local equivalent agencies.

Any alteration, such as preservation, restoration, or rehabilitation, must be conducted according to the <u>local</u> or <u>national standards</u> for rehabilitation, wherever applicable. If the building is not subject to historic review, a **preservation professional** that meets the <u>United States' federal qualifications for historic architects</u> (or a local equivalent for projects located outside the United States) should be included in the project team, and the preservation professional must confirm conformance to the **Secretary of Interior's Standards for the Treatment of Historic Properties** (or a local equivalent for projects located outside the United States).

One thing to note under this option is that this option does not have any threshold for compliance. In other words, the credit does not define any area of the building to be reused or altered. It only requires the "historic" designation status of the building to be still valid after the construction, according to the appropriate standards and agencies. If the building's "historic" status is revoked after the historic review, this option can no longer be pursued. (In that case, project teams may pursue Option 3—Building and Material Reuse if they can meet its requirements.) And if the building is not subject to any historic review, the preservation professional must ensure conformance with the Secretary of Interior's Standards for the Treatment of Historic Properties (or a local equivalent for projects located outside the United States).

> 📄 Project teams should document the historic designation status of the reused historic building, the description of how additions and alterations (if applicable) meet the local review board requirements, and a narrative describing demolition (if applicable).

OR

OPTION 2: RENOVATION OF ABANDONED OR BLIGHTED BUILDING — (5 Points)

Under this option, project teams should maintain at least **50%**, by surface area, of the existing **building structure** (e.g., foundation, floor, roof decking), **enclosure** (e.g., skin, framing), and **interior structural elements** (e.g., walls, doors, floor coverings, ceiling systems) for buildings that meet local criteria of abandoned buildings or are considered blighted. An abandoned or blighted property is a property that is permanently and intentionally left behind and that the former owner does not intend to come back to or use. Project teams should check this definition with the local jurisdiction and confirm whether the building meets the abandoned criteria.

The building must be renovated to a state of productive occupancy to fulfill this option. If there is any deterioration or damage, up to **25%** of the building surface area may be excluded from credit calculation. If the deteriorated or damaged part of the building is more than 25% of the building surface area, project teams should proceed with demolishing those parts and neglect pursuing this option. Additionally, window assemblies and any hazardous materials that are remediated as a part of the project should also be excluded from the calculations.

Following is the equation to be used for this option:

$$\text{Abandoned or blighted building reuse} = \left(\frac{\text{Surface area reused}}{\text{Existing building surface area} - \text{Hazardous or unsafe materials demolished area}} \right) \times 100$$

Equation 25. Percentage of abandoned or blighted building reuse

📄 Project teams should document a description of the abandoned or blighted status of the building and submit the reused elements table and calculations.

OR

OPTION 3: BUILDING AND MATERIAL REUSE – (2-4 Points)

Under this option, projects should be using existing buildings and materials, as well as using salvaged materials off-site. Projects will reuse or salvage building materials <u>on-site</u> or <u>off-site</u> as a percentage of the <u>surface area</u> and earn points according to table 28. **Structural elements** (e.g. foundation, floors, roof decking), **enclosure materials** (e.g., skin, framing), and **permanently installed interior elements** (e.g., walls, doors, floor coverings, ceiling systems) should all be <u>included</u> in the credit calculations. Window assemblies and any hazardous materials that are remediated as a part of the project are excluded from the calculations.

In "Option 2: Renovation of Abandoned or Blighted Buildings," salvaged materials off-site that will be installed in the building cannot be included in the credit calculations, though that option is more about keeping and reusing the <u>existing</u> building materials as much as possible. However, in this option project teams can use salvaged materials off-site and count them as "surface areas reused" in the credit calculations. Since option 2 is for abandoned or blighted buildings, the option also allows project teams to demolish any <u>damaged</u> parts of the building, up to 25% of the building's surface area, and exclude them from the credit calculations. However, that is not the case for this option. In this option, project teams can only exclude the removed hazardous materials from the credit calculations. However, the calculations should include any removed surface area (if nonhazardous), even if it was removed because of damage or deterioration.

Another important thing to note under this credit is that off-site products that are used for this credit **cannot contribute toward the** "Building Product Disclosure and Optimization—Sourcing of Raw Materials" credit.

% of completed project surface area reused	Points LEED BD+C except Core and Shell	Points LEED BD+C: Core and Shell
25%	2	2
50%	3	3
75%	4	5

Table 28. Points awarded according to the percentage of completed project surface area reused

Following is the equation to be used under this option;

$$\text{Existing building reuse} = \left(\frac{\text{Surface area reused from off-site} + \text{Surface area reused from on-site}}{\text{Existing building surface area} - \text{Hazardous materials surface area}} \right) \times 100$$

Equation 26. Percentage of existing building reuse

📄 Projects should document the reused elements table and calculations.

OR

OPTION 4: WHOLE-BUILDING LIFE-CYCLE ASSESSMENT — (3 Points)

For new construction (buildings or portions of buildings), project teams should conduct a life-cycle assessment of the project's structure and enclosure, which should demonstrate **a minimum of 10% reduction**, compared with the baseline building, in at least three of the six impact categories listed below, <u>one of which must be global warming potential:</u>

- Global warming potential (greenhouse gases), in CO_2e;
- Depletion of the stratospheric ozone layer, in kg CFC-11;
- Acidification of land and water sources, in moles H+ or kg SO_2;
- Eutrophication, in kg nitrogen or kg phosphate;
- Formation of tropospheric ozone, in kg NOx, kg O_3 eq, or kg ethene; and
- Depletion of nonrenewable energy resources, in MJ.

No impact category evaluated as part of the life-cycle assessment may increase by more than **5%** compared with the baseline building. In other words, project teams will first conduct an LCA for the baseline building, and next, by applying different design solutions, project teams will evaluate the LCA for the current design and confirm that a minimum of 10% reduction is established in at least three of the six impact categories listed above, and one of them has to be global warming potential. Finally, project teams will ensure that no impact category has increased more than 5% compared with the baseline building.

In order to achieve these reductions, project teams can conduct building scenarios and compare the results by implementing different design alternatives, such as evaluating different structural system types, different building products and assemblies, and more.

The LCA should cover the structure and enclosure, including the footings, foundations, structural wall assemblies from cladding to interior finishes, structural floors, ceilings (excluding finishes), and roof assemblies. The mechanical, electrical, and plumbing systems, as well as the excavation and other site development activities, should be <u>excluded</u> from the LCA.

Additional building elements such as nonstructural walls or finishes can be included or excluded from the LCA in the project teams' discretion.

In the LCA calculations, the building should fully account for maintenance and replacement for at least **60 years**. For example, if a product used in the building has a 10-year service life, project teams should multiply its impacts by 6 to truly evaluate its effect on the LCA. Additionally, for the LCA calculations, data sets must be compliant with **ISO 14044**.

Another thing to note under this option is that, when comparing the designed building with the baseline building, the system boundary, gross floor area, building orientation, location, and building functions should be the same. For example, if the building orientation differs in the actual building design when compared with the baseline building, the LCA results cannot be really comparable since different exposure to sun will strongly affect the building's energy use and many other aspects. Or if the gross floor area changes, again the LCA results will not be comparable. However, projects are free to modify building massing or the shape of the envelope or any other aspects as long as the mentioned items remain the same.

For "LEED BD+C: Healthcare" projects only:
For all options in this credit, if "LEED BD+C: Healthcare" projects have demolished building materials to create courtyards for increasing daylighting, those demolished parts can be considered as "retained" in the credit calculations. However, the new courtyards must meet the requirements of the "Daylight" credit.

> 📄 Project teams should document the LCA summary showing outputs of the proposed building with the percentage change from the baseline building for all the impact indicators, and they should submit a description of LCA assumptions, scope, and analysis process for the baseline building and the proposed building.

SURFACE AREA CALCULATIONS FOR OPTIONS 2 AND 3

When doing the surface area calculations for determining the reused portion of the building, project teams should consider the following:

- Each assembly included in the credit calculations, both vertical and horizontal, can be calculated for up to **three layers** of surface area.

    For example, if a wall assembly consists of bricks on the exterior side, backer board, metal studs, insulation, and drywall on the interior side, project teams should include only three out of five layers in the credit calculations, which may be the bricks as the "enclosure," metal studs as the "structure," and drywall as the "interior finish." Or it could be the bricks as the "enclosure," insulation as the "structure," and drywall as the "interior finish."

- For vertical building elements, the three layers are <u>enclosure</u>, <u>interior finish</u>, and <u>structure</u>.

- For horizontal building elements, the three layers are <u>ceiling finish</u>, <u>structure</u>, and <u>floor finish</u>.

- If an existing layer is removed and replaced with new materials, project teams must include that layer in the credit calculations. However, if the layer is removed and not replaced, the layer can be excluded.

- Structural support elements such as beams, studs, and columns will be considered part of the larger surface they support, such as a wall or a floor. For example, let us say that a wall assembly consists of 3,000 square feet of bricks (reused) on the exterior side, 3,000 square feet of backer board (reused), metal studs at an unknown quantity (reused), and 3,000 square feet of drywall (reused) on the interior side. And the project team decides to include the metal studs in the credit calculations instead of the backer board. The area of the metal studs will be calculated as the area of the wall that the metal studs support. So basically, since the whole wall is covered with bricks on the exterior side and drywall on the interior side, the area of the brick, drywall, and metal studs will be the same, which is in this case 3,000 square feet. And with these values, the project teams can create the following table for the wall assembly:

Wall Assembly	Existing area (sqft)	Reused area (sqft)	% reused
Bricks	3,000	3,000	100%
~~Backer board~~	~~3,000~~	-	-
Metal studs	3,000	3,000	100%
Drywall	3,000	3,000	100%
Total	**9,000**	**9,000**	**100%**

As previously noted, if an existing layer is removed and replaced with new materials, project teams must include that layer in the credit calculations. To illustrate, let's say that a wall assembly has four layers: 5,000 square feet of drywall (replaced) on the exterior side, metal studs (replaced), 5,000 square feet of batt insulation (reused), and 5,000 square feet of drywall (replaced) on the interior side. In this scenario, the three layers to be included in the credit calculations should be the drywall on the exterior side, metal studs, and the drywall on the interior side.

Even though the insulation was reused, it cannot be included in the credit calculations instead of the metal studs because any existing layer that is removed and replaced with new materials <u>must</u> be included in the credit calculations. With these values, the project team can create the following table for the wall assembly:

Wall Assembly	Existing area (sqft)	Reused area (sqft)	% reused
Drywall (exterior side)	5,000	0	0%
Metal studs	5,000	0	0%
~~Batt insulation~~	~~5,000~~	-	-
Drywall (interior side)	5,000	0	0%
Total	**15,000**	**0**	**0%**

Now let's take a look at another previously listed item. As previously noted, if the layer is removed and not replaced, the layer can be excluded from the credit calculations. To illustrate, this time let's say that a floor assembly in a building contains three layers: 15,000 square feet of acoustical ceiling tiles, 15,000 square feet of structural slab, and 15,000 square feet of carpeting. The project teams decide to reuse the existing acoustical ceiling tiles and structural slab, but will remove carpeting without replacing it in order to use the exposed structural concrete as the finish material. In this case, the project teams will exclude the carpeting from the credit calculations, since it was not replaced by another material. With these values, the project teams can create the following table for the floor assembly:

Floor Assembly	Existing area (sqft)	Reused area (sqft)	% reused
Acoustical ceiling tiles	15,000	15,000	100%
Structural Slab	15,000	15,000	100%
~~Carpeting~~	~~15,000~~	~~0~~	-
Total	**30,000**	**30,000**	**100%**

If the carpeting was replaced by a new carpeting material, the previous table would look like the following table:

Floor Assembly	Existing area (sqft)	Reused area (sqft)	% reused
Acoustical ceiling tiles	15,000	15,000	100%
Structural Slab	15,000	15,000	100%
Carpeting	15,000	0	0%
Total	**45,000**	**30,000**	**66.66%**

If a wall or a floor assembly contains fewer than three layers, such as two, the calculations will be based on those two layers.

Up to this point, we have evaluated the rules to consider when calculating the "percentage reused" when reusing the existing building materials. Now let's take a look at the considerations for calculating the salvaged materials in addition to the reused surfaces, which only applies to option 3 (since using salvaged materials does not count in option 2).

If a material salvaged off-site replaces all or a part of an existing layer, project teams should count the existing surface as the area of the entire existing layer. In other words, if a building contains a 50,000-square-foot wall assembly with ceramic tiles, and the project team decides to reuse 15,000 square feet of it and replace the remaining 35,000 square feet by using 10,000 square feet of salvaged tiles and 25,000 square feet of new tiles, the reuse area for only this layer of the flooring assembly would be (according to equation 26):

$$\text{Existing building reuse} = \left(\frac{15,000 + 10,000}{50,000 - 0} \right) \times 100 = 50\%$$

Let us illustrate what would happen if a team with a project containing 30,000 square feet of flooring assembly covered by carpeting planned to remove the whole carpet. The project team might decide to install salvaged wooden flooring for the 8,000 square feet of the slab, install salvaged marble for the 12,000 square feet, and use the remaining 10,000 square feet as exposed concrete as the finished floor. Since the 8,000 square feet of the removed carpeting will be replaced with salvaged wooden flooring, this will result in a 100% reuse. Installing salvaged marble for the 12,000-square-foot portion of the removed carpet would again result in a 100% reuse. And for the remaining 10,000 square feet, since the removed carpeting will not be replaced with a new material, that portion will be excluded from the calculations, and in total, the whole layer will be counted as 100% reused.

As mentioned, each assembly included in the credit calculations, both vertical and horizontal, can be calculated up to **three layers** of surface area. However, note that this does not mean considering only one type of material in each layer.

As can be noted in the previous example, we have considered the floor finish as one layer, and inside that layer there were two different materials, which are the salvaged wooden flooring and the salvaged marble.

Once more, in option 2, if there is any deterioration or damage in the building, up to **25%** of the building surface area will be excluded from these credit calculations. In addition window assemblies and all hazardous materials that are remediated as a part of the project will be excluded from the credit calculations. In option 3, only the window assemblies and the hazardous materials that are remediated as a part of the project are excluded from the calculations, not the damaged building layers.

EXEMPLARY PERFORMANCE

Projects pursuing options 1 and 2 cannot qualify for exemplary performance. To qualify for exemplary performance under this credit, projects pursuing option 3 should reuse **95%** of the building, and projects pursuing option 4 should achieve improvement over the required credit thresholds in **all the six impact measures**.

KEY THINGS TO REMEMBER

- Names of the impact categories under option 4.
- Global warming is the top priority of LEED. This is the reason that the life-cycle assessment (LCA) reductions should be made in at least three of the six impact categories listed above, and <u>one of those must be the global warming potential</u>.
- Off-site products that are used for this credit cannot contribute toward the "Building Product Disclosure and Optimization—Sourcing of Raw Materials" credit.
- Under "Option 1: Historic Building Reuse," if the building is not subject to historic review, a **preservation professional** that meets the <u>federal qualifications for historic architects</u> (or a local equivalent for projects located outside the United States) should be included in the project team, and the preservation professional must confirm conformance to the <u>Secretary of Interior's Standards for the Treatment of Historic Properties</u> (or a local equivalent for projects located outside the United States).
- Under "Option 2: Renovation of Abandoned or Blighted Building," if there is any deterioration or damage, up to **25%** of the building surface area may be excluded from credit calculation. If the deteriorated or damaged part of the building is more than 25% of the building surface area, project teams should proceed with demolishing those parts and neglect pursuing this option. Additionally, window assemblies and any hazardous materials that are remediated as a part of the project will also be excluded from the calculations.

- For options 2 and 3, each assembly included in the credit calculations, both vertical and horizontal, can be calculated for up to **three layers** of surface area.
- Under "Option 3: Building and Material Reuse," window assemblies and any hazardous materials that are remediated as a part of the project are excluded from the calculations.
- Under "Option 4: Whole-Building Life-Cycle Assessment," no impact category evaluated as part of the life-cycle assessment may increase by more than **5%** compared with the baseline building.
- Under option 4, the building should fully account for maintenance and replacement for at least **60 years.** For the calculations, data sets must be compliant with **ISO 14044.**
- Under option 4, when comparing the designed building with the baseline building, the system boundary, gross floor area, building orientation, location, and building functions should be the same.
- For all options in this credit, if "LEED BD+C: Healthcare" projects have demolished building materials to create courtyards for increasing the daylighting, those demolished parts can be considered as "retained" in the credit calculations. However, the new courtyards must also meet the requirements of the "Daylight" credit.

BPDO Environmental Product Declarations—Credit

■ Applicable to: All the LEED BD+C Rating Systems

All the LEED BD+C Rating Systems	1 – 2 points

CREDIT SUMMARY

This credit encourages the use of **permanently installed products and materials** with preferred life-cycle impacts. Environmental Product Declarations (EPD) show a product's raw material extraction effects to the environment, energy use, chemical makeup, waste generation, and any emissions made to water, air, and soil during the entire sourcing and manufacturing process. Supporting the use of products with EPDs will increase the number of environmentally friendly manufacturers. However, the credit only accepts EPDs that conform to ISO standards.

An EPD is typically created from a **product category rule (PCR)**, which defines how to standardize the EPD for each product type. The PCR defines the scope, system boundary, and measurement procedures as well as the other technical requirements. That means all the EPDs of a certain product type from different manufacturers can be compared with each other. In other words, typically, every EPD has a corresponding PCR that was used during the creation of the EPD. And under this credit, the EPDs submitted for credit compliance should also have corresponding PCRs.

Option 1 of the credit requires the use of permanently installed products manufactured by the companies that provide EPDs for their products. Projects should use **at least 20 different permanently installed products** sourced from **at least five different manufacturers** that also meet the requirements of option 1. However, all product EPDs are not equally weighted with regard to the credit achievement calculations, as will be discussed under the credit requirements. For example, a product with an industry-wide (generic) EPD will be counted as a half (1/2) product, while a product with product-specific Type III EPD will be counted as one (1) product. And according to the valuation criteria, the sum of the products should add up to 20.

Option 2, which refers to multiattribute optimization, requires the use of third-party- certified, permanently installed products that are proven to have less environmental impact compared to the regular products in **at least 3 of the 5 impact categories**. The applicable impact categories are the global warming potential, the depletion of the stratospheric ozone layer, the acidification of land and water sources, eutrophication, the formation of tropospheric ozone and depletion of nonrenewable energy resources.

In order to show compliance to this credit's option 2, the project teams need to calculate the cost of materials in compliance with the option 2 requirements, and they need to multiply their cost by a valuation factor to show that **50%** of all the permanently installed building products have preferred life-cycle impacts. For example, a product with a global warming potential, eutrophication, and a formation of tropospheric ozone values below the industry average according to third-party certification will be valued at 100% of its cost. However, if that product is sourced (**extracted**, **manufactured**, and **purchased**) within **100 miles** (160 kilometers)—the location valuation factor of LEED—of the project site, the product will be valued at **200%** of its cost.

During the construction phase, as the project teams procure materials, they should regularly enter the procured materials' data to the **BPDO calculator** in USGBC's website or use any other tool to ensure their level of compliance.

CREDIT INTENT

To encourage the use of products and materials with declared life-cycle information and have environmentally, economically, and socially preferable life-cycle impacts. To award project teams for selecting products from manufacturers that have been verified to improve environmental life-cycle impacts.

CREDIT REQUIREMENTS

Project teams should achieve one or both of the following options, for a maximum of 2 points.

OPTION 1: ENVIRONMENTAL PRODUCT DECLARATION (EPD) — (1 Point)

Under this option, project teams should use at least **20 different permanently installed products**, sourced from **at least five different manufacturers** which meet one of the following disclosure criteria:

- Product-specific declarations: Only the products with a publicly available, critically reviewed life-cycle assessment conforming to **ISO 14044** and having at least a **cradle-to-gate scope assessment** will qualify under these criteria. Cradle-to-gate assessment is the product assessment covering the stages from the sourcing of the raw materials to the finished product at the factory gate ready for sale. For the purposes of credit-achievement calculations, these products will be valued as **one quarter (1/4) of a product**.

- Environmental Product Declarations: To qualify for an EPD, a product must conform to ISO 14025, 14040, 14044, and EN 15804 or ISO 21930, and the EPD should have at least a cradle-to-gate scope assessment. Next, for the purposes of credit achievement calculations, the EPDs will be valued according to their types as follows:

    a. **Industry-wide (generic) Type III third-party certification EPD**: This includes products with **industry-wide (generic) Type III third-party certification** (including external certification that the manufacturer is recognized as the participant by the program operator). These products will be valued as **one-half (1/2) of a product** for the purposes of credit-achievement calculations.

    b. **Product-specific Type III third-party certification EPD**: This includes products with **product-specific Type III third-party certification** (including external certification that the manufacturer is recognized as the participant by the program operator). These products will be valued as **one whole (1) product** for the purposes of credit achievement calculations.

- Other USGBC-approved program: This category includes products that comply with other USGBC-approved environmental product declaration frameworks.

Similar products from the same manufacturer can be counted as separate products as well, but their formulations must be different.

Below is the credit's equation to be used for option 1:

$$\text{Total number of products with declaration} = \left(\begin{array}{c} \text{Number of products with product specific declarations} \end{array} \times 0.25 \right) + \left(\begin{array}{c} \text{Number of products with industry specific declarations} \end{array} \times 0.5 \right) + \left(\begin{array}{c} \text{Number of products with product specific type III EPD} \end{array} \times 1 \right)$$

Equation 27. Total number of products with environmental product declarations

> 📄 Project teams should document the MR building product disclosure and optimization calculator or an equivalent tracking tool and submit the EPD and LCA reports or compliant summary documents for all the products contributing to the credit.

AND/OR

OPTION 2: MULTI-ATTRIBUTE OPTIMIZATION — (1 Point)

Under this option, **50%** (by cost) of the permanently installed products used in the project must comply with one of the following criteria.

- ➤ Third-party-certified products that demonstrate impact reduction below the industry average **in at least three** of the following five impact categories are valued at **100%** of their cost for credit-achievement calculations.

  - Global warming potential (greenhouse gases), in CO_2e;
  - Depletion of the stratospheric ozone layer, in kilograms of CFC-11;
  - Acidification of land and water sources, in moles of H+ or kilograms of SO_2;
  - Eutrophication, in kilograms of nitrogen or kilograms of phosphate;
  - Formation of tropospheric ozone, in kilograms of NO_x or kilograms of ethane; and depletion of nonrenewable energy resources, in million joules (MJ).

- ➤ Other USGBC-approved programs—This category includes products that comply with other USGBC-approved multiattribute frameworks.

It is important to note that, for the credit achievement calculations, products that are sourced (extracted, manufactured, purchased) within **100 miles** (160 kilometers) of the project site will be valued at **200%** of their base contributing cost. And this will only happen under option 2, not option 1. Additionally, under option 2, structure and enclosure materials cannot constitute more than **30%** of the value of compliant building products. In LEED, to qualify as a structure material, the material should either carry vertical or horizontal loads. And to qualify as an enclosure element, the element must separate conditioned space from the outside or from an unconditioned space.

Below is the credit's equation to be used for option 2.

$$\text{\% of materials cost} = \frac{\left(\begin{array}{c}\text{Product} \\ \text{cost 1}\end{array} \times \begin{array}{c}\text{Criterion} \\ \text{valuation} \\ \text{factor 1}\end{array} \times \begin{array}{c}\text{Location} \\ \text{valuation} \\ \text{factor}\end{array}\right) + \left(\begin{array}{c}\text{Product} \\ \text{cost 2}\end{array} \times \begin{array}{c}\text{Criterion} \\ \text{valuation} \\ \text{factor 2}\end{array} \times \begin{array}{c}\text{Location} \\ \text{valuation} \\ \text{factor}\end{array}\right) + \dots}{\text{Cost of all permanently installed products}} \times 100$$

Equation 28. Percentage of compliant' materials cost

📄 Project teams should document the MR building product disclosure and optimization calculator or an equivalent tracking tool, and they should submit documentation showing compliance with a USGBC-approved program.

As discussed, all the qualifying products must be <u>permanently installed</u> products for both options 1 and 2. For LEED, <u>mechanical</u>, <u>electrical</u>, <u>plumbing</u>, and <u>furniture</u> items are not considered permanently installed building products and are typically excluded from the credit calculations. However, if the project team considers them "permanently installed building products," they can be included in the credit calculations as long as they are also included in the other BPDO credits, which are "BPDO: Sourcing of Raw Materials" and "BPDO: Material Ingredients."

EXEMPLARY PERFORMANCE

To qualify for exemplary performance under this credit, project teams pursuing option 1 should source at least **40 qualifying products** from **five different manufacturers**.

Project teams pursuing option 2 should purchase **75%** (by cost) **of permanently installed building products** that meet the requirements.

KEY THINGS TO REMEMBER

- For the credit achievement calculations, in "Option 1—Environmental Product Declarations," project teams should consider the <u>number</u> of products used, while in "Option 2—Multi-attribute Optimization," project teams should consider the <u>cost</u> of products used.
- Under this credit, all the qualifying products must be <u>permanently installed products</u>.
- Valuation factors for each criterion defined under both options.
- In LEED, all the qualifying EPDs should conform to ISO 14025, 14040, 14044, and EN 15804 or ISO 21930, and they should have at least a cradle-to-gate scope assessment.
- For the credit achievement calculations under option 2, products extracted, manufactured, and purchased within 100 miles (160 kilometers) of the project site are valued at **200%** of their base contributing cost; that is the location valuation factor of LEED.
- The names of the five impact categories defined in this credit's option 2.
- Under option 2, structure and enclosure materials cannot constitute more than **30%** of the value of compliant building products.

BPDO Sourcing of Raw Materials—Credit

■ Applicable to: All the LEED BD+C Rating Systems

All the LEED BD+C Rating Systems	1 – 2 points

CREDIT SUMMARY

The principles employed during the raw material extraction process are very important for reducing the environmental impacts resulting from the creation of a product. Think about a wood supplier that cuts trees without planting any new ones. This approach can only result in a loss of habitat and in deforestation.

In order to prevent similar environmental impacts, "Option 1: Raw Material Source and Extraction Reporting" encourages the use of products that are sourced from ecologically responsible raw material suppliers. The raw material suppliers with third-party-verified corporate sustainability reports (CSR) and self-declared reports should be chosen by project teams in order to encourage sustainable raw material source and extraction principles.

This credit's "Option 2: Leadership Extraction Practices" promotes the use of materials that are either bio-based, **Forest Stewardship Council (FSC)**-certified, reused, have recycled content (both postconsumer and preconsumer recycled content) or contain a producer responsibility program.

The Forest Stewardship Council is a voluntary program that sets standards for wood product manufacturers to ensure responsible forest management in order to prevent deforestation and loss of habitat. The FSC provides a **chain of custody (CoC)** certification that entails a procedure that tracks a product from the point of harvest/extraction to its distribution.

Preconsumer recycled content is the content of a material that is recycled before being used by a consumer. An example of this would be sawdust generated during the manufacture of a wood product. The by-product (sawdust) is then recycled in order to be used inside an MDF board (medium density fiberboard). Thus, the sawdust was never consumed by anyone, and it was directly recycled into a totally different product. Other types of materials with preconsumer recycled content are wood chips, tree bark, magazine overruns, and a number of supplemental cementitious materials (SCMs) such as fly ash.

Postconsumer recycled content is the recycled content of a used material. For example, recyclable printer paper can be sent to be recycled after being used and can then become a part of new printer paper. Other types of materials with postconsumer recycled content are aluminum cans, water bottles, most types of glass, wood and steel products, newspapers, and many others.

Extended Producer Responsibility (EPR) is a product stewardship policy approach that holds consumer goods companies responsible for managing their own products and packaging when consumers are finished with them. There are typically two types of EPR programs available. The first type is the "manufacturer-based program," in which the manufacturer has a take-back or a recycling program for its products sold. The second type is the "third-party program," in which third-party entities transport materials back to the manufacturer.

Lastly, **bio-based materials** are products other than food that are biological products, renewable agricultural materials, or forestry materials. Bio-based materials are derived from biomass. Plants and animals can be examples of bio-based materials; however, hide products, such as leather and other animal skin material, are excluded in LEED calculations.

As in the previous "BPDO—Environmental Product Declarations" credit, project teams need to do some credit achievement calculations in order to show compliance with the credit. Again, the valuation factors will be different for each criterion in the credit's requirements.

CREDIT INTENT

To encourage the use of products and materials that have declared life-cycle information and have environmentally, economically, and socially preferable life-cycle impacts. To award projects for selecting products verified to be extracted or sourced in a responsible manner.

CREDIT REQUIREMENTS

Project teams should achieve one or both of the following options for a maximum of 2 points.

OPTION 1: RAW MATERIAL SOURCE AND EXTRACTION REPORTING – (1 Point)

Under this option, project teams should use at least **20 permanently installed building materials** from **at least five different manufacturers**, which have:

- publicly released a report from their raw material suppliers that includes raw material extraction locations;
- a commitment to long-term ecologically responsible land use;
- a commitment to meeting applicable standards or programs that address responsible sourcing criteria; and
- a commitment to reducing environmental harms created from the extraction/manufacturing process.

Following are the valuation criteria for this option;

- Products sourced from manufacturers with self-declared reports are valued at **one-half (1/2) of a product** in the credit achievement calculations.
- Products with third-party verified corporate sustainability reports that include environmental impacts of extraction operations and activities related to the manufacturer's product and the product's supply chain are valued as **one whole (1) product** for credit-achievement calculation. Acceptable CSR frameworks include:

  - Global Reporting Initiative (GRI) Sustainability Report
  - Organisation for Economic Co-operation and Development (OECD) Guidelines for Multinational Enterprises
  - UN Global Compact: Communication of Progress
  - ISO 26000: 2010 Guidance on Social Responsibility
  - Other USGBC-approved programs

Similar products with <u>distinct formulations</u> from the same manufacturer can be counted as separate products.

All the reports documented for the credit achievement should be current at the products' time of installation.

Following is the equation to be used for option 1:

$$\text{Total number of products} = \left(\begin{array}{c} \text{Number of products with} \\ \text{manufacturer declared} \\ \text{(self-declared) reports} \end{array} \times 0.5 \right) + \left(\begin{array}{c} \text{Number of} \\ \text{products with} \\ \text{third-party-} \\ \text{verified reports} \end{array} \times 1 \right)$$

Equation 29. Total number of products with material raw extraction reporting

> 📄 Project teams should document the MR building product disclosure and optimization calculator or an equivalent tracking tool, and they should submit corporate sustainability reports for all the products contributing to this credit.

AND/OR

OPTION 2: LEADERSHIP EXTRACTION PRACTICES – (1 Point)

Under this option, project teams should use products that meet <u>at least one</u> of the following responsible extraction criteria for at least **25%** (by cost) **of the total value of permanently installed building products** in the project.

- **Extended producer responsibility (EPR):** This includes products purchased from a manufacturer that is involved in an extended-producer-responsibility program or is directly responsible for extended producer responsibility. Products meeting this criterion are valued at **50%** of their cost in the credit-achievement calculations.
- **Bio-based materials:** Bio-based products that meet the <u>Sustainable Agriculture Network's Sustainable Agriculture Standard</u>. Bio-based raw materials must be tested using <u>ASTM Test Method D6866</u> and be legally harvested. **Hide products**, such as leather and other animal skin material, are <u>excluded</u>. Products meeting bio-based material criteria are valued at **100%** of their cost in the credit-achievement calculation.
- **Wood products:** Wood products must be certified by the **Forest Stewardship Council (FSC)** or another USGBC-approved equivalent. Products meeting wood products criteria are valued at **100%** of their cost in the credit-achievement calculation. One thing to note under this criterion is that, if the purchased wood product only has some percentage of FSC-certified wood content (which means the remaining percentage of wood inside the product is not FSC-certified), such as "FSC Mix 60%," the product must be valued according to that percentage. In this case it could be valued at 60% of its cost.
- **Materials reuse:** This criterion includes salvaged, refurbished, or reused products. Products meeting materials reuse criteria are valued at **100%** of their cost in the credit-achievement calculation. (For example, a reused "wood" product can be valued at 100% of its cost, <u>without</u> being FSC-certified, under this criterion. This criterion only considers whether the product is salvaged, refurbished, reused, or not.)

To determine the cost of the reused material, project teams can use the "actual cost" paid for the material or the replacement value (which is basically the cost of that material in new condition), whichever is higher. To calculate the replacement value of a used material, project teams can check the price of a comparable material in the market. To illustrate, let's say that a project bought 20 windows from a store that sells those reused windows for $150 each. The project team confirms that the market price for the same windows in "new" condition is $1,000 each. The value of the equivalent windows should be calculated at $1,000 each, not $150 each.

➤ **Recycled content:** For LEED, recycled content is the sum of <u>postconsumer recycled</u> content plus <u>one-half of the preconsumer recycled content</u>. This is based on <u>cost</u>. Products meeting recycled-content criteria are valued at **100%** of their cost in the credit achievement calculation. These products must conform to ISO 14021-1999.

➤ **Any other USGBC-approved program:** Any other USGBC-approved program meeting leadership extraction criteria can be used.

Even if a product meets more than one criterion above, its valuation cannot exceed 100% of its actual cost in the credit-achievement calculations. In other words, double counting a product is not permitted. However, in the credit achievement calculations, materials sourced (extracted, manufactured, or purchased) within **100 miles** (160 kilometers) (which is the location valuation factor of LEED) of the project site will be valued at **200%** of the base contributing cost. (This rule is just the same as in option 2 of the "BPDO: Environmental Product Declarations" credit.) For example, if the project is using an FSC- certified wood product that is also sourced within 100 miles of the project site, and the product costs $100,000, the product will be counted with the following formulas:

$100,000 x 100% (FSC certified product valuation factor) = $100,000

$100,000 x 200% (location valuation factor) = **$200,000**

The base location for the "reused" materials will be considered as follows: If the material is taken directly from another building, the base location will be that building. If the material is bought from a store, the base location will be the store.

Another important thing to note under this option is that <u>structure</u> and <u>enclosure materials</u> cannot constitute more than **30% of the compliant building products** by cost. Once this threshold is reached, these materials cannot be considered compliant materials from that point forward.

However, 100% of the products' cost will be included inside the "total value of the permanently installed building materials" used in the project. In other words, 100% of their cost should be included in the denominator on the following equation for option 2. Note that the following equation is exactly the same as the equation under option 2 of the "BPDO: Environmental Product Declarations" credit.

$$\% \text{ of materials cost} = \frac{\left(\text{Product cost 1} \times \text{Criterion valuation factor 1} \times \text{Location valuation factor}\right) + \left(\text{Product cost 2} \times \text{Criterion valuation factor 2} \times \text{Location valuation factor}\right) + \dots}{\text{Cost of all permanently installed products}} \times 100$$

Equation 30. Percentage of compliant' materials cost

> 📄 Project teams should document the MR building product disclosure and optimization calculator or an equivalent tracking tool, and they should submit documentation of product claims under the credit requirements.

As can be seen in both of the options, the credit only considers the "permanently installed building products." For LEED, mechanical, electrical, plumbing, and furniture items are not considered permanently installed building products and are typically excluded from the credit calculations. However, if the project team considers them "permanently installed building products," they can be included in the credit calculations as long as they are also included in other BPDO credits. They are "BPDO: Environmental Product Declarations" and "BPDO: Material Ingredients." (Again, this rule is just the same as in the "BPDO: Environmental Product Declarations" credit.)

Project teams can use the "MR Building Product Disclosure and Optimization" calculator in LEED Online, or they can use an equivalent tool. They can input information as the materials are procured. With this approach, project teams can review progress toward the credit achievement and ensure compliance.

EXEMPLARY PERFORMANCE

To qualify for exemplary performance, project teams pursuing option 1 should source at least **40 qualifying products** from five different manufacturers. The project teams pursuing option 2 should purchase **50%** (by cost) **of the permanently installed building products** that meet the extraction criteria.

CASE STUDY

To illustrate, let's say that project teams decided to buy 40 doors to be used in the project, and those doors cost $2,000 each. The project teams use the "MR Building Product Disclosure and Optimization" calculator in LEED Online, and they want to input this new information in the calculator to review its progress toward the credit achievement.

Let's say 40% of each door, by weight, contains FSC-certified wood that is sourced 1,000 miles (1,609 kilometers) away from the project site. And the other 60% of each door, by weight, is preconsumer waste steel that meets the ISO 14021 requirement and is sourced 50 miles (80 kilometers) away from the project site. From this information, we can say that the steel part of the door will qualify for the location valuation factor of LEED and will be counted as 200% of its cost.

The project teams proceed with calculations and create the following table:

Component of each door	Percentage of the component by weight (per door)	Component value per door	Criterion valuation factor	Location valuation factor	Qualifying value by each component
FSC certified wood	40%	$800	100%	-	$800
Preconsumer waste steel	60%	$1,200	100%	200%	$2,400
Actual value of each door		$2,000	Value of each door in the credit calculations		$3,200

Since the project has 40 of these doors, the total value of the doors to be used for credit compliance would be as follows:

$3,200 x 40 = **$128,000**

From the table, we can say that the value of each door has jumped from $2,000 to $3,200 because of the location valuation factor effect, which was significant for the steel part of the door. The project teams can now input this value and review their progress toward credit compliance.

As can be noted from this case study, in the credit calculations, a portion or portions of a product can count as long as they are compliant with the credit's requirements. In other words, if a door is made up of steel, aluminum, and wood, and only the wood portion meets the credit's requirements, project teams can find the percentage of the qualifying wood by weight and multiply that percentage by the total value of the door and find the "qualifying value" of the door.

KEY THINGS TO REMEMBER

- Under option 1, the raw material supplier or the manufacturer of a qualifying product should have publicly released a report that includes <u>raw material extraction locations</u>, <u>commitment to long-term ecologically responsible land use</u>, <u>commitment to meeting applicable standards or programs that address responsible sourcing criteria</u>, and <u>commitment to reducing environmental harms created from the extraction/manufacturing process</u>.

- Know the acceptable CSR frameworks under option 1.

- To qualify as a bio-based product, the product should meet the <u>Sustainable Agriculture Network's Sustainable Agriculture Standard</u>, must be tested using <u>ASTM Test Method D6866</u>, and must be legally harvested. Hide products, such as leather and other animal skin material, are <u>excluded</u> in LEED calculations, and they do not count as bio-based materials.

- Under option 2, structure and enclosure materials cannot constitute more than **30%** of the compliant building products by cost.

- The Forest Stewardship Council (FSC) is a very important organization to know for exam purposes.

- Criterion valuation factors for each criterion defined under both options.

- Under option 2, materials sourced (extracted, manufactured, or purchased) within **100 miles** (160 kilometers) of the project site are valued at **200%** of their cost. That's using the location valuation factor of LEED.

- Recycled content is the sum of <u>postconsumer recycled content</u> plus <u>one-half the preconsumer recycled content</u>, which is based on cost.

BPDO Material Ingredients—Credit

- Applicable to: All the LEED BD+C Rating Systems

All the LEED BD+C Rating Systems	1 – 2 points

CREDIT SUMMARY

In the United States, 96% of 85,000 products have not been screened for possible health effects.[5] The use of persistent bioaccumulative and toxic chemicals (PBTs) and persistent organic pollutants (POPs) are mostly found in building products, and the PBTs and POPs cause serious harm to organisms and can even affect the health of animals and plants living miles away.

This credit encourages the use of chemically screened products and aims to transform the market so that producers pay more attention to chemical screenings.

Green chemistry is the design of chemical products and processes that eliminate the use and generation of hazardous substances.[6] Therefore, it should be implemented for all products. Manufacturers should disclose information about the ingredients in their products so that consumers can make better decisions when choosing environmentally friendly products.

Cradle to Cradle Certification (C₂C), **GreenScreen,** and **REACH Optimization** are also mentioned in the credit, in which the Cradle to Cradle Certification (C₂C) assesses the ingredients of a product for environmental and human health hazards and awards a Basic-, Bronze-,

Silver-, Gold-, or Platinum-level Cradle to Cradle Certification to the products with preferable life-cycle impacts.

Figure.1 Cradle-to-Cradle Products Innovation Institute

GreenScreen is a method used to identify chemicals of high concern and also safer alternatives to those chemicals. GreenScreen is developed by Clean Production Action, a nonprofit organization.

Figure.2 GreenScreen—Chemical Hazard Assessment Method

REACH Optimization—which stands for Registration, Evaluation, Authorization and Restriction of Chemicals—is a European Union regulation that requires all chemicals sold to be evaluated based on their hazard profiles. Only projects outside the United States can use REACH Optimization, as an alternative compliance path (ACP).

As with the previous BPDO credits, project teams need to do some credit achievement calculations in order to show compliance with the credit, and the valuation factors will be different for each criterion in the credit's requirements.

CREDIT INTENT

To encourage the use of products and materials with declared life-cycle information and have environmentally, economically, and socially preferable life-cycle impacts. To award project teams for choosing products with chemical ingredients that are inventoried using an accepted methodology and to award them for using products evaluated to minimize the use and generation of harmful substances. To award raw material manufacturers who produce products verified to have improved life-cycle impacts.

CREDIT REQUIREMENTS

Projects can earn a maximum of **two points** under this credit by achieving the requirements of two out of the following three options:

OPTION 1: MATERIAL INGREDIENT REPORTING — (1 Point)

Under this option, project teams should use at least **20 different permanently installed building products** from **at least five different manufacturers** that use any of the following programs to demonstrate the chemical inventory of the product to at least **0.1%** (1,000 parts per million) of its ingredients;

- **Manufacturer Inventory:** The manufacturer should have published the complete content inventory of the product by showing all the ingredients identified by name and Chemical Abstract Service Registration Number (CASRN). The manufacturer may decline to show the name and/or CASRN for materials that are defined as trade secrets or intellectual property, but it should still disclose the role, amount, and GreenScreen benchmark according to a GreenScreen v1.2 assessment. (A GreenScreen benchmark indicates a chemical's danger level for health.)

- **Health Product Declaration:** The manufacturer should provide an HPD for its end-use product, with full disclosure of known hazards in compliance with the Health Product Declarations open standard.

➤ **Cradle to Cradle Certified (C_2C):** The product should be certified to the <u>Cradle to Cradle v2 Basic level</u> or <u>Cradle to Cradle v3 Bronze level</u>.

➤ **Other USGBC-approved programs.**

Similar products with <u>distinct formulations</u> from the same manufacturer can be counted as separate products.

> 📄 Project teams should document the MR building product disclosure and optimization calculator or an equivalent tracking tool, and they should submit documentation of chemical inventory through HPD, Cradle to Cradle certification labels, manufacturers' lists of ingredients with GreenScreen assessment reports for confidential ingredients, or other USGBC-approved programs.

AND/OR

OPTION 2: MATERIAL INGREDIENT OPTIMIZATION — (1 Point)

Under this option, project teams should use products from manufacturers that document the products' material ingredient optimizations using the following paths for at least **25%** (by cost) **of the total value of permanently installed products** in the project:

➤ **GreenScreen v1.2 Benchmark:** This covers the products that have fully inventoried chemical ingredients to 100 ppm, and the ingredients do not contain "Benchmark 1" hazards. (For GreenScreen v1.2 "Benchmark 1 hazards" are the most dangerous chemicals for health, while "Benchmark 4 hazards" are the least dangerous.)

  ▪ If any ingredients are assessed with the **"GreenScreen List Translator,"** project teams will value these products at **100%** of their costs.

  ▪ If all ingredients have undergone a full **"GreenScreen Assessment,"** project teams will value these products at **150%** of their costs.

➤ **Cradle to Cradle Certified:** This covers the products that have Cradle to Cradle certification. The valuation criteria for these products in the credit calculations will change according to the certification levels as follows:

  ▪ <u>Cradle to Cradle v2 Gold</u>: value these products at **100%** of their costs.
  ▪ <u>Cradle to Cradle v2 Platinum</u>: value these products at **150%** of their costs.
  ▪ <u>Cradle to Cradle v3 Silver</u>: value these products at **100%** of their costs.
  ▪ <u>Cradle to Cradle v3 Gold or Platinum</u>: value these products at **150%** of their costs.

- ➤ **International Alternative Compliance Path—REACH Optimization**: Projects outside the United States can use products and materials that do not contain substances that meet REACH criteria for "substances of very high concern." If the product does not contain any ingredients listed on the <u>REACH Authorization</u> or <u>Candidate list</u>, the product will be valued at **100%** of its cost in credit calculations.
- ➤ **Other USGBC-approved programs**: This covers the other USGBC- approved building product optimization criteria.

To summarize, option 1 of this credit asks for screening a product for all the ingredients to at least **0.1%** (1,000 ppm), identifying and disclosing those ingredients, and indicating the potential risks of those ingredients. However, in option 2, the requirements go beyond that, and it ensures that ingredients of high concern are not even included inside the products used.

Below is the equation to be used for option 2 (note that the following equation is exactly the same as the equation under option 2 of the "BPDO: Environmental Product Declarations" and "BPDO: Sourcing of Raw Materials" credits):

$$\%\text{ of materials cost} = \frac{\left(\begin{array}{c}\text{Product}\\\text{cost 1}\end{array} \times \begin{array}{c}\text{Criterion}\\\text{valuation}\\\text{factor 1}\end{array} \times \begin{array}{c}\text{Location}\\\text{valuation}\\\text{factor}\end{array}\right) + \left(\begin{array}{c}\text{Product}\\\text{cost 2}\end{array} \times \begin{array}{c}\text{Criterion}\\\text{valuation}\\\text{factor 2}\end{array} \times \begin{array}{c}\text{Location}\\\text{valuation}\\\text{factor}\end{array}\right) + \dots}{\text{Cost of all permanently installed products}} \times 100$$

Equation 31. Percentage of compliant' materials cost

> 🖺 Projects should document the MR building product disclosure and optimization calculator or an equivalent tracking tool used in the credit calculations. Additionally, projects should document the verification of ingredient optimizations through Cradle to Cradle certification labels, manufacturers' lists of ingredients with GreenScreen benchmarks listed for all ingredients, or manufacturers' declarations for REACH Optimization or other USGBC- approved programs.

AND/OR

OPTION 3: PRODUCT MANUFACTURER SUPPLY CHAIN OPTIMIZATION – (1 Point)

Unlike option 2, in which the criterion valuation factors vary according to the criterion met, every product meeting the requirements of this option will be valued at **100%** of its cost. (However, this option is more about the product's manufacturer than the properties of the product itself.) Let's take a closer look at the option's requirements.

Under this option, project teams should use building products for at least **25%** (by cost) **of the total value of permanently installed products** in the project that

- ✒ are sourced from manufacturers that engage in validated and robust safety, health, hazard, and risk programs and also, at a minimum, document at least **99%** (by weight) of the ingredients used to make the building product or building material; and
- ✒ are sourced from manufacturers with independent <u>third-party verification</u> of their supply chain that at a minimum verifies the following:
  - ▪ Processes are in place to communicate and transparently prioritize chemical ingredients along the supply chain according to available hazard, exposure, and use information to identify those that require more detailed evaluation.
  - ▪ Processes are in place to identify, document, and communicate information on health, safety, and environmental characteristics of chemical ingredients.
  - ▪ Processes are in place to implement measures to manage health, safety, and environmental hazards and risks of chemical ingredients.

📄 Projects should document supply chain optimization.

For both options 2 and 3, products that are sourced (extracted, manufactured, or purchased) within **100 miles (160 kilometers)** of the project site are valued at **200%** of their cost. (That is the same rule as in option 2 of the "BPDO: Environmental Product Declarations" and "BPDO: Sourcing of Raw Materials" credits.)

In the credit calculations, if a product meets the requirements of both option 2 and option 3, the product can be counted only once under one option. That's in case the project team is pursuing both of the options. In other words, double counting of the same product under two different options is prohibited.

Another important thing to note under option 2 and option 3 is that <u>structure</u> and <u>enclosure materials</u> cannot constitute more than **30% of the compliant building products** by cost. Once this threshold is reached, these materials cannot be considered as compliant materials from that point forward. (Again, this was the case in option 2 of the "BPDO: Environmental Product Declarations" and "BPDO: Sourcing of Raw Materials" credits.)

Project teams can use the "MR Building Product Disclosure and Optimization" calculator in LEED Online, or an equivalent tool, and input information as the materials are procured. With this approach, project teams can review progress toward the credit achievement and ensure compliance.

EXEMPLARY PERFORMANCE

To qualify for exemplary performance under this credit, projects pursuing option 1 should source **at least 40** qualifying products that meet the requirements of option 1. For projects pursuing option 2, **50%** (by cost) **of the permanently installed building products** in the project should meet the requirements of option 2.

KEY THINGS TO REMEMBER

- Projects can earn a maximum of two points under this credit by achieving two out of the three options.
- Under option 1, the chemical inventory of the product assessed should be at least down to **0.1%** (1,000 ppm) of its ingredients.
- In GreenScreen v1.2, "Benchmark 1 hazards" are the most dangerous chemicals for health, and "Benchmark 4 hazards" are the least dangerous.
- Definition of green chemistry.
- GreenScreen.
- Cradle to Cradle Certification.
- REACH Optimization.
- Know the criterion valuation factors under option 2.
- Projects outside the United States can use products and materials that do not contain substances that meet REACH criteria for **"substances of very high concern."**
- Under option 2 and option 3, structure and enclosure materials cannot constitute more than **30% of the compliant building products** by cost.
- For both option 2 and 3, products that are sourced (extracted, manufactured, or purchased) within **100 miles (160 kilometers)** of the project site are valued at **200%** of their cost.

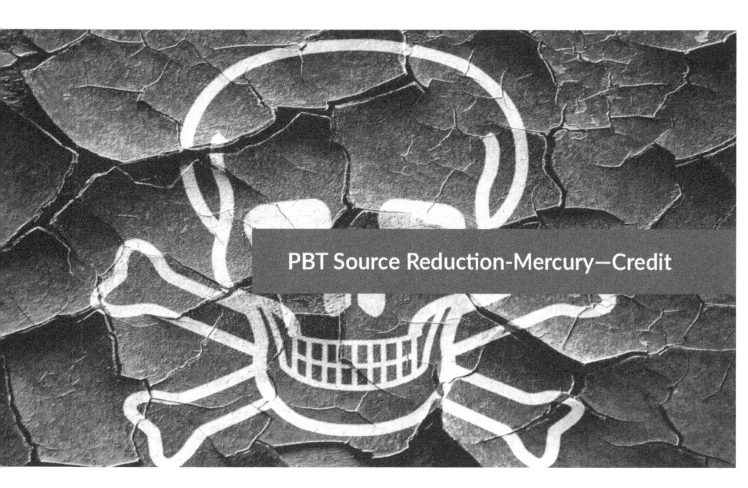

PBT Source Reduction-Mercury—Credit

■ Applicable to: **Healthcare**

Healthcare	1 point

CREDIT SUMMARY

This is the credit of the "PBT Source Reduction—Mercury" prerequisite, with additional requirements. The credit requires project teams to use fluorescent lamps low in mercury content, and it additionally <u>specifies minimum lamp life (in hours)</u> and <u>ballast type</u> in order to ensure use of long-lasting mercury fluorescent lights and contribute to lower mercury use because of the less-frequent replacement needed. The "PBT Source Reduction—Mercury" prerequisite does not address the lamp life or the ballast type.

CREDIT INTENT

Reduction of the release of persistent, bioaccumulative, and toxic chemicals (PBTs) related to the life cycle of building products.

CREDIT REQUIREMENTS

Project teams should specify and install fluorescent lamps with both low mercury content and long lamp life. Projects should not install any circular fluorescent lamps or probe start metal halide lamps. Probe start metal halide lamps have short lamp life. Instead, projects can use pulse start metal halide lamps.

Project teams should specify the use of those lamps that meet the credit criteria for increased lamp life, should specify linear and U-bend fluorescent lamps to meet the rated hours and ballast type criteria, and should also consider installing high-efficiency lamps with no mercury content, such as LEDs, to replace high-pressure sodium (HPS) lamps. Next, projects should create a lighting schedule and track purchased lamps during construction with a material checklist.

If lamps required by operating rooms, dental treatment rooms, dental labs, and other spaces in medical military spaces comply with UFC 4-501-01 but cannot satisfy the credit requirements, those lamps may be excluded from the credit. If the credit requirements conflict with the local code or regulations, the affected lamps may be excluded from the credit, but projects should retain a copy of the local code.

> 🖹 Projects should document lighting schedules that also includes the lamps' hours of life, a narrative explaining lamps that are excluded from the credit, and USGBC's MR PBT source reduction calculator or equivalent documentation.

EXEMPLARY PERFORMANCE

This credit does not qualify for exemplary performance.

KEY THINGS TO REMEMBER

- This credit is only applicable to healthcare projects.
- The credit specifies requirements for the mercury content in milligrams, lamp life in hours, and ballast type. The "PBT Source Reduction—Mercury" prerequisite does not address lamp life.
- Projects should not install circular fluorescent lamps or probe start metal halide lamps.

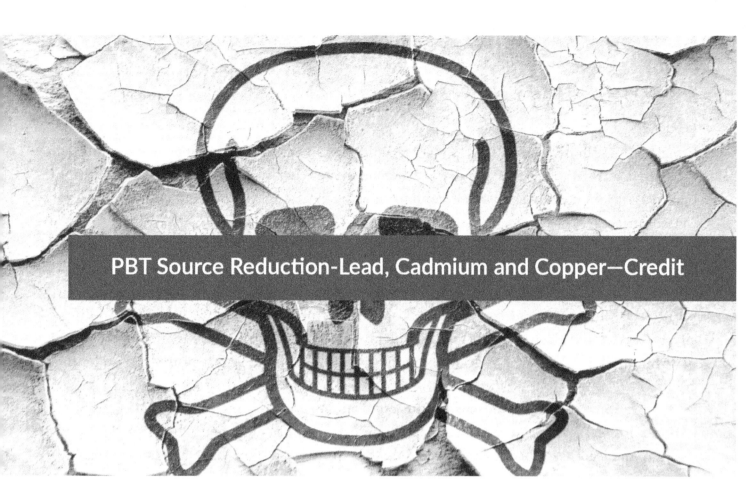

PBT Source Reduction-Lead, Cadmium and Copper—Credit

■ Applicable to: **Healthcare**

Healthcare	2 points

CREDIT SUMMARY

Lead, cadmium, and copper are other persistent bioaccumulative toxic chemicals (PBTs) that can present a great deal of harm to both human health and the environment. That being said, healthcare projects, which are the most critical facilities for improving human health, should set strict requirements for their use.

This credit addresses lead, cadmium, and copper usage, and it requires projects to limit their PBTs to certain minimums.

CREDIT INTENT

To reduce the release of persistent, bioaccumulative, and toxic chemicals (PBTs) related to the life cycle of building products.

CREDIT REQUIREMENTS

<u>For lead:</u>

Project teams should specify and use solder and flux to connect plumbing pipe on site that meet the **California AB1953** standard, which stipulates that solder should not contain more than 0.2% lead and flux should not contain more than a weighted average of 0.25% lead for wetted surfaces.

For water that is intended for human consumption, project teams should specify and use pipes, pipe fittings, plumbing fittings, and faucets that meet the **California AB1953** standard of a weighted average lead content of the wetted surface area of no more than 0.25% lead.

Projects should use lead-free roofing, flashing, interior paint, and exterior paint. Additionally, the cables and electrical wires used in the project should have lead content of less than 300 parts per million. The use of interior or exterior paints containing lead is prohibited under this credit.

Renovation projects should ensure the removal and disposal of disconnected wires with lead stabilizers, according to the **2002 National Electric Code requirements**.

Only the lead used for radiation shielding and copper used for MRI shielding are exempt from the credit's requirements.

<u>For cadmium:</u>

Projects should not use any interior or exterior paints containing intentionally added cadmium.

<u>For copper:</u>

Project teams should reduce or eliminate joint-related sources of copper corrosion in the copper pipe applications by the use of mechanically crimped copper joint systems. And the project teams should ensure that all solder joints and flux comply with **ASTM B828 2002**, and **ASTM B813 2010** respectively.

> 🗎 Project teams should submit manufacturers' data or a proof of certification to demonstrate that the credit criteria have been met. Additionally, projects should submit a narrative about the pipe jointing process (for copper pipes only), verification of appropriate disposal of wires and lead stabilizers (for renovation projects), and a narrative describing any excluded material.

EXEMPLARY PERFORMANCE

This credit does not qualify for exemplary performance.

KEY THINGS TO REMEMBER

- This credit is only applicable to healthcare projects.
- PBTs are substances that pose high long-term risks to humans and the environment and can remain in the environment for long periods and can travel far from their original source.
- LEED addresses copper by reducing or eliminating joint-related sources of copper corrosion.
- With respect to cadmium, projects should not use any interior or exterior paints containing intentionally added cadmium.
- In LEED, the California AB1953 standard is used to address lead, and the ASTM B828 2002 and ASTM B813 2010 standards are used to address copper.

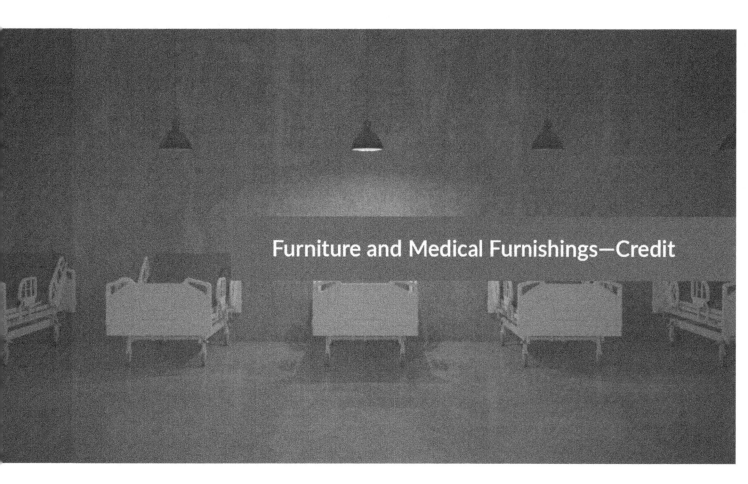

Furniture and Medical Furnishings—Credit

■ Applicable to: **Healthcare**

Healthcare	1 - 2 points

CREDIT SUMMARY

Just like lamps, pipes, roofing materials, or paints can contain mercury, lead, cadmium, or copper, furnishings can also contain persistent bioaccumulative toxic chemicals (PBTs) and can seriously affect indoor air quality and human health. That being said, healthcare projects, which are the most critical facilities for improving human health, should address the potential harm of PBTs in furniture and medical furnishings.

CREDIT INTENT

To enhance the environmental and human health performance attributes related to freestanding furniture and medical furnishings.

CREDIT REQUIREMENTS

Under this credit, at least **30%** (1 point) or **40%** (2 points), by cost, of all the freestanding furniture and medical furnishings—such as mattresses, foams, panel fabrics, cubicle curtains, and other textiles—that meet the criteria in one of the following three options should be used by projects. Projects should include any built-in casework and built-in millwork in the calculations, even if they are manufactured off-site.

OPTION 1: MINIMAL CHEMICAL CONTENT

Under this option, all components that constitute **at least 5%,** by weight, of a furniture or medical furnishing assembly—including textiles, finishes, and dyes—should contain less than **100 parts per million** (ppm) of at least four of the five following chemical groups:

- Urea formaldehyde
- Heavy metals, including mercury, cadmium, lead, and antimony
- Hexavalent chromium in plated finishes consistent with the European Union Directive on the Restriction of the Use of Certain Hazardous Substances (EU RoHS)
- Stain and nonstick treatments derived from perfluorinated compounds (PFCs), including perfluorooctanoic acid (PFOA)
- Added antimicrobial treatments.

AND/OR

OPTION 2: TESTING AND MODELING OF CHEMICAL CONTENT

Under this option, all components of a furniture or medical furnishing assembly, including textiles, finishes, and dyes, must contain **less than 100 parts per million** (ppm) of at least two of the five chemicals or materials listed in option 1.

And any new furniture or medical furnishing assemblies must be in accordance with **ANSI/BIFMA Standard Method M7.1–2011.** Projects should comply with **ANSI/BIFMA e3-2010 Furniture Sustainability Standard, Sections 7.6.1 and 7.6.2** using either the concentration modeling approach or the emissions factor approach. Projects should model the test results using the open plan, private office, or seating scenario in **ANSI/BIFMA M7.1.** USGBC-approved equivalent testing methodologies and contaminant thresholds will also be acceptable.

Salvaged and reused furniture, more than one-year-old at the time of use, is considered compliant if it meets the requirements for any site-applied paints, coatings, adhesives, and sealants.

AND/OR

OPTION 3: MULTI-ATTRIBUTE ASSESSMENT OF PRODUCTS

Under this option, projects should use products that meet at least one of the criteria below. Each product can receive credit for each criterion met. The scope of any environmental product declaration (EPD) must be at least cradle to gate. (This option is similar to the BPDO credits.)

- **Product-specific declarations**: Products with a publicly available, critically reviewed life-cycle assessment conforming to ISO 14044 that have at least a cradle to gate scope are valued as one-quarter (1/4) of a product for the purposes of credit-achievement calculation.
- **Environmental Product Declarations**: These conform to ISO 14025, 14040, 14044, and EN 15804 or ISO 21930 and have at least a cradle to gate scope.
    - **Industry-wide (generic) EPD**: Products with third-party certification (Type III)—including external verification in which the manufacturer is explicitly recognized as a participant by the program operator—are valued as one-half (1/2) of a product for purposes of credit-achievement calculation.
    - **Product-specific Type III EPD**: Products with third-party certification (Type III)—including external verification in which the manufacturer is explicitly recognized as the participant by the program operator—are valued as one whole product for purposes of credit-achievement calculation.
- **Materials reuse**: Use salvaged or reused products.
- **Recycled content**: Use products with recycled content. Remember that the recycled content is the sum of post-consumer recycled content plus one-half of the preconsumer recycled content.
- **Extended producer responsibility**: Products purchased from a manufacturer that participates in an extended producer responsibility program or is directly responsible for extended producer responsibility.
- **Bio-based materials**: Bio-based products must meet the **Sustainable Agriculture Network's Sustainable Agriculture Standard**. Bio-based raw materials must be tested using ASTM Test Method D6866 and be legally harvested, as defined by the exporting and receiving country. Again, hide products, such as leather and other animal skin material, are excluded.
- **Wood products**: Wood products must be certified by the Forest Stewardship Council or USGBC-approved equivalent.

Just like in the BPDO credits, products sourced (extracted, manufactured, purchased) within 100 miles (160 kilometers) of the project site are also valued at 200% of their base contributing cost under this credit.

📄 Project teams should document the use of the MR furniture and medical furnishings calculator provided by USGBC, and they should provide documentation of product claims for any option pursued.

EXEMPLARY PERFORMANCE

To qualify for exemplary performance under this credit, **at least 50%** (by cost) of all freestanding furniture and medical furnishings should meet the credit criteria.

KEY THINGS TO REMEMBER

- This credit is only applicable to healthcare projects.
- Under this credit, projects should use at least **30%** (1 point) or **40%** (2 points), by cost, of all the freestanding furniture and medical furnishings—such as mattresses, foams, panel fabrics, cubicle curtains, and other textiles—that meet the criteria in one of the three options.

Design for Flexibility—Credit

■ Applicable to: **Healthcare**

Healthcare	1 point

CREDIT SUMMARY

Conservation of materials starts by eliminating the need for new materials. Adaptive reuse strategies, which can also be called "designing for flexibility, should be well considered in the buildings that may need frequent changes in layouts or floor plans. Healthcare projects can be a good example. For instance, a flexible floor plan for a hospital building can allow simple changes to be made regarding the sizes of rooms due to the changes in the medical equipment that occur with rapid evolution of technology. Through the use of movable wall partitions or the use of modular systems, the layout of hospital plans can be changed without going into a complete renovation. Or with the use of interstitial space, which is an intermediate space between the floors of the building used to run the majority of the building systems (mainly electrical and mechanical), projects can have a much easier time when adding or modifying any building system during the future adaptation of the building.

This credit encourages healthcare projects to design for flexibility and reduce the need for new materials that can result from future changes in the building.

CREDIT INTENT

Conserve resources related to the construction and management of buildings by designing for flexibility. Ease future building adaptation and increase the service life of components and assemblies.

CREDIT REQUIREMENTS

With the early commitment of the project team and the owner, projects should increase building flexibility by employing at least three of the following strategies:

- Install interstitial space and design distribution zone utility systems and equipment (HVAC, plumbing, electrical, information technology, medical gases, and life safety systems) to serve the occupied zones. Also, have the capacity to control multiple zones in clinical spaces.

- Provide programmed **soft space**, such as administration or storage space, equal to at least **5%** of **departmental gross area** (**DGA**). DGA is the area for diagnostics and treatment in clinical departments, and it is calculated from the centerline of the surrounding walls. (Any wall and circulation space within the department is included; inpatients units are excluded.) Soft space is the type of space whose function can be easily changed. For instance, a management office in a hospital could become a laboratory. Soft spaces should be located adjacent to clinical departments that anticipate future changes and growth. Additionally, projects should determine a strategy for future accommodation of the displaced soft space.

- Provide shell space equal to **at least 5% of DGA**. Shell space is the type of space that is designed to be used in future expansion. It is space that is typically left unfinished. Projects should locate the shell spaces so that they can be occupied without displacing occupied space.

- Determine horizontal expansion capacity for diagnostic and treatment uses or other clinical space equal to **at least 30% of existing floor area**, excluding inpatient units, without demolition of the occupied space.

- Design for future vertical expansion on **at least 75% of the roof**. The existing operations and service systems should be able to continue at or near capacity during the expansion.

- Assign spaces for future above-grade parking structures equal to **50% of existing on-grade parking capacity**, with direct access to the main hospital lobby or circulation.

- Use demountable partitions for **50% of applicable areas**.

- Use movable or modular casework for at least **50% of casework and millwork**.

📄 Project teams should document a narrative of the flexible design strategy, and they should submit the following as applicable:

- The floor plans or other submittal for areas using flexible design strategies
- Calculations for departmental gross area, showing areas required for each strategy selected
- Calculations of floor area for soft space, shell space, and capacity for expansion and future parking
- Calculations of linear area for demountable partitions and a narrative about the areas excluded
- Calculation of product costs for movable and modular casework

EXEMPLARY PERFORMANCE

This credit does not qualify for exemplary performance.

KEY THINGS TO REMEMBER

- Under this credit, projects can provide soft space and shell space equal to at least **5% of DGA**.
- Definitions of soft space, shell space, and departmental gross area.
- This credit is only applicable to healthcare projects.

Construction and Demolition Waste Management—Credit

■ Applicable to: All the LEED BD+C Rating Systems

| All the LEED BD+C Rating Systems | 1 – 2 points |

CREDIT SUMMARY

This is the credit of the "Construction and Demolition Waste Management Planning" prerequisite. If the project teams implement their construction and demolition waste management (CWM) plans, as developed in the prerequisite, and reach the diversion thresholds specified in this credit, they would earn the credit.

In the prerequisite, project teams set the diversion rates without a minimum threshold. However, the diversion rates in this credit are set by the USGBC. It is important to remember that the project teams will not create a separate CWM plan for this credit, and instead will use the CWM plan created under the prerequisite. This is the reason that the CWM plan created under the prerequisite should also comply with the credit's thresholds, assuming the project teams aim for this credit.

The credit contains two options and the first option contains two paths. In option 1 — path 1, projects can divert **50%** of the total construction and demolition material with **at least three material streams** to earn one point. In option 1 — path 2, projects can choose to divert **75%** of the total construction and demolition material with **at least four material streams** and earn two points.

The best technique to eliminate project waste is source reduction, which is to plan the materials to be produced at exact sizes through prefabrication, modular construction, or a similar method so that no waste is generated on-site at all. Option 2 of this credit awards 2 points for the reduction of total waste material. Projects that do not generate more than **2.5 pounds of construction waste per square foot (12.2 kilograms of waste per square meter) of the building's gross floor area** will earn the credit under option 2.

CREDIT INTENT

To reduce construction and demolition waste disposed of in landfills and incineration facilities by reusing, recycling, and recovering materials.

> ♥ The same intent as that of the "Construction and Demolition Waste Management Planning" prerequisite.

CREDIT REQUIREMENTS

To earn this credit under option 1, project teams should recycle and/or salvage nonhazardous construction and demolition materials. Calculations can be either by weight or volume, but they should be consistent throughout.

Excavated soil, land-clearing debris, alternative daily cover (ADC) and hazardous materials should always be excluded in LEED diversion calculations. (Even though ADC will not count as a diversion, it should still be included as a portion of the total construction waste generated.) However, wood waste that is converted to fuel (bio-fuel) can be included in the credit calculations as a diversion. But other types of waste-to-energy products should be excluded from credit calculations unless the project teams cannot meet the credit requirements by reusing or recycling.

In the case of projects that cannot meet credit requirements using reuse and recycling methods, waste-to-energy systems may be considered waste diversion if the **European Commission Waste Framework Directive 2008/98/EC** and **Waste Incineration Directive 2000/76/EC** are followed and if waste-to-energy facilities meet the applicable **European Committee for Standardization (CEN) EN 303** standards.

Project teams should choose either one the following options:

OPTION 1: DIVERSION — (1-2 Points)

Under this option, project teams should choose one of the following paths.

PATH 1: DIVERT 50% AND THREE MATERIAL STREAMS — (1 Point)

Under this path, projects should divert at least **50%** of the total construction and demolition material. Diverted materials should include **at least three material streams**.

OR

PATH 2: DIVERT 75% AND FOUR MATERIAL STREAMS — (2 Points)

Under this path, projects should divert at least **75%** of the total construction and demolition material. Diverted materials should include **at least four material streams**.

Diversion rate = (Total waste diverted from landfill / Total waste produced by the project) x 100

Equation 32. Diversion rate

📄 Project teams should document the use of the MR Construction and Demolition Waste Management Calculator, or an equivalent tool, tracking the total and diverted waste amounts and material streams. Additionally, as applicable, project teams should provide documentation for the recycling rates of the commingled facilities, a narrative about the use of waste-to-energy strategy, and proof showing that the waste-to-energy facilities comply with the relevant EN standards.

OR

OPTION 2: REDUCTION OF TOTAL WASTE MATERIAL — (2 Points)

Under this option, projects should not generate more than **2.5 pounds of construction waste per square foot (12.2 kilograms of waste per square meter) of the building's gross floor area**.

Waste per area = (Total construction and demolition waste generated / Project gross floor area) x 100

Equation 33. Waste per area

📄 Projects should document total waste per area.

Achieving both options 1 and 2 will not bring additional points under this credit. However, that achievement will qualify the project for exemplary performance and cause the reward of a bonus point under the "Innovation" credit. (Exemplary performance points are always awarded under the "Innovation" credit, which will be discussed in the following chapters.)

EXEMPLARY PERFORMANCE

To qualify for exemplary performance under this credit, projects should achieve both option 1 (any path in option 1) and option 2.

KEY THINGS TO REMEMBER

- Excavated soil, land-clearing debris, alternative daily cover (ADC), and hazardous materials do not count as materials diverted.
- The diversion rate formula in option 1 (the same as the formula in the prerequisite) and the waste-per-area formula in option 2.
- Diversion calculations can be by weight or volume, but they should be consistent throughout.
- As is the case with the "Construction and Demolition Waste Management Planning" prerequisite, wood waste, which is converted to fuel (bio-fuel), can be included in LEED diversion calculations without complying with additional LEED requirements.

CHAPTER 9

INDOOR ENVIRONMENTAL QUALITY (EQ)

This credit category is about the strategies related to indoor air quality and thermal, visual, and acoustic comfort. A good standard of indoor environmental quality is essential in green buildings to protect the health and comfort of building occupants. Moreover, the thermal, visual, and acoustic qualities of a building are important in increasing occupants' comfort level and productivity.

In order to increase the indoor air quality of a building, the sources of contaminants should first be identified, and necessary measures should be taken to prevent them from reaching the indoors, which is also called source control. Studies show that poor indoor air quality can result in respiratory disease, allergies, asthma, and sick building syndrome (SBS) or other building-related illnesses (BRI).

All LEED BD+C projects must comply with certain aspects of the ASHRAE 62.1 standard (which is a ventilation standard used to achieve acceptable indoor air quality) or the local codes as part of the "Minimum Air Quality Performance" prerequisite. After the minimum air quality standards have been met, monitoring the indoor air quality is essential since, in some cases, providing sufficient amounts of fresh air to the building may not be enough.

Material off-gassing will also seriously affect indoor air quality and human health. The amount of volatile organic compounds (VOCs), such as formaldehyde, contained in construction materials will affect the health of both the construction workers and the building occupants. Many building materials, such as adhesives, sealants, composite wood, paints, coatings, floorings, furniture, wall coverings, and other products such as photocopy machines can contain harmful levels of VOCs.

Project teams should develop and implement an indoor air quality (IAQ) plan in order to protect the health of both the construction workers and the building occupants. Think about the HVAC ducts stored on-site without any protection and collecting all the dust before getting installed. Even if the building has increased its ventilation rates, all the air that will be supplied by the ducts will be contaminated air, which will decrease the indoor air quality as a consequence.

With the completion of construction, project teams should make sure that any contamination and dust are cleared before the building occupants arrive. To ensure sufficient air quality after the completion of construction, an air quality test can be conducted. Or the project team can choose to conduct a flush-out, which is a process of supplying ample amounts of fresh air to the building before or during occupancy; this process will take away the contaminated air and establish the desired level of indoor air quality.

Since fresh air is by far the most important element of indoor air quality, during the building operations phase, supplying ample amounts of fresh air inside the building will strongly affect the indoor air quality. This can be established by increasing the ventilation rates of the HVAC system, which will result in lowering the ratio of poor air and increase the removal of indoor contaminants. Otherwise, if the climate in the project location is appropriate, natural ventilation can be established by the opening of windows and doors, which would also reduce the building operating costs.

Occupant comfort is another factor that will be addressed under the "Indoor Environmental" credit category. Building occupants need to feel comfortable and in control of their environment in order to be healthy, happy, and productive in their buildings. There are several factors that will affect the comfort of an occupant. These include the following:

- Thermal comfort
- Daylighting
- Views
- Acoustics
- Lighting controls
- Temperature controls
- Ergonomics

However, merely addressing these factors will not be enough. Occupant surveys are also essential to ensure occupant comfort. By receiving occupant feedback, the building management can pinpoint areas that need to be improved.

"Thermal comfort" is much more than merely adjusting the room temperature. It includes air movement and humidity as well. An occupant cannot feel comfortable under an HVAC duct that blows directly on him or her or if the unit does not provide even temperatures in all spaces.

"Daylighting," a very important resource to use in green buildings, will increase the occupants' health, comfort, and productivity while also reducing building operating costs by using less artificial lighting inside the building. While too much daylighting can create discomfort, through means such as glare or direct sunlight to the occupant, an effective lighting design can overcome these consequences.

Having "quality views" in a building is another factor that will increase an occupant's comfort and productivity. Even if the building is in a great location that can provide wonderful views, the design of the building should still maximize the use of those views to the building occupants.

Building acoustics are an important part of the green building design that will affect an occupant's health, comfort, communication, and productivity. Students in schools can easily be disturbed by outside noise. Hospital patients can have even more problems and privacy issues related to poor acoustics.

Providing individual "lighting controls" with adjustable lighting levels will also increase occupant comfort and reduce lighting costs. If a big office space does not contain any individual lighting controls, all the lights should be "on," even if there are few people working in the office. Additionally, installing occupancy sensors will shut off light when an occupant is away from his or her desk and also reduce lighting usage. A major aspect of lighting that will affect occupant comfort is lighting quality. The layout and intensity of lighting fixtures should be thoroughly evaluated during the design. Excess brightness and glare are factors that will cause discomfort to building users.

As for "temperature controls," every individual has different temperature preferences. A certain temperature in an office building can make some people happy, while other people can try to warm themselves up by putting on their sweaters or jackets. Providing "thermal comfort controls" for individual spaces can allow building users to set their desired space temperature.

Finally, let's discuss "ergonomics." Office layouts, individual workstation design, furnishings, and equipment all contribute to the "ergonomics" of a building. Since every individual has different needs, the project team should consult and analyze the occupants' needs. Worker education and training should also be provided upon installation of furniture and equipment. Key ergonomic principles to be implemented should include flexibility, versatility, fit, and postural change.

This chapter will discuss the LEED requirements for the "Indoor Environmental Quality" credit category. The credit category contains the following prerequisites/credits:

- ➥ Minimum Indoor Air Quality Performance—Prerequisite
- ➥ Environmental Tobacco Smoke Control—Prerequisite
- ➥ Minimum Acoustic Performance—Prerequisite
- ➥ Enhanced Indoor Air Quality Strategies—Credit
- ➥ Low-Emitting Materials—Credit
- ➥ Construction Indoor Air Quality Management Plan—Credit
- ➥ Indoor Air Quality Assessment—Credit
- ➥ Thermal Comfort—Credit
- ➥ Interior Lighting—Credit
- ➥ Daylight—Credit
- ➥ Quality Views—Credit
- ➥ Acoustic Performance—Credit

SPACE CATEGORIZATION

As will be mentioned shortly, in some "Indoor Environmental Quality" prerequisites/credits, the "spaces" inside the building are categorized as "occupied spaces," or as "unoccupied space." Furthermore, "occupied spaces" are further categorized as "regularly occupied spaces" or as "nonregularly occupied" spaces. (For exam purposes, it is important to know the distinctions between them.)

For LEED, "occupied spaces" are active spaces intended for human activity, such as private offices, dorm rooms, restrooms, or corridors. "Unoccupied spaces" are inactive spaces that are occupied occasionally for short periods of time, such as the emergency exit corridor, mechanical rooms, or electrical rooms.

When further categorizing the "occupied spaces" as "regularly occupied spaces" or as "nonregularly occupied spaces," the duration of occupancy is considered. "Regularly occupied spaces" are spaces where people spend time of more than **one hour of continuous occupancy** per person per day, on average. If a space is not used daily, but people spend more than one hour when using that space, it should still be considered "regularly occupied space." Examples of regularly occupied spaces would be auditoriums, private offices, dorm rooms, meeting rooms, or reception desks.

"Nonregularly occupied spaces" are types of spaces that do not meet the definition of the "regularly occupied spaces." Examples of "nonregularly occupies spaces" would be corridors, locker rooms, or stairways.

In some credits, "occupied spaces" will also need to be categorized as "individual occupant spaces" or as "shared multioccupant spaces," based on the number of occupants using the space and their activities. An "individual occupant space" is a type of space where a person performs distinct tasks, such as the private office, reception desk, or hotel guest room. On the other hand, the "shared multioccupant space" is a type of space where people pursue collaborative and overlapping tasks, such as the gymnasium, classroom, meeting room, hotel lobby, or auditorium.

Minimum Indoor Air Quality Performance—Prerequisite

■ Applicable to: All the LEED BD+C Rating Systems

PREREQUISITE SUMMARY

Most of us predominantly spend our time inside buildings, breathing the air coming from the HVAC systems without being able to breathe fresh, outside air. The ventilation rates of the HVAC systems and the contamination inside the ducts are important factors to consider. HVAC systems may cause serious health effects since properly ventilated spaces always contain fewer contaminants than poorly ventilated areas.

This prerequisite aims for buildings to maintain enough fresh air rates to building occupants by forcing indoor air quality standards for both ventilation and air monitoring.

PREREQUISITE INTENT

Contribute to the well-being and comfort of building occupants by setting minimum standards for indoor air quality.

PREREQUISITE REQUIREMENTS

<u>For all LEED BD+C projects, except "LEED BD+C: Healthcare"</u>:
Project teams should meet the requirements for both <u>ventilation</u> and <u>monitoring</u>.

<u>Ventilation:</u>

This prerequisite has different ventilation requirements for "mechanically ventilated spaces" and for "naturally ventilated spaces".

<u>Mechanically ventilated spaces</u>:

For the mechanically ventilated spaces (and for mixed-mode systems when the mechanical ventilation is activated), projects located in the US should pursue "Option 1", while the projects located outside the US can pursue "Option 2".

OPTION 1: ASHRAE STANDARD 62.1–2010

Under this option, project teams should determine the <u>minimum outdoor air intake flow</u> for mechanical ventilation systems using the ventilation rate procedure from **ASHRAE 62.1-2010** or a local equivalent, whichever is more stringent. Additionally, projects should meet the <u>minimum requirements</u> of **ASHRAE Standard 62.1–2010**, **Sections 4–7**, Ventilation for Acceptable Indoor Air Quality (with errata) or a local equivalent, whichever is more stringent.

OPTION 2: CEN STANDARDS EN 15251–2007 AND EN 13779–2007

Projects located outside the US may choose to meet the minimum outdoor air requirements of Annex B of **Comité Européen de Normalisation (CEN) Standard EN 15251–2007**, Indoor environmental input parameters for design and assessment of energy performance of buildings addressing indoor air quality, thermal environment, lighting and acoustics. And projects should additionally meet the requirements of **CEN Standard EN 13779–2007**, Ventilation for nonresidential buildings, Performance requirements for ventilation and room conditioning systems.

<u>Naturally ventilated spaces</u>:

For naturally ventilated spaces, and for mixed-mode systems when the mechanical ventilation is inactive, project teams should determine the <u>minimum outdoor air opening</u> and <u>space configuration</u> requirements using the natural ventilation procedure from **ASHRAE Standard 62.1–2010**, or a local equivalent, whichever is more stringent.

Ceiling heights, location and size of the natural ventilation openings should be all designed to meet the requirements of the mentioned standard.

Project teams should confirm that natural ventilation is an effective strategy for the project by following the flow diagram in the **Chartered Institution of Building Services Engineers (CIBSE) Applications Manual** AM10, March 2005, Natural Ventilation in Nondomestic Buildings, Figure 2.8, and meet the requirements of **ASHRAE Standard 62.1-2010, Section 4**, or a local equivalent, whichever is more stringent.

For all spaces:

The indoor air quality procedure mentioned in the ASHRAE Standard 62.1–2010 may not be used to comply with this prerequisite.

Monitoring:

This prerequisite has different monitoring requirements for the "mechanically ventilated spaces" and for the "naturally ventilated spaces".

Mechanically ventilated spaces:

Projects containing variable air volume systems should monitor the minimum outdoor air intake flow with a direct **outdoor airflow measurement device**. This device should measure the minimum outdoor air intake flow, as defined by the ventilation requirements with an accuracy of **+/–10%** of the designed minimum outdoor airflow rate. An alarm should be activated when the outdoor airflow value varies by **15% or more** from the outdoor airflow setpoint.

Projects that use constant-volume systems, should balance outdoor airflow to the minimum outdoor airflow design rate defined by **ASHRAE Standard 62.1–2010 (with errata)**, or higher. Projects should install a current transducer on the supply fan, an airflow switch, or a similar monitoring device.

Naturally ventilated spaces:

For the naturally ventilated spaces and for the mixed-mode systems when the mechanical ventilation is inactivated, project teams should comply with at least one of the following strategies:

- Provide a direct **exhaust airflow measurement device** placed at the exhaust location. The device must be capable of measuring the exhaust airflow with an accuracy of **+/–10%,** and an alarm should be activated when airflow values vary by **15% or more** from the design exhaust rate.

➤ Provide **automatic indication devices** on <u>all natural ventilation openings</u>. An alarm should be activated when any one of the openings is closed during the occupied hours.

➤ Monitor **carbon dioxide concentrations** within <u>each thermal zone</u>. Carbon dioxide monitors must be between 3 and 6 feet (900 and 1,800 millimeters) above the floor and should be placed within each thermal zone. The monitoring devices should have an audible or visual indicator or should alert the building automation system, if carbon dioxide concentration levels exceeds the setpoints by more than 10%. The setpoints should be calculated by using the methods in ASHRAE 62.1–2010, Appendix C.

The mechanical equipment installed for the "LEED BD+C: Core and Shell" projects should be capable of meeting projected ventilation rates and monitoring requirements of the future tenants.

<u>Additional requirements for "residential" projects</u>:
Residential projects should comply with the previous requirements and additionally meet the following requirements in each dwelling unit:

➤ Unvented combustion appliances are not allowed in any unit.

➤ Carbon monoxide monitoring devices must be installed on each floor of each unit.

➤ All indoor fireplaces and woodstoves should have glass enclosures or doors that seal when closed.

➤ Any indoor fireplaces and woodstoves that are not closed combustion or power-vented should pass a backdraft potential test in order to confirm that depressurization of the combustion appliance zone is less than 5 Pa.

➤ Space- and water-heating equipment that involves combustion must be designed and installed with closed combustion or with power-vented exhaust, or should be located in a detached utility building or open-air facility.

➤ If the project is inside the high-risk areas for radon (EPA Radon Zone 1, or local equivalent for projects outside the US), projects should design and construct any dwelling unit –on levels one through four above grade– with radon-resistant construction techniques. Project teams should follow the techniques prescribed in EPA Building Radon Out; NFPA 5000, Chapter 49; International Residential Code, Appendix F; CABO, Appendix F; ASTM E1465; or a local equivalent, whichever is most stringent.

💡 "LEED BD+C: Data Center" and "LEED BD+C: Warehouses and Distribution Center" project teams should meet the previous requirements in all the occupied spaces.

📄 For documentation, as applicable, project teams should submit confirmation that the project meets the minimum requirements of the applicable standards, submit the ventilation procedures, MERV ratings, natural ventilation rate calculations, CIBSE flow diagram, and controls drawings showing the monitoring devices.

For "LEED BD+C: Healthcare" projects:
Healthcare projects should meet the following requirements for both <u>ventilation</u> and <u>monitoring</u>.

Ventilation:
This prerequisite has different ventilation requirements for the "mechanically ventilated spaces" and for the "naturally ventilated spaces".

Mechanically ventilated spaces:
For mechanically ventilated spaces and for mixed-mode systems when the mechanical ventilation is activated, healthcare projects should determine the minimum outdoor air intake flow rates by using the ventilation rates in **ASHRAE Standard 170–2008**, Section 7; the requirements of the **2010 FGI Guidelines for Design and Construction of Health Care Facilities** (Table 2.1–2); or a local equivalent, whichever is most stringent.

For any area not covered in the ASHRAE Standard 170-2008 or in the FGI guidelines, project teams should follow the ASHRAE 62.1 or a local equivalent, whichever is more stringent and meet the <u>minimum requirements</u> of ASHRAE Standard 170–2008, Sections 6–8, Ventilation of Health Care Facilities (with errata) or a USGBC-approved equivalent standard for projects outside the US.

Naturally ventilated spaces:
For naturally ventilated spaces (and for mixed-mode systems when the mechanical ventilation is inactivated), healthcare projects should determine the minimum <u>outdoor air opening</u> and <u>space configuration</u> requirements using the natural ventilation procedure of **ASHRAE Standard 62.1–2010 (with errata)** or a local equivalent, whichever is more stringent. Project teams should confirm that natural ventilation is an effective strategy for the project by following the flow diagram in Figure 2.8 of the **CIBSE Applications Manual AM10**, March 2005, Natural Ventilation in Nondomestic Buildings.

Monitoring:

Mechanically ventilated spaces:

For mechanically ventilated spaces (and for mixed-mode systems when the mechanical ventilation is activated), healthcare projects should provide a direct **outdoor airflow measurement device**, in order to measure the minimum outdoor air intake flow. The measurement device should be capable of measuring the minimum outdoor air intake flow with an accuracy of **+/−10%** and an alarm should alert staff whenever the outdoor airflow value varies by **15% or more** from the outdoor airflow setpoint.

Naturally ventilated spaces:

(Note that the following monitoring requirements are just the same with the previously described monitoring requirements that are applicable to the other LEED BD+C projects.)

For naturally ventilated spaces and for mixed-mode systems when the mechanical ventilation is inactivated, healthcare projects should comply with <u>at least one</u> of the following strategies:

- ⤳ Provide a direct **exhaust airflow measurement device** placed at the exhaust location. The device must be capable of measuring the exhaust airflow with an accuracy of **+/−10%,** and an alarm should be activated when airflow values vary by **15% or more** from the design exhaust rate.
- ⤳ Provide **automatic indication devices** on <u>all natural ventilation openings</u>. An alarm should be activated when any one of the openings is closed during the occupied hours.
- ⤳ Monitor **carbon dioxide concentrations** within <u>each thermal zone</u>. Carbon dioxide monitors must be between 3 and 6 feet (900 and 1,800 millimeters) above the floor and should be placed within each thermal zone. The monitoring devices should have an audible or visual indicator, or should alert the building automation system, if carbon dioxide concentration levels exceeds the setpoints by more than 10%. The setpoints should be calculated by using the methods in ASHRAE 62.1–2010, Appendix C.

📄 For documentation, as applicable, healthcare project teams should submit confirmation that the project meets the minimum requirements of the applicable standards, submit the air balance summary table, the ventilation rate procedure calculations, the CIBSE flow diagram process, natural ventilation procedure calculations / ventilation opening information, any natural ventilation exception from mechanical ventilation system, any exception from authority having jurisdiction, and submit controls drawing showing the monitoring devices.

KEY THINGS TO REMEMBER

■ ASHRAE's standard numbers and their scopes are favorite test questions. **ASHRAE Standard 62.1-2010** is used under this prerequisite to address indoor air quality.

■ For residential projects, the prerequisite requires additional criteria.

■ For "LEED BD+C: Healthcare" projects, the prerequisite also refers to the **2010 FGI Guidelines for Design and Construction of Health Care Facilities** and **ASHRAE Standard 170–2008,** for ventilation of the mechanically ventilated spaces.

■ All LEED BD+C projects using natural ventilation should confirm that natural ventilation is an effective strategy for the project by following the flow diagram in Figure 2.8 of the **Chartered Institution of Building Services Engineers Applications Manual** AM10, March 2005, Natural Ventilation in Nondomestic Buildings.

Environmental Tobacco Smoke Control—Prerequisite

■ Applicable to: All the LEED BD+C Rating Systems

PREREQUISITE SUMMARY

This prerequisite requires strict requirements to prevent smoking both outside and inside the building, thereby increasing the air quality and at the same time saving nonsmokers from the effects of secondhand smoke.

For schools, the prerequisite restricts smoke on the entire site, without any exceptions. And for residential projects, the prerequisite has additional requirements if smoking is permitted in residential units.

PREREQUISITE INTENT

To prevent or minimize the exposure of building users, indoor areas, and ventilation air distribution systems to environmental tobacco smoke.

PREREQUISITE REQUIREMENTS

Project teams should prohibit smoking inside the building and additionally prohibit smoking outside the building except in designated smoking areas located at least **25 feet (7.5 meters)** from all entries, outdoor air intakes, and operable windows. Furthermore, smoking should be prohibited outside the property line in the spaces used for business purposes.

If the requirement to prohibit smoking within 25 feet (7.5 meters) cannot be implemented because of any code or regulation, project teams should provide documentation.

Signage must be posted within **10 feet** (3 meters) of all building entrances, and it should indicate the no-smoking policy.

"LEED BD+C: School" projects must **prohibit smoking on the entire site** and post signage indicating the no-smoking policy.

> 📄 For all projects where smoking is prohibited, project teams should document a narrative about the project's no-smoking policy and describe how the policy is enforced with respect to building occupants. Moreover, project teams should document a scaled site plan/map indicating the designated outdoor smoking and no-smoking areas showing their 25-foot (7.5-meter) distances from building openings, submit the drawings/photos of no-smoking signage, and any code or landlord restriction that inhibits the establishment of no-smoking requirements.

For residential projects only:
Residential projects should meet one of the following options.

OPTION 1: NO SMOKING

Residential projects that prohibit smoking inside the entire building are eligible to pursue this path. Project teams should meet the previous requirements just like the other rating systems, and they should prohibit smoking inside the entire building.

OR

OPTION 2: COMPARTMENTALIZATION OF SMOKING AREAS

If smoking will not be prohibited inside the whole building, residential projects should pursue this option. Under this option, projects must prohibit smoking inside all common areas, and this prohibition must be written in the building rental or lease agreements.

The rest of the mentioned requirements still apply to residential projects; projects must prohibit smoking outside the building except in designated smoking areas located at least **25 feet** (7.5 meters) from all entries, outdoor air intakes, and operable windows. And smoking should be prohibited outside the property line in the spaces used for business purposes.

If the requirement to prohibit smoking within 25 feet (7.5 meters) cannot be implemented because of any code or regulation, project teams should provide documentation.

And signage indicating the no-smoking policy must be posted within **10 feet** (3 meters) of <u>all building entrances.</u>

Since this option is for residential projects that will allow smoking inside the residential units, each unit must be compartmentalized to prevent excessive leakage between units. Plus, the following would apply:

- All exterior doors and operable windows in the residential units should be weather-stripped to minimize leakage from outdoors.
- All doors leading from residential units into common hallways should be weather-stripped.
- By sealing penetrations in the walls, ceilings, and floors and by sealing vertical chases, minimize uncontrolled pathways for the transfer of smoke and other indoor air pollutants between residential units.
- Demonstrate a maximum leakage of 0.23 cubic feet per minute per square foot at 50 Pa of the enclosure. This would include surfaces enclosing the apartment, exterior and party walls, floors, ceilings, or any similar surfaces.

📄 For residential projects where smoking is permitted, project teams should provide documentation with a narrative about the project's no-smoking policy (outside of the residential units) and describe how policy is enforced with building occupants. Moreover, project teams should provide documentation with a scaled site plan/map indicating the designated outdoor smoking and no-smoking areas and showing their 25-foot (7.5 meter) distances from building openings. Moreover, projects should submit drawings/photos of no-smoking signage, the differential air pressure test report, and door schedule indicating the weather stripping at the exterior unit doors and the doors leading from units to common hallways.

KEY THINGS TO REMEMBER

■ For schools, the prerequisite restricts smoking on the entire site, without any exceptions.

■ Projects should prohibit smoking outside the building except in designated smoking areas located at least **25 feet (7.5 meters)** from all entries, outdoor air intakes, and operable windows.

■ Signage that indicates the no-smoking policy must be posted within **10 feet** (3 meters) of <u>all building entrances.</u>

■ Residential projects should prohibit smoking inside all <u>common areas</u>, and this prohibition must be written in the building rental or lease agreements. In residential projects, each residential unit must be compartmentalized to prevent excessive leakage between units if smoking is permitted inside them.

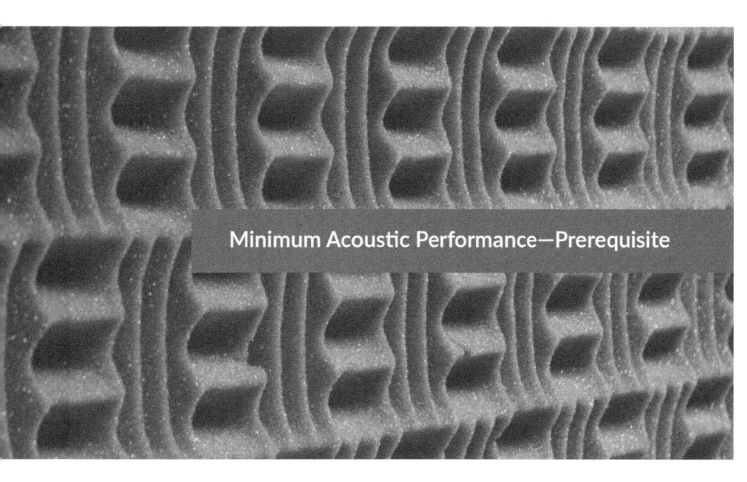

Minimum Acoustic Performance—Prerequisite

■ Applicable to: **Schools**

PREREQUISITE SUMMARY

Acoustic design is an important part of the green building design that will affect an occupant's health, comfort, communication, and productivity. Students in schools and people working in open office environments can easily be disturbed by outside noise. Hospital patients can have even more problems and privacy issues related to poor acoustics.

However, this prerequisite only covers the "LEED BD+C: Schools" projects, and requires all LEED-certified schools to implement an effective acoustic design by addressing the prerequisite requirements for HVAC background noise, exterior noise, and reverberation time.

In the following pages, there is also the "Acoustic Performance" credit, which awards a point or points to projects for implementing measures to improve the acoustic performance of a building.

PREREQUISITE INTENT

To provide classrooms that facilitate teacher-to-student and student-to-student communication by implementing effective acoustic design.

PREREQUISITE REQUIREMENTS

Every school project should first identify all <u>classrooms</u> and <u>other core learning spaces</u> and address the following requirements for HVAC background noise, exterior noise, and reverberation time. For LEED, classroom or core learning space refers to any space that is regularly used for educational activities.

<u>HVAC Background Noise:</u>

School projects should achieve a maximum background noise level of **40 dBA** from the HVAC systems in the classrooms and other core learning spaces. Projects should follow the recommended methodologies for the mechanical system noise control in **ANSI Standard S12.60–2010**, Part 1, Annex A.1; **2011 HVAC Applications ASHRAE Handbook**, Chapter 48, Noise and Vibration Control (with errata); **AHRI Standard 885–2008** or a local equivalent for projects located outside the United States.

To satisfy this requirement, project teams can locate the HVAC equipment in such a way as to minimize the noise in the classrooms and other core learning spaces, or they can choose to insulate the HVAC equipment to reduce background noise. (For example, internal duct insulation is known to reduce background noise, but it also increases energy usage.)

When the necessary measures are taken, project teams will measure the HVAC background noise according to the mentioned standards when no occupants are present, all the furnishings are installed, and the noises from other sources are minimized. During the measurements, the HVAC equipment should be operating under typical conditions.

<u>Exterior Noise:</u>

In school projects that are exposed to high noise levels—peak-hour L_{eq} above **60 dBA** during school hours—project teams should design acoustic treatment and other measures to reduce the noise intrusion from exterior sources and control the sound transmission between classrooms and other core learning spaces. L_{eq} is a method to describe a varying sound level over time. Think about the variation of the noise levels on highways; as more cars and trucks pass, more sound is produced, and the traffic on the highway varies with each minute. To describe the noise level of such a highway, using the L_{eq} value can be useful, as there will be only one value to describe the highway's noise level. The L_{eq} value is found by calculating an average of these varying noise levels. (It's not an arithmetic average; it's a logarithmic average.)

Projects that are located at least <u>one-half mile</u> (800 meters) from any significant noise source, such as airports, industry, highways, etc., are exempt from this requirement.

If there are noise-producing sources located within one-half mile (800 meters) of the project, the project teams should conduct acoustic readings during normal school hours. If the peak-hour L_{eq} is above 60 dBA, the team must implement noise reduction measures.

Some possible strategies may be to use architectural barriers, sound sealants, efficient window and door gaskets, and more. After the necessary measures are taken, the project teams must again conduct acoustic readings and confirm that the peak-hour L_{eq} is below 60 dBA.

Reverberation Time:

Reverberation time is the time span between when a sound is produced and when it dies away. Actually, sounds do not merely die away. In fact, they are absorbed by materials, furniture, and isolation products while they reach zero amplitude.

To address reverberation time, school projects should meet the following requirements according to their classroom and core learning space size.

For classrooms and core learning spaces that are less than 20,000 cubic feet (566 cubic meters):

Project teams should design classrooms and other core learning spaces with sufficient sound-absorptive finishes and comply with the reverberation time requirements specified in ANSI Standard S12.60–2010, Part 1, Acoustical Performance Criteria, Design Requirements and Guidelines for Schools, or a local equivalent for projects outside the United States.

Project teams should determine the sound absorption properties of the absorptive materials at 500 Hz, 1,000 Hz, and 2,000 Hz. The sound absorptive materials can be applied to any planar surface in the space.

Next, project teams should choose and pursue one of the following options.

OPTION 1:

Under this option, for each room, projects should confirm that the total surface area of acoustic wall panels, ceiling finishes, and other sound-absorbent finishes equals or exceeds the total ceiling area of the room (excluding grilles, light fixtures, and diffusers). The acoustic materials must have noise reduction coefficients (NRCs) of 0.70 or higher in order to be included in this calculation.

For example, if the whole surface of the classroom ceiling (excluding grilles, light fixtures, and diffusers) is covered by sound absorptive material with an NRC of 0.70 or higher, the project team will automatically earn this prerequisite by documenting the manufacturers' testing data for the material used. If some portion of the ceiling is not covered by sound absorptive material, the project team may choose to install sound absorptive material with an NRC of 0.70 or higher to the walls to compensate for that portion.

OR

OPTION 2:

Under this option, projects should confirm through calculations that rooms are designed to meet reverberation time requirements as specified in the <u>ANSI Standard S12.60-2010</u> standard. Reverberation time should again be verified at 500 Hz, 1,000 Hz, and 2,000 Hz.

<u>For classrooms and core learning spaces that are equal to or bigger than 20,000 cubic feet (566 cubic meters)</u>:

Project teams should meet the recommended reverberation times for classrooms and core learning spaces as specified in the <u>NRC-CNRC Construction Technology Update No. 51, Acoustical Design of Rooms for Speech (2002)</u>, or a local equivalent for projects outside the United States. Reverberation time should be verified at 500 Hz, 1,000 Hz and 2,000 Hz.

<u>Prerequisite Exceptions</u>:

Projects with a limited scope of work or projects that must obey historic preservation requirements may be considered exempt from this prerequisite's requirements according to GBCI's considerations. In those instances, the project teams can come up with new solutions for acoustic treatment, provide a narrative about the things that are not under the control of the project teams, and the new strategies taken to address acoustics.

This prerequisite also does not cover auditoriums, natatoriums, music performance spaces, teleconferencing rooms, or special education rooms. It only covers classrooms and core learning spaces.

> Project teams should provide documentation with the summary report of measurements and calculations for "background noise." They should submit a description of the exterior noise sources within one-half-mile (800 meter) radius of the project site, submit L_{eq} calculations and a narrative describing when measurements were taken, and submit a description or drawings of measures implemented for the "exterior noise." They should also submit documentation or calculations for "reverberation time" that show that the reverberation time requirements have been met.

KEY THINGS TO REMEMBER

- This prerequisite is only applicable to "LEED BD+C: Schools" projects.
- This prerequisite does not cover auditoriums, natatoriums, music performance spaces, teleconferencing rooms, or special education rooms. It only covers classrooms and core learning spaces.
- School projects should achieve a maximum background noise level of **40 dBA** from HVAC systems in classrooms and other core learning spaces.
- School projects that are exposed to high noise levels—peak-hour L_{eq} above **60 dBA** during school hours—should design acoustic treatment and other measures to reduce the noise intrusion from exterior sources and control the sound transmission between classrooms and other core learning spaces.
- The L_{eq} value is found by calculating an average of these varying noise levels (not an arithmetic average but a logarithmic average).

Enhanced Indoor Air Quality Strategies—Credit

■ Applicable to: All the LEED BD+C Rating Systems

All the LEED BD+C Rating Systems	1 – 2 points

CREDIT SUMMARY

This is the credit of the "Minimum Indoor Air Quality Performance" prerequisite. It goes beyond the prerequisite and aims to enhance indoor air quality by requiring the installation of entryway systems to prevent contaminants from being brought inside the building, by setting increased ventilation rates, by encouraging the use of enhanced filtration media, and by monitoring building air quality.

The credit requires certain minimum efficiency reporting value (MERV) ratings to be achieved in the air filters used in the project even though using air filters with a higher MERV will result in greater energy usage. The minimum efficiency reporting value (MERV) rates the air filters according to their performance in removing particles from the air, and the higher the MERV, the more particles will be removed.

The credit contains two options and projects can pursue both of them to earn more points.

CREDIT INTENT

Promoting building occupants well-being, comfort and productivity by enhancing the indoor air quality.

CREDIT REQUIREMENTS

OPTION 1: ENHANCED IAQ STRATEGIES — (1 Point)

In the **mechanically ventilated spaces**, project teams should comply with the following strategies as applicable:

A. Entryway systems;

B. Interior cross-contamination prevention; and

C. Filtration.

In the **naturally ventilaed spaces**, project teams should apply the following strategies:

A. Entryway systems; and

B. Natural ventilation design calculations.

For the **mixed-mode systems**, project teams should apply the following strategies:

A. Entryway systems;

B. Interior cross-contamination prevention;

C. Filtration;

D. Natural ventilation design calculations; and

E. Mixed-mode design calculations.

Let's take a closer look at the requirements of each strategy:

A. <u>Entryway systems</u>: Under this strategy, projects should install **permanent entryway systems** at least 10 feet (3 meters) long in the primary direction of travel at the <u>regularly used exterior entrances</u>, in order to prevent dirt and particulates from reaching indoors. Some example entryway systems may be **grilles, grates, slotted systems,** and **rollout mats,** or any other entryway system with equivalent or better performance. Entryway systems should be maintained on a weekly basis.

"LEED BD+C: Warehouses and Distribution Centers" are not required to install entryway systems at the doors leading from the exterior to the loading dock or garage. However, entryway systems should be installed between these spaces and adjacent office spaces.

"LEED BD+C: Healthcare" projects should additionally provide pressurized entryway vestibules at the building entrances with high-volume.

B. <u>**Interior cross-contamination prevention**</u>: Under this strategy, projects should exhaust spaces that may contain hazardous materials or chemicals (according to the exhaust rates determined in the "Minimum Indoor Air Quality Performance" prerequisite or a minimum of 0.5 cfm per square foot), in order to create negative pressure with respect to the adjacent spaces when the doors to the room are closed. These types of spaces should also contain self-closing doors and deck-to-deck partition or a hard-lid ceiling. Some example spaces that may contain hazardous materials or chemicals would be the garages, laundry areas, or the copying and printing rooms.

C. <u>**Filtration**</u>: Each ventilation system that supplies outdoor air to the occupied spaces should contain particle filters or air cleaning devices that has a **MERV rating 13 or higher**, in accordance with the **ASHRAE 52.2-2007**, or **Class F7 or higher** as defined by the CEN standard **EN 779-2002**, Particulate Air Filters for General Ventilation, Determination of the Filtration Performance.

All filters should be replaced after construction and before occupancy. For "LEED BD+C: Data Centers", the mentioned requirement will only be applicable to the regularly occupied spaces.

D. <u>**Natural ventilation design calculations**</u>: Under this strategy, the natural ventilation design for the occupied spaces should employ the appropriate strategies in **CIBSE Applications Manual AM10, March 2005, Natural Ventilation in Non-Domestic Buildings, Section 2.4**.

E. <u>**Mixed-mode design calculations**</u>: The mixed-mode system design for the occupied spaces should comply with **CIBSE Applications Manual 13-2000, Mixed Mode Ventilation**.

    📄 Project teams should document;
- <u>For entryway systems</u>: Scaled floor plans indicating locations and measurements of the entryway systems.
- <u>For interior-cross contamination prevention</u>: List of rooms, areas, exhaust rate and separation method.
- <u>For filtration</u>: Mechanical schedules highlighting MERV or class ratings for all the supply air units.
- <u>For natural ventilation design</u>: Calculations and narrative explaining strategies per referenced standard.
- <u>For mixed mode design</u>: Calculations and narrative explaining strategies per referenced standard.

AND/OR

OPTION 2: ADDITIONAL ENHANCED IAQ STRATEGIES — (1 Point)

For the **mechanically ventilated spaces**, project teams should comply with <u>one</u> of the following strategies:

A. Exterior contamination prevention;

B. Increased ventilation;

C. Carbon dioxide monitoring; or

D. Additional source control and monitoring.

For the **naturally ventilated spaces**, project teams should comply with <u>one</u> of the following strategies:

A. Exterior contamination prevention;

B. Additional source control and monitoring; or

C. Natural ventilation room by room calculations.

For the **mixed-mode systems**, project teams should comply with <u>one</u> of the following strategies:

A. Exterior contamination prevention;

B. Increased ventilation;

C. Additional source control and monitoring; or

D. Natural ventilation room-by-room calculations.

Note that option 1 of this credit requires implementing all of the strategies applicable to the project's ventilation type, while option 2 requires implementing only one strategy applicable to the project's ventilation type.

Let's take a closer look at the requirements of each strategy:

A. <u>**Exterior contamination prevention**</u>: Under this strategy, project teams should design the building to minimize and to control the entry of pollutants into the building. Through the **computational fluid dynamics modeling, Gaussian dispersion analyses, wind tunnel modeling,** or **tracer gas modeling**, project teams should ensure that the outdoor air contaminant concentrations at the outdoor air intakes are following the requirements listed in the following table:

Pollutants	Maximum concentration	Referenced Standard
The pollutants regulated by **National Ambient Air Quality Standards**	Allowable annual average OR 8- or 24-hour average where an annual standard does not exist OR Rolling 3 month average	National Ambient Air Quality Standards

Table 29. Maximum concentrations of pollutants at outdoor air intakes

In order to fulfill this strategy, the outdoor air intakes should be located away from the sources of pollutants. Next, the project teams will select one of the mentioned modeling tools and model the contaminant travel at worst case meteorological conditions. The model will be conducted according to the National Ambient Air Quality Standards and will confirm that the concentrations of the pollutants regulated by the National Ambient Air Quality Standards are below the threshold values.

B. <u>**Increased ventilation**</u>: This strategy requires projects to increase the breathing zone ventilation air rates by **at least 30%** above the minimum rates determined in the "Minimum Indoor Air Quality Performance" prerequisite, in all the occupied spaces.

C. <u>**Carbon dioxide monitoring**</u>: In all the densely occupied spaces, projects should monitor carbon dioxide levels. For LEED, densely occupied spaces the areas that contain at least 25 people per 1,000 square feet (93 square meters). Carbon dioxide monitoring devices should have an audible or visual indicator, or alert the building automation system if the carbon dioxide concentrations exceeds the setpoint by **10%** (carbon dioxide setpoint should be calculated using the methods in ASHRAE 62.1-2010, Appendix C).

D. <u>**Additional source control and monitoring**</u>: For all the spaces that area likely to contain contaminants, project teams should address additional contaminants besides carbon dioxide. Firstly, the project teams should plan to reduce the likelihood of contaminant release. Next, monitoring systems with sensors and alarm should be installed to monitor the presence of specific contaminants.

E. <u>**Natural ventilation room by room calculations**</u>: Under this strategy, projects should implement **CIBSE AM10, Section4, Design Calculations** to confirm that room-by-room airflows will provide effective natural ventilation.

📄 Project teams should document;

- **For exterior contamination prevention:** Narrative specifying type of modeling used and provide the model output reports.
- **For increased ventilation:** Since the calculations for increased ventilation are documented under the "Minimum Indoor Air Quality Performance" prerequisite, project teams will only submit a confirmation under this credit.
- **For carbon dioxide monitoring:** List of densely occupied spaces, space type, design CO_2 concentrations, floor plans with sensor locations, and a narrative describing the CO_2 setpoints.
- **For additional source control and monitoring:** A narrative about the likely air contaminants and how they are identified, description of the material handling plan, and plans showing the monitoring system.
- **For natural ventilation:** Room by room calculations, narrative and diagrams demonstrating effective natural ventilation per the referenced standard.

EXEMPLARY PERFORMANCE

To qualify for exemplary performance under this credit, project teams should achieve both "Option 1" and "Option 2", in addition to incorporating an additional "Option 2" strategy.

KEY THINGS TO REMEMBER

- Knowing the title of each strategy and their corresponding ventilation type mentioned under "Option 1" and "Option 2" is essential.
- Grilles, grates, slotted systems, rollout mats can be used in exterior building entrances to capture dirt under the entryway systems strategy. The installed entryway systems should be at least 10 feet (3 meters) long in the primary direction of travel at the regularly used exterior entrances.
- For LEED, densely occupied spaces the areas that contain at least 25 people per 1,000 square feet (93 square meters).
- Under the exterior contamination prevention strategy, through the **computational fluid dynamics modeling**, **Gaussian dispersion analyses**, **wind tunnel modeling**, or **tracer gas modeling**, according to the **National Ambient Air Quality Standards**.
- For enhanced indoor air quality, projects should use supply (outdoor) filters with a MERV rating 13 or higher according to the ASHRAE 52.2-2007.

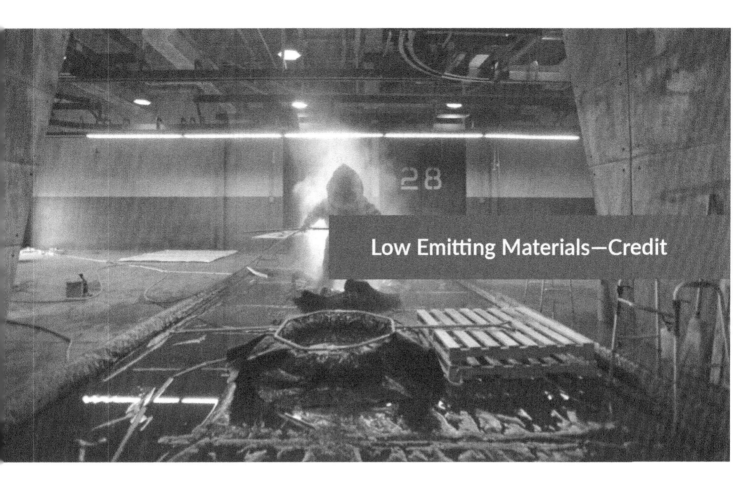

Low Emitting Materials—Credit

▨ Applicable to: All the LEED BD+C Rating Systems

All the LEED BD+C Rating Systems	1 – 3 points

CREDIT SUMMARY

The level of the VOCs contained in the building materials are important to address since during the installation and operation phase of a material, the material will release VOCs indoors; consequently, this will present a serious health hazard to both the construction workers and the building occupants.

Think about epoxy-based paints. During the painting process, their smell is not pleasant at all. They release very strong odors, which can even create a burning feeling in the throat and lungs. This is what a high VOC level can do. In addition to causing harm to the environment, materials with high levels of VOCs can cause asthma, chronic obstructive pulmonary disease, and cancer.

This credit requires certain VOC levels to be met according to both material type and their location in the building; the materials are categorized as either interior material or exterior material. **In LEED, "building interior" is defined as everything inside the waterproofing membrane. "Building exterior" is everything outside the waterproofing membrane inclusive of the waterproofing membrane.**

If the project meets the VOC requirements for some of the building materials, the project teams can use the **budget calculation method** to earn the credit and show that the overall VOC level in the building is less than the required level by calculating the weighted averages of building materials' VOC levels. In LEED, the term "<u>low emitting</u>" always refers to the VOC content.

Inherently nonemitting sources that are products without any VOC emissions do not need to be tested and will be exempt from this credit. Examples of inherently nonemitting sources are ceramic, stone, powder-coated metals, concrete, glass, anodized metal, clay brick, and untreated solid wood flooring.

CREDIT INTENT

Reducing the concentrations of chemical contaminants that may damage air quality, human health, productivity, and the environment.

CREDIT REQUIREMENTS

OPTION 1: PRODUCT CATEGORY CALCULATIONS — (1–3 Points)

There are **7 product categories** with different requirements (the seventh product category is only for "LEED BD+C: Schools" and "LEED BD+C: Healthcare" projects). If the products used on-site achieve the required threshold values of the applicable product categories, then this option could be pursued. If there are some products that can't meet the VOC requirements, project teams should pursue "Option 2" to offset the non-compliant products and earn any partial credit.

Under this option, project teams should identify all applicable products according to the product categories and obtain manufacturer documentation to confirm compliance. The following table shows the product categories and their requirements.

Product categories	Threshold	Emissions and content requirements
Interior paints and coatings applied on-site	At least 90%, by volume, should comply with "general emissions evaluation"; 100% should comply with VOC content requirements	▪ "General emissions evaluation" for paints and coatings applied to walls, floors, and ceilings ▪ VOC content requirements for wet-applied products
Interior adhesives and sealants applied on site (including flooring adhesive)	At least 90%, by volume, should comply with "general emissions evaluation"; 100% should comply with VOC content requirements	▪ "General emissions evaluation" ▪ VOC content requirements for wet-applied products
Flooring	100% should comply	"General Emissions Evaluation"
Composite wood	100% not covered by other categories, should comply	"Composite wood evaluation"
Ceilings, walls, thermal, and acoustic insulation	100% should comply	▪ "General emissions evaluation" ▪ "Additional insulation requirements" (for LEED BD+C: Healthcare and Schools only)
Furniture (include in calculations if part of scope of work)	At least 90%, by cost, should comply	"Furniture evaluation"
Healthcare and Schools only: Exterior applied products	At least 90%, by volume, should comply	"Exterior applied products"

Table 30. Thresholds of compliance with emissions and content standards for 7 material categories

Projects will be awarded points based on the number of compliant product categories as shown on the following table.

Number of compliant product categories	Points
All LEED BD+C projects except "LEED BD+C: Schools" and "LEED BD+C: Healthcare" without furniture	
2	1
4	2
5	3
All LEED BD+C projects except "LEED BD+C: Schools" and "LEED BD+C: Healthcare" with furniture	
3	1
5	2
6	3
LEED BD+C: Schools and Healthcare without furniture	
3	1
5	2
6	3
LEED BD+C: Schools and Healthcare with furniture	
4	1
6	2
7	3

Table 31. Point or points awarded for number of compliant categories of products

Let's take a closer look at the emission and content requirements shown on table 30.

- **General emissions evaluation**: This criterion requires products to be tested and determined compliant in accordance with the **California Department of Public Health (CDPH) Standard Method v1.1-2010.**
- **VOC content requirements for wet-applied products**: Wet-applied products must meet the previous "General emissions evaluation" requirements and additionally meet the applicable limits of the **California Air Resources Board (CARB) 2007, Suggested Control Measure for Architectural Coatings**, or the **South Coast Air Quality Management District (SCAQMD) Rule 1113.**
- **Composite wood evaluation**: Composite wood products should have low formaldehyde emissions and must meet the **California Air Resources Board** formaldehyde requirements.

- ➤ <u>**Furniture evaluation**</u>: New furniture and furnishings items should be tested according to the **ANSI/BIFMA Standard Method M7.1-2011**, and meet the **ANSI/BIFMA e3-2011 Furniture Sustainability Standard Sections 7.6.1 and 7.6.2.**
- ➤ <u>**Additional insulation requirements (for LEED BD+C: Healthcare and School only)**</u>: Batt insulation should not contain formaldehyde.
- ➤ <u>**Exterior applied products (for LEED BD+C: Healthcare and School only)**</u>: Sealants, adhesives, roofing, coatings, and waterproofing materials applied on-site should meet the VOC limits of **California Air Resources Board 2007 Suggested Control Measure for Architectural Coatings** <u>and</u> **South Coast Air Quality Management District, Rule 1168.**

Inherently non-emitting sources do not need to be tested and will be exempt from this credit.

To illustrate let us say that a "LEED BD+C: Retail" project meets the requirements of the following product categories;

- ➤ Flooring
- ➤ Composite word
- ➤ Interior paints and coatings applied on site

However, cannot meet the requirements of the following product categories;

- ➤ Interior adhesives and sealants applied on site
- ➤ Ceilings, walls, thermal, and acoustic insulation

By complying with 3 product categories, the project will receive 1 point under this option (see table 31). Please note that if a project contains furniture in its scope of work, the points awarded will also vary under this option.

OR

OPTION 2: BUDGET CALCULATION METHOD — (1–3 Points)

This option does not contain product categories, rather it organizes the **building interior** into six assemblies (the sixth assembly is only for "LEED BD+C: School" and "LEED BD+C: Healthcare" projects):

- ➤ Flooring
- ➤ Ceilings
- ➤ Walls
- ➤ Thermal and acoustic insulation
- ➤ Furniture (should be included if in the scope of work, otherwise exclude)
- ➤ Exterior applied products (for "LEED BD+C: Schools" and "LEED BD+C: Healthcare" only)

For each assembly type, projects should determine the percentage of compliant materials. The compliant materials should meet the emission and content requirements mentioned under "Option 1".

Once the percentage of compliant materials is calculated for each assembly type, project teams will find their average to determine the points earned. In other words, this option will consider the overall VOC content and emissions. A project with higher VOC content for flooring, but no VOC content for walls, may offset the higher VOC content of flooring and earn points.

To calculate the percentage of compliant materials for each <u>assembly type</u>, project teams will use the following equation:

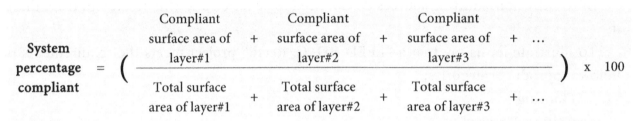

Equation 34. System percentage compliant

If 90% of an assembly meets the criteria, the whole assembly will be counted as 100% compliant. If less than 50% of an assembly meets the criteria, the whole assembly will be counted as 0% compliant. To illustrate, if 45% of the "ceiling" assembly is compliant with the credit's criteria, project teams will need to count it as 0% compliant.

To calculate percentage compliance of the furniture assembly, project teams will need to use the following equation, since the percentage compliance for furniture should be based on cost.

$$\% \text{ Compliance for furniture} = \left(\frac{0.5 \times \text{Cost compliant with 7.6.1 of ANSI/BIFMA} + \text{Cost compliant with 7.6.2 of ANSI/BIFMA}}{\text{Total furniture cost}} \right) \times 100$$

Equation 35. Percentage compliance for furniture

Once the project teams calculate the percentage of compliant products for each assembly type, one of the following equations will be used to determine the total percentage compliance (projects that include furniture in their scope of work will use the equation 37):

$$\text{Total \% compliant for projects without furniture} = \left(\frac{\text{\% compliant walls} + \text{\% compliant ceilings} + \text{\% compliant flooring} + \text{\% compliant insulation}}{4} \right)$$

Equation 36. Total % compliant for projects without furniture

$$\text{Total \% compliant for projects with furniture} = \left(\frac{\text{\% compliant walls} + \text{\% compliant ceilings} + \text{\% compliant flooring} + \text{\% compliant insulation} + \text{\% compliant furniture}}{5} \right)$$

Equation 37. Total % compliant for projects with furniture

According to the total percentage compliance, points will be awarded as follows:

Points for percentage compliance under "Option 2"	
Percentage of total	Points
Between 50% and 69%	1
Between 70% and 89%	2
Equal to or more than 90%	3

Table 32. Point or points for percent compliance

Since the "LEED BD+C: Healthcare" and "LEED BD+C: School" projects will also need to consider the "exterior finishes" as another assembly, they need to use one of the two following formulas to calculate the total percentage compliance:

$$\text{Total \% compliant for projects without furniture} = \left(\frac{\text{\% compliant walls} + \text{\% compliant ceilings} + \text{\% compliant flooring} + \text{\% compliant insulation} + \text{\% compliant exterior finishes}}{5} \right)$$

Equation 38. Total % compliant for projects without furniture for LEED BD+C: Healthcare and Schools

$$\text{Total \% compliant for projects with furniture} = \left(\frac{\text{\% compliant walls} + \text{\% compliant ceilings} + \text{\% compliant flooring} + \text{\% compliant insulation} + \text{\% compliant exterior finishes} + \text{\% compliant furniture}}{6} \right)$$

Equation 39. Total % compliant for projects with furniture for LEED BD+C: Healthcare and Schools

📄 For both "Option 1" and "Option 2", project teams should document the USGBC's low-emitting materials calculator, and the products' information such as MSDS, third-party certifications, or testing reports.

EXEMPLARY PERFORMANCE

To qualify for exemplary performance under this credit, projects pursuing option 1 should earn all points and reach **100%** of products. Projects pursuing option 2 should reach **100%** of products.

CASE STUDY

To illustrate, let us think that a "LEED BD+C: Retail" project aiming for this credit wants to calculate compliance under "Option 2". The project team calculates the percentage of compliant materials for each assembly type, and creates the following table:

Assembly type	% compliant
Flooring	92%
Ceilings	85%
Walls	45%
Thermal and acoustic insulation	80%
Furniture	70%

Please remember, that if 90% of an assembly meets the criteria, the whole assembly will be counted as 100% compliant. If less than 50% of an assembly meets the criteria, the whole assembly will be counted as 0% compliant. With this requirement, the project team adjusts the previous table:

Assembly type	% compliant
Flooring	100%
Ceilings	85%
Walls	0%
Thermal and acoustic insulation	80%
Furniture	70%

With these values, the project team calculates the total percentage compliance according to equation 37:

$$\left(\frac{100 \ + \ 85 \ + \ 0 \ + \ 80 \ + \ 70}{5} \right) \ = \ \textbf{67\%}$$

The project team earns 1 point.

KEY THINGS TO REMEMBER

- Definition of building interior and building exterior.
- Definition of inherently non-emitting sources.
- Purpose of the budget calculation method.
- "LEED BD+C: Healthcare" and "LEED BD+C: School" projects will also need to consider the exterior applied products.
- In "Option 2" if 90% of an assembly meets the criteria, the whole assembly will be counted as 100% compliant. If less than 50% of an assembly meets the criteria, the whole assembly will be counted as 0% compliant.
- Know the product categories and their thresholds under "Option 1", and the assembly types under "Option 2".
- The standards mentioned under this credit and their applicable product types.

Construction Indoor Air Quality Management Plan—Credit

■ Applicable to: All the LEED BD+C Rating Systems

All the LEED BD+C Rating Systems	1 point

CREDIT SUMMARY

This credit requires the implementation of an indoor air quality management plan to reduce exposure of the building occupants to construction dust, toxic substances, or other contaminants. During construction, dust results in indoor contamination, which can stay in the building long after the construction is complete.

Think about the HVAC ducts stored inside the construction area without any dust protection, which after their installation are supposed to provide fresh air to the building occupants; it is clear that the dusty fresh air they will supply will not be very healthy for the building occupants.

This credit sets requirements to ensure a good standard of indoor air quality for building occupants immediately following the construction period. These requirements include the implementation of SMACNA IAQ guidelines, the replacement of the HVAC filtration media before occupancy (if HVAC is used during construction), and prohibiting smoking inside and within 25 feet (7.5 meters) of the building during the construction phase.

In addition, projects also need to implement an **indoor air quality management plan** during the construction and preoccupancy phases in order to prevent molds and moisture damage and increase the HVAC equipment's performance and durability.

For healthcare projects, the credit sets different requirements.

CREDIT INTENT

To promote the well-being of construction crews and building occupants by minimizing indoor air quality problems associated with construction and renovation.

CREDIT REQUIREMENTS

Projects should develop and implement an **indoor air quality** (IAQ) **management plan** for both the <u>construction</u> and <u>preoccupancy phases</u> of the building. The plan must address all of the following:

- During construction, projects should meet or exceed all applicable control measures of the **Sheet Metal and Air Conditioning National Contractors Association (SMACNA) IAQ Guidelines for Occupied Buildings under Construction, 2nd edition, 2007, ANSI/SMACNA 008–2008, Chapter 3**. This really means that project teams should incorporate these standards into the drawings and specifications before construction.

- Projects should protect absorptive materials, which are installed or stored on-site, from moisture damage. (Project teams will also need to photograph their actions and upload those photographs to LEED Online.)

- Permanently installed air-handling equipment should not be operated during construction unless it is operated with filtration media having a minimum efficiency reporting value of **8**, as determined by **ASHRAE 52.2–2007**, with errata,(or as defined in the CEN Standard EN779-2002, Particulate Air Filters for General Ventilation, Determination of the Filtration Performance with filtration media class of **F5 or higher**). The filtration media are installed at each return air grille and return or transfer duct inlet opening. Project teams should ensure that there is no bypass around the filtration media. Just before the occupancy, all the filtration media should be replaced with the designed filtration media.

- The use of tobacco products inside the building and within **25 feet** (7.5 meters) of the building entrance <u>during construction</u> should be prohibited.

It is also strongly advised to use materials with low VOC levels they will seriously affect the indoor air quality. Projects should look for ways to prevent circulation of contaminated air.

📄 All project teams should document compliance with the IAQ management plan or detailed checklist highlighting the no-smoking policy (except "LEED BD+C: Healthcare"), submit a narrative describing protection measures for absorbent materials, submit annotated photos of indoor air and environmental quality measures, and submit a record of the filtration media.

Only for "LEED BD+C: Healthcare" projects:
Healthcare projects should develop an **environmental quality management plan** (EQMP) instead of developing an indoor air quality (IAQ) management plan, and they should address the following requirements;

➥ **Moisture:** Project teams should develop and implement a **moisture control plan** to protect building materials from moisture damage. Any material susceptible to microbial growth should be replaced with new, undamaged material. Project teams should also include strategies for protecting the building from moisture intrusion and for preventing occupants' exposure to mold spores.

➥ **Particulates:** Projects should not operate permanently installed air handling equipment during construction unless filtration media with a certain minimum efficiency are installed at each return air grille and return or transfer duct inlet opening such that there is no bypass around the filtration media. The filtration media must have a minimum efficiency reporting value of **8**—as determined by **ASHRAE 52.2–2007**, with errata (or equivalent filtration media with a class of **F5 or higher**, as defined by CEN Standard EN 779–2002, Particulate Air Filters for General Ventilation, Determination of the Filtration Performance). Immediately before occupancy, project teams should replace all filtration media with the final design filtration media.

➥ **VOCs:** Project teams should take all necessary measures to minimize exposure of absorbent materials to VOC emissions. Project teams should complete painting and sealing before installing the nonemitting materials so that those materials will not accumulate contaminants. Fuels, solvents, and other sources of VOCs should be stored separately from the absorbent materials.

➥ **Outdoor emissions:** For renovation projects involving waterproofing, repairing asphalt roofing, sealing parking lots, or other outdoor activities that generate high VOC emissions, project teams should develop a plan to manage fumes and avoid infiltration to the occupied spaces. Project teams should comply with the procedures established by **NIOSH**, Asphalt Fume Exposures during the Application of Hot Asphalt to Roofs (Publication 2003–112).

➥ **Tobacco:** During construction, project teams should prohibit the use of tobacco products inside the building and within **25 feet** (7.5 meters) of the building entrance.

- **Noise and vibration:** Project teams should develop a plan based on the British Standard (BS 5228) to reduce noise emissions and vibrations from construction equipment and other nonroad engine, by specifying low-noise emission design or the lowest decibel level available that meets performance requirements in the British Standard. Construction crews must wear ear protection in areas where sound levels exceed **85 dB** for extended periods.

- **Infection control:** For renovations and additions adjacent to occupied facilities or for phased occupancy in new construction, project teams should follow the **FGI 2010 Guidelines for Design and Construction of Health Care Facilities** and the **Joint Commission on Standards** to evaluate infection control risk. After the evaluation, the required precautions should be documented in a project-specific plan. Projects should use the infection control risk assessment standard published by the **American Society for Healthcare Engineering** and the **Centers for Disease Control and Prevention (CDC)** as a guideline to evaluate risk and to take necessary mitigation measures during construction.

> Healthcare project teams should document an EQMP or detailed checklist while highlighting a no-smoking policy, submit a narrative describing protection measures for absorbent materials, submit the annotated photos of indoor air and environmental quality measures, and submit a record of the filtration media.

EXEMPLARY PERFORMANCE

This credit does not qualify for exemplary performance.

KEY THINGS TO REMEMBER

- During construction, projects should meet or exceed all applicable control measures of the **Sheet Metal and Air Conditioning National Contractors Association (SMACNA) IAQ Guidelines for Occupied Buildings under Construction, 2nd edition, 2007, ANSI/SMACNA 008–2008, Chapter 3**.
- Project teams should not operate permanently installed air handling equipment during construction unless there is filtration media with a rating of MERV **8**, as determined by **ASHRAE 52.2–2007, with errata** or equivalent filtration media with a class of **F5 or higher**, as defined by CEN Standard EN 779–2002.
- Healthcare projects should develop an environmental quality management plan (EQMP).
- Healthcare projects should address <u>moisture</u>, <u>particulates</u>, <u>VOCs</u>, <u>outdoor emissions</u>, <u>tobacco</u>, <u>noise and vibrations</u>, and <u>infection control</u>.

Indoor Air Quality Assessment—Credit

■ Applicable to: All the LEED BD+C Rating Systems, except **Core and Shell**

All the LEED BD+C Rating Systems except Core and Shell	1 - 2 points

CREDIT SUMMARY

This credit is very similar to the previous "Construction Indoor Air Quality Management Plan" credit, but its requirements are different. The goal is again to provide good indoor air quality to the building occupants after the construction period. However, with this credit, project teams should either remove the air pollution resulting from the construction activities by conducting a **flush-out,** or they should conduct air testing inside the building to determine the air contamination levels and take the necessary actions to clean the contamination. A flush-out refers to the process of supplying a sufficient amount of fresh air to the building before or during occupancy to take away the contaminated air and establish the desired level of indoor air quality.

CREDIT INTENT

To establish better indoor air quality inside the building after construction and during the occupancy phase.

CREDIT REQUIREMENTS

Project teams should choose one of the following options and implement its requirements right after construction ends and the building is completely cleaned. All interior finishes (doors, carpets, ceilings, furnishings, etc.) must be installed, and major VOC punch list items should be completed by the time one of the options below is performed.

OPTION 1: FLUSH-OUT — (1 Point)

Under this option, project teams must pursue one of the following paths: path 1: before occupancy flush-out; or path 2: during occupancy flush-out.

PATH 1: BEFORE OCCUPANCY

As the name implies, under this path, the flush out must be completed before the occupancy.

Projects should install new filtration media after the construction and perform a building flush-out. During the flush-out, **14,000 cubic feet of outdoor air per square foot of gross floor area** should be supplied to the space while maintaining an internal temperature between **60° F and 80° F** (15° C–27° C) and relative humidity no higher than **60%**. The flush-out should be completed in every space of the building.

If any partial work occurs during the flush-out in any space (such as installing furnishings), the flush-out process must be restarted from the beginning for that space. Another thing to note under this option is that, if the project teams use the permanent HVAC system for the flush-out, they will also need to replace the used filters (this is applicable to both path 1 and path 2).

> 💡 Typical ventilation systems supply an airflow of 0.7 cubic feet per minute (cfm) per square foot. The 14,000 cubic feet of outdoor air per square foot of gross floor area value is found by supplying this 0.7 cubic feet per minute (cfm) continuously for two weeks, twenty-four hours a day.

OR

PATH 2: DURING OCCUPANCY

If the project teams choose to conduct the flush out mainly during the occupancy period, this path can be chosen. Under this path, before the occupancy, a minimum of **3,500 cubic feet of outdoor air per square foot of gross floor area** must be provided to the space while maintaining an internal temperature between **60° F and 80° F** (15° C–27° C) and relative humidity no higher than **60%**.

This flush-out process should continue until a <u>total</u> of **14,000 cubic feet of outdoor air per square foot of gross floor area** is delivered to the space. In other words, if the project teams provide 3,500 cubic feet of outdoor air per square foot of gross floor area during the preoccupancy flush-out, the teams will need to provide the remaining 10,500 cubic feet of outdoor air per square foot of gross floor area during the postoccupancy.

After a minimum of 3,500 cubic feet of outdoor air per square foot of gross floor area is provided, the space must be ventilated at a minimum rate of **0.30 cubic foot per minute (cfm) per square foot of outdoor air**, or it should be ventilated at the **design minimum outdoor air rate** determined in the "Minimum Indoor Air Quality Performance" prerequisite, whichever is greater. (If a shorter duration is desired for the flush-out, project teams can choose to increase the ventilation rate with additional equipment.)

During each day of the flush-out, the ventilation should start **three hours before the occupancy** and **continue during the occupancy**. Again, the flush-out should be completed in <u>every space</u> of the building, and if any partial work occurs during the flush-out in any space (such as installing furnishings), the flush-out process must be started from the beginning for that space.

> 🖹 Project teams pursuing any path of option 1 should document the flush-out report. This includes all the HVAC units used (temporary or permanent) and the description of flush-out procedures.

OR

OPTION 2: AIR TESTING — (2 Points)

Under this option, project teams will need to conduct air testing to determine if the contamination levels are above or below the credit's threshold values. If the contamination exceeds the credit's threshold values, project teams should clear the contamination and conduct another test.

To pursue this option, right after construction and **before occupancy**, under the ventilation conditions typical for occupancy, project teams should conduct **baseline indoor air quality testing** by using methods set forth by the USGBC; those are the **ASTM**, **EPA**, and **ISO** methods. The laboratory that will conduct the tests should be accredited under ISO/IEC 17025 for the test methods they use.

The test will evaluate the concentrations of the following:

- Formaldehyde
- Particulates
- Ozone
- Total volatile organic compounds (TVOCs)
- Carbon monoxide (CO)
- Target chemicals listed in the California Department of Public Health (CDPH) Standard Method v1.1, Table 4-1, except formaldehyde

The measurements for the test must take place during normal occupied hours but <u>before the occupancy</u>. The building ventilation system should be running at the normal daily start time and operated at the minimum outdoor airflow rate, just as it would during the occupied hours, throughout the test. So basically, all the conditions should be the same as a typical day in the building, but without the occupants inside the building. It is also important to mention that this option follows the **California Department of Public Health Standard Method v1.1** for testing procedures for VOCs.

Project teams should choose the testing locations with the greatest VOC concentration levels, and the tests must be conducted by accredited personnel. There must be at least one test in each floor of the building. If there are identical spaces (such as the same type of hotel rooms with the same type of materials installed in a hotel project), the project team can conduct the test in every one out of seven rooms, thereby avoiding testing in each identical space. During the test, the measurement equipment must be positioned between **3** and **6 feet** (90 and 180 centimeters) **above the floor**, which is the breathing zone.

The test results should show that the maximum concentration levels of the mentioned contaminants do not exceed the threshold levels set forth by this credit. If any contaminant concentration exceeds the credit's threshold, project teams should take corrective actions and conduct a retest for the noncompliant contaminants at the same **sampling points** (the points where the test was conducted) until all the contamination levels are below the credit's thresholds.

> 🗎 Project teams should provide documentation for the IAQ testing report, including a narrative about the testing procedures that describes how the test locations were chosen, and they should submit the test results.

EXEMPLARY PERFORMANCE

This credit does not qualify for exemplary performance.

CASE STUDY

In this case study, we will demonstrate how a project team will perform the credit calculations for "Option 1—Path 2: During Occupancy." Let's calculate the necessary flush-out volumes and durations for the flush-out of 50,000 square feet of space in an office building. (The project teams should do this flush-out calculation for every space.)

Under this path, the project teams will first need to provide a minimum of 3,500 cubic feet of outdoor air per square foot of gross floor area while maintaining an internal temperature between 60° F and 80° F (15° C–27° C) and relative humidity not higher than 60%.

Net space area: 50,000 square foot

Total outdoor air to be provided before occupancy:

50,000 x 3,500 = **175,000,000 cubic feet**

And let us say that the air handler's air capacity is **10,000 cubic feet per minute**.

Using that information, the duration of the preoccupancy flush-out would be as follows:

175,000,000 / 10,000 = **17,500 minutes**, if we convert this number to days;

17,500 / (60x24) = **12.15 days**

Now we can say that if the project teams operate the air handler 24 hours a day during the preoccupancy flush-out, they will need to continue the process for 12.15 days.

Now let's calculate the necessary flush-out durations for the postoccupancy period. The project team now needs to provide the remaining 10,500 cubic feet of outdoor air per square foot of gross floor area while maintaining an internal temperature between 60° F and 80° F (15° C–27° C) and relative humidity not higher than 60%.

Total outdoor air to be provided after occupancy:

50,000 x 10,500 = **525,000,000 cubic feet**

But the air handler's air capacity is **10,000 cubic feet per minute**.

Remember that under path 2, the space must be ventilated at a minimum rate of 0.30 cubic feet per minute (cfm) per square foot of outdoor air, or it must be ventilated at the design minimum outdoor air rate determined in the "Minimum Indoor Air Quality Performance" prerequisite, whichever is greater.

If we say that the design minimum outdoor air rate determined in the "Minimum Indoor Air Quality Performance" prerequisite is 0.20 cubic feet per minute (cfm) per square foot of outdoor air, the project teams will need to ventilate the building at a minimum rate of 0.30 cubic feet per minute (cfm) per square foot of outdoor air. Let's confirm if the air handler can provide that rate:

0.30 x 50,000 = 15,000 cubic feet per minute

The air handler's air capacity is 10,000 cubic feet per minute, so in this case, the project team should find more equipment to provide the additional 5,000 cubic feet per minute to the space. If we assume that the additional equipment is installed to provide the remaining 5,000 cubic feet per minute to the space, the duration of the postoccupancy flush-out would be:

525,000,000 / 15,000 = **35,000 minutes**, if we convert this number to days;

35,000 / (60x24) = **24.30 days**

Now we can say that if the project team operates the air handler and the additional equipment 24 hours a day during the postoccupancy flush-out, the process will take 24.3 days.

Below is the credit's formula for these calculations. However, it's not recommend to memorize it since it can be easily created on the exam by thoroughly understanding the calculations.

$$\textbf{Duration of flush-out (days)} = \frac{\text{Area (ft}^2\text{) x 14,000 cfm}}{\text{Air handler capacity (days) / (1440 minutes/day)}}$$

Equation 40. Duration of flush-out

Note that in the formula, the 14,000 cfm value will be changed according to each path under option 1 of this credit. So it could also become 10,500 cfm or 3,500 cfm. Also note that the air handler capacity in the formula is in days, not minutes.
That's the reason the formula contains the 1440 minutes/day value. (There are 1,440 minutes in a day—60 minutes per hour x 24 hours per day = 1440.)

KEY THINGS TO REMEMBER

■ All interior finishes (<u>doors</u>, <u>carpets</u>, <u>ceiling</u>, <u>furnishings,</u> etc.) must be installed, and major VOC punch list items should be completed by the time one of the two options is performed.

■ During the flush-out, an internal temperature between **60° F and 80° F** (15° C–27° C) and relative humidity no higher than **60%** should be maintained, and the flush-out should be completed in <u>every space</u> of the building.

■ Under option 2, project teams should conduct **baseline indoor air quality testing** by using methods set forth by the USGBC, which are **ASTM**, **EPA**, and **ISO** methods.

■ Option 2 of this credit follows the **California Department of Public Health Standard Method v1.1** for the VOCs' testing procedures.

■ The air test in Option 2 will evaluate the concentrations of formaldehyde, particulates, ozone, total volatile organic compounds (TVOCs), carbon monoxide (CO), and some chemicals listed in the California Department of Public Health (CDPH) Standard Method v1.1, Table 4-1, except formaldehyde, and the measurements for the test must take place during normal occupied hours, but before the occupancy.

Thermal Comfort—Credit

- Applicable to: All the LEED BD+C Rating Systems, except **Core and Shell**

All the LEED BD+C Rating Systems except Core and Shell	1 point

CREDIT SUMMARY

Thermal comfort is one of the top priority measures to increase occupant comfort, which is defined by a combination of six factors: air temperature, humidity, surface temperature, air movement, metabolic rate, and clothing. The thermal comfort ranges will be different for different individuals in an office space.

Building users who are given thermal controls for their spaces will exhibit additional satisfaction and productivity. Giving occupants local temperature controls for **+/- 5⁰ F** will be enough to increase their productivity by 2.7% to 7%.[1]

The credit requires projects to increase the comfort of the building occupants through the implementation of quality thermal comfort design and the provision of thermal comfort controls to at least **50%** of the individual occupant spaces.

CREDIT INTENT

To promote building occupants' productivity, comfort, and well-being by providing quality thermal comfort.

CREDIT REQUIREMENTS

Project teams must meet the requirements for both <u>thermal comfort design</u> and <u>thermal comfort control</u>.

Thermal comfort design:

<u>For all LEED BD+C projects, except "LEED BD+C: Warehouses and Distribution Centers"</u>: (This credit doesn't apply to LEED BC+C: Core and Shell)

To address thermal comfort design, project teams must choose one of the following options (Whether the building uses natural ventilation, mechanical ventilation, or mixed-mode ventilation, the following requirements should be reflected according to the ventilation type as stated in the standard.)

OPTION 1: ASHRAE STANDARD 55-2010

Under this option, project teams should design <u>HVAC systems</u> and the <u>building envelope</u> to meet the requirements of **ASHRAE Standard 55–2010, Thermal Comfort Conditions for Human Occupancy, with errata** or a local equivalent.

For natatoriums only, projects should demonstrate compliance with **ASHRAE HVAC Applications Handbook, 2011 edition, Chapter 5, Places of Assembly, Typical Natatorium Design Conditions, with errata.**

OR

OPTION 2: ISO AND CEN STANDARDS

Under this option, project teams should design the <u>HVAC systems</u> and the <u>building envelope</u> to meet the requirements of the following applicable standard:

- **ISO 7730:2005, Ergonomics of the Thermal Environment, analytical determination and interpretation of thermal comfort** using calculation of the predicted mean vote (PMV) and predicted percentage of dissatisfied (PPD) indices and local thermal comfort criteria (The PMV and PPD indices are found by placing test participants in climate chambers and recording their level of comfort on a scale.)

- **CEN Standard EN 15251:2007, Indoor Environmental Input Parameters for Design and Assessment of Energy Performance of Buildings**, addressing indoor air quality, thermal environment, lighting, and acoustics, Section A2.

"LEED BD+C: Data Center" projects should meet one of these options only for the <u>regularly occupied spaces</u> since the data storage rooms will require different thermal qualities.

One thing to note under this credit is that project teams choosing option 1 of the thermal comfort design, which is ASHRAE Standard 55-2010, should oversee acceptable comfort ranges at all the combinations of conditions that are expected to occur, and they may also need to estimate personal factors such as clothing and activity levels and then install systems that can maintain the calculated comfort levels under all of these conditions.

Option 2 of the thermal comfort design, which has the ISO and CEN standards, also requires similar actions, so the project teams should address different ranges of comfort for specific building types and number of occupants in accordance with the applicable standards. For example, in ISO 7730:2005 and EN 15251:2007, the suggested PMV levels change for different occupant types, such as sensitive occupants like elderly or ill people.

<u>For "LEED BD+C: Warehouses and Distribution Centers":</u>
For the office portions of the building, "LEED BD+C: Warehouses and Distribution Centers" projects should meet the requirements above like the other rating systems.

Additionally, for the regularly occupied spaces of the building's <u>bulk storage</u>, <u>sorting</u>, and <u>distribution areas</u>, project teams should implement one or more of the following design alternatives:

- Radiant flooring
- Circulating fans
- Passive systems, such as heat venting, nighttime air, or wind flow
- Localized active cooling (refrigerant- or evaporative-based systems) or heating systems
- Localized, hard-wired fans that provide air movement for occupants' comfort
- Other equivalent thermal comfort strategies

Thermal comfort control:

<u>For all LEED BD+C projects, except "LEED BD+C: Healthcare"</u>:
(This credit doesn't apply to LEED BD+C Core and Shell)

To address thermal comfort controls, projects should provide <u>individual thermal comfort controls</u> to **at least 50% of the individual occupant spaces**. Additionally, projects should provide <u>group thermal comfort controls</u> for all shared multioccupant spaces. (Again, whether the building uses natural ventilation, mechanical ventilation, or mixed-mode ventilation, the following requirements should be reflected according to the ventilation type under the mentioned standards.)

The acceptable thermal comfort controls would be adjustable underfloor diffusers, operable windows, task mounted controls, or more. Any thermal comfort control without any accessible control or adjustable control cannot satisfy the credit's requirements.

All the thermal comfort controls provided should allow occupants to adjust at least one of the following in their local environment: <u>air temperature</u>, <u>radiant temperature</u>, <u>air speed</u>, and <u>humidity</u>.

For "LEED BD+C: Retail" projects, project teams should meet the mentioned requirements for **50%** of the individual occupant spaces in <u>office</u> and <u>administrative areas</u>.

For the projects under the "LEED BD+C: Hospitality" rating system, LEED assumes that these projects already provide adequate thermal comfort controls to the guest rooms, and therefore it excludes them from credit calculations.

<u>For "LEED BD+C: Healthcare"</u>:
To address thermal comfort controls, "LEED BD+C: Healthcare" projects should provide <u>individual thermal comfort controls</u> for **every patient room** and at least **50% of the remaining individual occupant spaces**. Additionally, projects should provide <u>group thermal comfort controls</u> for all shared multioccupant spaces.

Again, all the thermal comfort controls provided, whether in individual spaces or shared multioccupant spaces, should allow occupants to adjust at least one of the following in their local environment: <u>air temperature</u>, <u>radiant temperature</u>, <u>air speed</u>, and <u>humidity</u>.

> 📄 For documenting option 1 of "Thermal Comfort Design," project teams should submit the weather data used and the calculation results that verify that the design parameters meet the required standards.

📄 For documenting option 2 of "Thermal Comfort Design," projects should submit verification that shows that thermally conditioned spaces meet the required standards.

📄 For documenting "Thermal Comfort Control," projects should submit the list of spaces by their type and the quantity of thermal comfort controls.

📄 Project teams of the "LEED BD+C: Warehouses and Distribution Centers" projects should document the list of regularly occupied bulk storage, sorting, and distribution areas, and they should submit a narrative describing the design strategy used in each space.

EXEMPLARY PERFORMANCE

This credit does not qualify for exemplary performance.

KEY THINGS TO REMEMBER

■ Thermal comfort is one of the top priority measures to increase occupant comfort. Thermal comfort is defined by a combination of six factors: air temperature, humidity, surface temperature, air movement, metabolic rate, and clothing.

■ All the thermal comfort controls provided should allow occupants to adjust at least one of the following in their local environment: air temperature, radiant temperature, air speed, and humidity.

■ "LEED BD+C: Retail" projects should meet the mentioned requirements for **50%** of the individual occupant spaces in office and administrative areas.

■ For "LEED BD+C: Hospitality", LEED assumes that projects already provide adequate thermal comfort controls to the guest rooms, and therefore it excludes them from the credit calculations.

■ To address thermal comfort controls, "LEED BD+C: Healthcare" projects should provide individual thermal comfort controls for every patient room and at least **50%** of the remaining individual occupant spaces.

■ **ISO 7730:2005, Ergonomics of the Thermal Environment** uses calculation of the predicted mean vote (PMV) and predicted percentage of dissatisfied (PPD) indices.

■ Applicable to: All the LEED BD+C Rating Systems, except **Core and Shell**

New Construction	1 – 2 points	Data Centers	1 – 2 points	Healthcare	1 point
Schools	1 – 2 points	Warehouses & Dist. Centers	1 – 2 points		
Retail	2 points	Hospitality	1 – 2 points		

CREDIT SUMMARY

Just like thermal comfort, interior lighting is a factor that affects the productivity and comfort of building occupants. In summary, carefully illuminated spaces with lighting controls provided for individuals and groups result in increased comfort levels and productivity rates.

This credit addresses interior lighting by requiring the projects to provide lighting controls for at least **90%** of the individual occupant spaces under option 1, and/or projects can follow the lighting quality standards defined under option 2 to implement a higher quality lighting design. For LEED BD+C: Retail and LEED BD+C: Healthcare, the credit requires different criteria and does not contain two options.

To measure the amount of illumination that falls onto a surface, the term **footcandle** is used; a footcandle is equal to one lumen per square foot.

CREDIT INTENT

To promote building occupants' productivity, comfort, and well-being by providing quality lighting.

CREDIT REQUIREMENTS

<u>For all LEED BD+C projects, except "LEED BD+C: Retail" and "LEED BD+C: Healthcare"</u>:
(This credit does not apply to LEED BD+C: Core and Shell)

Project teams should pursue one or both of the following two options.

OPTION 1: LIGHTING CONTROL – (1 Point)

Under this option, project teams should provide <u>individual lighting controls</u> that enable occupants to adjust the lighting to suit their preferences for **at least 90% of the individual occupant spaces**. The individual lighting should contain **at least three lighting levels (on, off, midlevel)**, and the midlevel should be between 30% and 70% of the maximum illumination level (daylight contributions are not included).

Additionally, for **all the shared multioccupant spaces**, projects should meet all of the following requirements:

- ➤ Provide <u>multizone control systems</u> that enable occupants to adjust the lighting to meet the group needs and preferences with at least three lighting levels or scenes (on, off, midlevel).
- ➤ Lighting for any presentation or projection wall should be separately controlled by the occupants.
- ➤ Switches or manual controls must be in the same space with the controlled luminaires. The person operating the controls should be able to have a direct line of sight to the controlled luminaires.

Note that 90% of the individual occupant spaces and 100% of the shared multioccupant spaces must meet the credit requirements, and these percentages are based on the <u>number of spaces</u> and are not based on the floor area.

For the projects under the "LEED BD+C: Hospitality" rating system, LEED assumes these projects already provide adequate lighting controls to the guest rooms and therefore <u>excludes</u> the guest rooms from the credit calculations. (This is similar to the "Thermal Comfort" credit; in this instance, LEED assumes that the "LEED BD+C: Hospitality" projects already provide adequate thermal comfort controls to the guest rooms and therefore excludes them from the credit calculations.)

📄 Project teams should document the table of individual occupant and multioccupant spaces and the lighting controls in each space.

AND/OR

OPTION 2: LIGHTING QUALITY — (1 Point)

Under this option, project teams should choose four of the following eight strategies.

1. Use lighting fixtures with a luminance of less than **2,500 cd/m² between 45 and 90 degrees from nadir** in the regularly occupied spaces. (Wallwash fixtures properly aimed at walls, indirect uplighting fixtures, and any other specific applications such as adjustable fixtures are excluded).

2. Use light sources with a **color rendering index (CRI) of 80 or higher** for the entire project. (Lamps or fixtures specifically designed to use color lighting for effect, site lighting, and any other special-use lighting are exempt.)

3. For at least 75% of the total connected lighting load, use light sources that have a rated life (or L70 for LED sources) of at least **24,000 hours** (at 3 hours per start, if applicable). To calculate the total connected lighting load, project teams can use the lighting power calculations prepared under the "Minimum Energy Performance" prerequisite.

4. Use <u>direct-only overhead lighting</u> for **25% or less of the total connected lighting load** for <u>all regularly occupied spaces</u>. Again, to calculate the total connected lighting load, project teams can use the lighting power calculations prepared under the "Minimum Energy Performance" prerequisite.

5. For at least 90% of the regularly occupied floor area, projects should meet or exceed the following thresholds for area-weighted average surface reflectance: 85% for ceilings, 60% for walls, and 25% for floors.

6. Select furniture (if included in the scope of work) to meet the following thresholds for area-weighted average surface reflectance: 45% for work surfaces and 50% for movable partitions.

7. For at least 75% of the regularly occupied floor area, the ratio of average <u>wall surface illuminance</u> (excluding fenestration) to average <u>work surface illuminance</u> should not exceed **1:10**. Projects must also meet strategy 5, strategy 6, or demonstrate an area-weighted surface reflectance of at least 60% for walls.

8. For at least **75% of the regularly occupied floor area**, the ratio of average <u>ceiling illuminance</u> (excluding fenestration) to <u>work surface illuminance</u> should not exceed **1:10**. Projects must also meet strategy 5, strategy 6, or demonstrate an area-weighted surface reflectance of at least 85% for ceilings.

Following is the equation to calculate the area-weighted average surface reflectances for strategies 5 and 6, which is basically the typical weighted average equation.

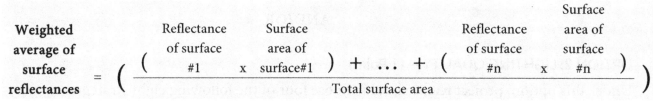

$$\text{Weighted average of surface reflectances} = \left(\frac{\left(\text{Reflectance of surface \#1} \times \text{Surface area of surface\#1} \right) + \dots + \left(\text{Reflectance of surface \#n} \times \text{Surface area of surface \#n} \right)}{\text{Total surface area}} \right)$$

Equation 41. Weighted average of surface reflectances

Following are the equations to be used for strategies 7 and 8 respectively:

$$\text{Wall to work plane illuminance ratio} = 1 : \left(\frac{\text{Average work surface illuminance}}{\text{Average wall surface illuminance}} \right)$$

Equation 42. Wall to work plane illuminance ratio

$$\text{Ceiling to work plane illuminance ratio} = 1 : \left(\frac{\text{Average work surface illuminance}}{\text{Average ceiling surface illuminance}} \right)$$

Equation 43. Ceiling to work plane illuminance ratio

These strategies may seem confusing at first, so let's discuss these strategies one by one:

1. This strategy is about minimizing lighting fixture luminance. To describe "luminance," we should first describe "illuminance." "Illuminance" is basically the intensity of light falling on a unit area on a surface. The higher the intensity of the light source, the higher the illuminance. Also, the closer to the light source, the higher the illuminance, and the farther away from the light source, the lower the illuminance. The "luminance" is the intensity of light emitted from a surface per unit area in a direction. So we are talking about the lighting intensity when the light—coming from a light source—hits an object and comes to your eye. Luminance does not define the direct light. When designing buildings, only considering the illuminance values would not create a quality lighting design; however, considering the luminance values will make a difference. That's because in this scenario, the lighting team will consider the amount of light reflected from the objects in addition to the intensity of light generated by the light source. That being said, the building materials' reflectance values will also have an impact on the "luminance" values. Going back to evaluating the strategy, this strategy requires projects to use lighting fixtures with a luminance of less than **2,500 cd/m² between 45 and 90 degrees from nadir** in the regularly occupied spaces in order to reduce discomforting glare.

2. This strategy is about increasing the rendering quality of the light source. The color rendering index (CRI), which is basically a scale between 0 and 100, measures the ability of

a light source to precisely render all the frequencies of its color. In other words, light sources with low CRI will reproduce fewer accurate colors, and the higher-CRI lamps will render color equally. To summarize, CRI is not about the color of the lamp but about the lamp's rendering quality. Under this strategy, LEED requires the use of light sources with **CRI above 80**, which is closer to natural lighting.

3. This strategy is about increasing the lamp life and promotes using longer-life light sources.

4. Using direct overhead lighting will increase glare and contrast. This strategy aims to reduce glare and contrast by encouraging projects to minimize direct overhead lighting.

5. Using surfaces with higher reflectance will make the space brighter because of the reflection that these surfaces will provide.

6. This strategy requires projects to use high-reflectance furniture and make the space brighter because of the reflection that these surfaces will provide.

7. This strategy aims to reduce the amount of contrast inside the space by designing for an illuminance ratio of 1:10 between the <u>wall</u> and the occupants' work surface.

8. As with the previous strategy, this strategy aims to reduce the amount of contrast inside the space by designing for an illuminance ratio of 1:10 between the <u>ceiling</u> and the occupants' work surface.

📄 For the corresponding strategy pursued, projects should document the following:

1. Table of regularly occupied spaces and associated lighting details, including manufacturer and model, estimation results, or in situ or laboratory photometric tests

2. Lighting details, including manufacturer and model, estimation results, or in situ or laboratory photometric tests

3. Calculations of total connected lighting loads and lighting details, including manufacturer and model, estimation results, or in situ or laboratory photometric tests

4. Table of regularly occupied spaces and associated lighting details, including manufacturer and model, estimation results, or in situ or laboratory photometric tests and calculations of total connected lighting load

5. List of ceiling, wall, and floor surfaces and their surface reflectance values and the average surface reflectance calculations

6. List of work surfaces and movable partitions with their surface reflectance values and the average surface reflectance calculations

7. List of work surfaces and illuminance values (lux) and illuminance ratio calculations

8. List of wall or ceiling surface with illuminance values (lux) and illuminance ratio calculations

For "LEED BD+C: Retail":

Retail projects only have one option, and they should provide <u>individual lighting controls</u> to **at least 90% of the individual occupant spaces** in <u>office</u> and <u>administrative areas</u>.

In the sales area, projects should provide controls that can reduce the ambient light levels to a midlevel. The midlevel should be between 30% and 70% of the maximum illumination level (daylight contributions are not included).

For "LEED BD+C: Healthcare":

Healthcare projects should provide individual lighting controls for at least **90% of individual occupant spaces in staff areas.**

For at least **90%** of patient positions, projects should provide lighting controls that are readily accessible from the patient's bed. In the <u>multioccupant patient spaces</u>, the controls must be individual lighting controls. In private rooms, project teams should additionally provide <u>exterior window shades</u>, <u>blinds</u>, or <u>curtain controls</u> that are readily accessible from the patient's bed. (In-patient critical care, pediatric, and psychiatric patient rooms are excluded.)

In all the shared multioccupant spaces (not the multioccupant <u>patient</u> spaces), projects should provide multizone control systems that enable occupants to adjust the lighting to meet group needs and preferences, with at least three lighting levels or scenes (on, off, midlevel). Again, the midlevel should be between 30% and 70% of the maximum illumination level (daylight contributions are not included).

EXEMPLARY PERFORMANCE

This credit does not qualify for exemplary performance.

KEY THINGS TO REMEMBER

- Option 2, strategy 1 excludes <u>wallwash fixtures properly aimed at walls</u>, <u>indirect uplighting fixtures</u>, and <u>any other specific applications</u> such as adjustable fixtures.
- Option 2, strategy 2 excludes <u>lamps or fixtures specifically designed to use color lighting for effect</u>, <u>site lighting</u>, or <u>any other special use lighting</u>.
- For the projects under the "LEED BD+C: Hospitality" rating system, LEED assumes these projects already provide adequate lighting controls to the guest rooms, and it therefore excludes the guest rooms from the credit calculations.
- In LEED, the lighting midlevel should be between 30% and 70% of the maximum illumination level. (Daylight contributions are not included.)
- Footcandle is a measurement of the amount of illumination that falls on a surface; one footcandle is equal to one lumen per square foot.
- For the lighting requirements, LEED commonly refers to the Illuminating Engineering Society (IES).

Daylight—Credit

■ Applicable to: All the LEED BD+C Rating Systems

New Construction	1 - 3 points	Retail	1 - 3 points	Hospitality	1 - 3 points
Core and Shell	1 - 3 points	Data Centers	1 - 3 points	Healthcare	1 - 2 points
Schools	1 - 3 points	Warehouses & Dist. Centers	1 - 3 points		

CREDIT SUMMARY

Studies show that increased access to daylight presents lots of benefits to human health and psychology. Exposure to daylight improves student performances[2] and patient healing times, increases productivity in offices,[3] and also helps to fight depression. By introducing daylight into interior spaces, the projects will also reduce their lighting costs. However, the project teams should also consider the heat gains and losses that will result from daylighting.

This credit sets requirements for daylight qualities and levels, and its points are awarded according to the daylight modeling process used and the percentage of floor area with daylight access.

To maximize daylight in interior spaces, transparent partitions—such as interior windows placed in walls or doors—or interior glazing can be used. Low-height partitions in open offices can also increase the amount of daylight.

One problem with daylighting is the glare. The use of glare control devices is required in this credit, such as operable window blinds or curtains.

Fixed-glare control devices—such as fixed exterior overhangs, fixed fins, fixed louvres, dark color glazing, frit glazing treatment, or additional glazing treatments—will not satisfy this credit. Acceptable glare control devices include interior window blinds, shades, curtains, moveable exterior louvres, moveable screens, and moveable awnings.

This credit also mentions **spatial daylight autonomy (sDA)**, which is a metric used to describe the annual sufficiency of ambient daylight in building interiors. In other words, sDA is the metric to describe if there is enough daylight in the space or not.

As mentioned, excessive daylighting can cause glare and excessive heat gains. This credit also mentions **annual sunlight exposure (ASE)**, which is a metric to describe the potential glare and potential heat gains in the space and is used to limit excessive daylighting. In other words, it shows the percentage of an area that exceeds the required direct sunlight illuminance level beyond a specified number of hours per year.

CREDIT INTENT

Connect building occupants with the outdoors, reinforce circadian rhythms, and reduce energy consumption of electrical lighting by using daylighting.

CREDIT REQUIREMENTS

Projects pursuing any option should provide **manual or automatic glare control devices with manual overrides for all the regularly occupied spaces.**

Project teams should select either one of the three options below. Option 1 and option 2 require a computer simulation, and option 3 does not require any modeling and is created mainly for renovation projects.

OPTION 1: SIMULATION: SPATIAL DAYLIGHT AUTONOMY AND ANNUAL SUNLIGHT EXPOSURE — (2-3 Points)

Under this option, project teams should implement a computer simulation and demonstrate that **spatial daylight autonomy 300/50%** (sDA300/50%) of at least **55%**, **75%**, or **90%** is achieved. All LEED BD+C projects except "LEED BD+C: Healthcare" should consider the **regularly occupied floor areas** in the simulation, while the "LEED BD+C: Healthcare" projects should consider the **perimeter area** determined under the "Quality Views" credit. (The "perimeter area" will be explained in depth under the "Quality Views" credit. For now, it can be defined as the floor area within 15 feet of the perimeter.) The following table shows the number of points awarded according to simulation results:

All LEED rating systems except LEED BD+C: Healthcare		Only for LEED BD+C: Healthcare	
sDA for regularly occupied floor area	Points	sDA for perimeter floor area	Points
55%	2	75%	1
75%	3	90%	2

Table 33. Points awarded according to the simulation results

After the sDA requirements have been met, the projects should additionally meet the ASE requirements. By performing computer simulations, project teams should demonstrate that **annual sunlight exposure 1000,250** (ASE1000,250) of **no more than 10%** is achieved for each analysis area. Project teams should use the regularly occupied floor spaces that are daylit per the sDA300/50% simulations.

For both simulations, an hourly time-step analysis based on meteorological data should be used, and projects should include any permanent interior obstructions to sunlight in the project model. Movable furniture and partitions can be excluded.

When doing the sDA and ASE calculations on the simulation, each space should be divided with horizontal grids, and the sDA and ASE measurements should be conducted in each little square that is formed by the grids. The credit requires dividing regularly occupied spaces with grids no more than 2 feet (60 centimeters) square at a work plane height of 30 inches (76 centimeters) above the finished floor.

For "LEED BD+C: Core and Shell" projects, if the finishes in the regularly occupied spaces will not be completed, projects can assume an 80% surface reflectance for ceilings, 20% surface reflectance for floors, and 50% surface reflectance for walls. The entire floor, except the core part, should be assumed to be a regularly occupied space.

- All project teams pursuing any option should submit floor plans highlighting the regularly occupied spaces. (Teams for healthcare projects should highlight the regularly occupied perimeter area.) Project teams should also submit a list of glare control devices for all the windows, including their control mechanism.
- Project teams pursuing option 1 should additionally document a list of compliant spaces with their annual summary values for sDA and ASE, geometric plot from simulations, and a narrative describing the daylight simulation program, inputs, and the weather file.

OR

OPTION 2: SIMULATION: ILLUMINANCE CALCULATIONS – (1-2 Points)

With the use of computer modeling, projects should demonstrate that the illuminance levels in the regularly occupied floor area would be **between 300 lux and 3,000 lux for 9:00 a.m. and 3:00 p.m.** (both on a clear-sky day at the equinox). Points will be awarded according to the compliant floor area percentages indicated in the table below. As is the case in option 1, all LEED BD+C projects except "LEED BD+C: Healthcare" should consider the **regularly occupied floor areas** while the "LEED BD+C: Healthcare" projects should consider the **perimeter area.**

All LEED rating systems except LEED BD+C: Healthcare		Only for "LEED BD+C: Healthcare	
% compliant regularly occupied floor area	Points	% compliant perimeter floor area	Points
75%	1	75%	1
90%	2	90%	2

Table 34. Points awarded according to the simulation results

Project teams should calculate the illuminance intensity for sun (direct component) and sky (diffuse component) to be used during the simulation. In order to calculate them, project teams will need to use the meteorological year data of the nearest available weather station. Next, project teams will select one day within **15 days of September 21** and the other day within **15 days of March 21** that will represent the <u>clearest sky condition</u>. After the two days are determined, the project teams will calculate and use the average of the hourly illuminance values for these two selected days.

With this data, project teams will conduct a simulation and calculate the percentage of floor area between 300 lux and 3,000 lux, at 9:00 a.m. and 3:00 p.m. to determine the point(s) earned. A floor area that is found to be 500 lux at 9:00 a.m. and 100 lux at 3:00 p.m. cannot be considered compliant. Compliant floor areas should meet the requirements for both 9:00 a.m. and 3:00 p.m. The compliant floor area can be a portion of the whole regularly occupied space as well. In other words, if the 900 square feet of the 1,000-sqare-foot regularly occupied space meets the requirements, this will mean that 90% of that floor area will still be considered compliant under this credit (see the "case study").

<u>Blinds</u> or <u>shades</u>, <u>moveable furniture</u>, and <u>partitions</u> may be excluded from the model. <u>Any permanent interior obstructions</u> to sunlight should be included.

As is the case for option 1, if the finishes in the regularly occupied spaces will not be completed for "LEED BD+C: Core and Shell" projects, project teams can assume an 80% surface reflectance for ceilings, 20% surface reflectance for floors, and 50% surface reflectance for walls. The entire floor, except the core part, should be assumed to be a regularly occupied space.

📄 All project teams pursuing any option should submit floor plans highlighting the regularly occupied spaces. (Teams for healthcare projects should highlight the regularly occupied perimeter area.) Project teams should also provide a list of glare control devices for all the windows, including their control mechanism.

📄 Additionally, projects pursuing option 2 should document geometric plot simulations, a narrative describing the daylight simulation program, inputs and weather file, and a list of compliant spaces with their calculated illuminance values.

OR

OPTION 3: MEASUREMENT — (2-3 Points)

Under this option, projects should achieve illuminance levels **between 300 lux** and **3,000 lux** for the percentage of floor area shown on table 36. One thing to note is that, in order to determine these illuminance levels, project teams will not create a simulation. Instead, they will conduct measurements on-site after the construction is complete and people have occupied the space.

As is the case for all the options in this credit, all LEED BD+C projects except "LEED BD+C: Healthcare" should consider the **regularly occupied floor areas** while the "LEED BD+C: Healthcare" projects should consider the **perimeter area**.

Between 9:00 a.m. and 3:00 p.m.—with furniture, fixtures and equipment all in place— project teams should measure the illuminance levels at appropriate work plane height. There must be two measurements. The first measurement should be in any **regularly occupied month**, while the second measurement should be in a regularly occupied month as specified in the following table. Regularly occupied month means that the measurement must be conducted during the building's regularly occupied periods. In other words, a school project cannot conduct a measurement in a month that is in the school break period.

If the first measurement is in,	then the second measurement should be in,
January	May–September
February	June–October
March	June–July, November–December
April	August–December
May	September–January
June	October–February
July	November–March
August	December–April
September	December–January, May–June
October	February–June
November	March–July
December	April–August

Table 35

Spaces larger than 150 square feet (14 square meters) should have their measurements on a maximum 10-foot (3-meter) square grid, and spaces smaller than 150 square feet (14 square meters) should have their measurements on a maximum 3-foot (900-millimeter) square grid.

Points will be awarded according to the compliant floor area percentages indicated in the following table.

All LEED rating systems except LEED BD+C: Healthcare		Only for LEED BD+C: Healthcare	
% compliant regularly occupied floor area	Points	% compliant perimeter floor area	Points
75%	2	75%	1
90%	3	90%	2

Table 36. Points awarded according to measurement results

📄 All project teams pursuing any option should submit floor plans highlighting the regularly occupied spaces. (Teams for healthcare projects should highlight the regularly occupied perimeter area.) Teams should also provide a list of glare control devices for all the windows, including their control mechanism.

📄 Project teams pursuing option 3 should document floor plans or a list of compliant spaces with their measured illuminance values for each node, and they should provide calculations that demonstrate the percentage of compliant spaces between 300 lux and 3,000 lux.

EXEMPLARY PERFORMANCE

This credit does not qualify for exemplary performance.

CASE STUDY

The project team of a LEED BD+C: New Construction project pursuing option 2 of this credit want to calculate compliance with this credit. The project teams create a list that shows all the regularly occupied spaces in the building and their corresponding floor area. Next, the project teams obtain the meteorological year data from the nearest weather station. According to their study, the project team determines that the clearest sky conditions that are within 15 days of September 21 and within 15 days of March 21, are on September 17 and March 27.

Now the project team calculates the average of the hourly illuminance values for September 17 and March 27.

With this data, project teams conduct a simulation and create the following table:

Regularly Occupied Space	Total floor area (sqft)	Compliant floor area (sqft)
Room 101	1,000	800
Room 102	2,000	1,800
Room 201	500	400
Room 203	900	500
Room 204	1,500	1,300
Total	5,900	4,800

The compliant floor area column of the table above indicates the floor area that is measured to be between 300 lux and 3,000 lux for both 9:00 a.m. and 3:00 p.m. With these results, the project teams confirm that **81%** of all the regularly occupied spaces meet the credit's requirements, and the project earns 1 point under option 2.

Remember that all projects should also provide manual glare control devices or automatic glare control devices with manual override for all the regularly occupied spaces.

KEY THINGS TO REMEMBER

- Definition of spatial daylight autonomy (sDA) and annual sunlight exposure (ASE).

- The use of glare control devices such as operable window blinds/curtains is required in this credit. In LEED, fixed glare control devices—like fixed exterior overhangs, fixed fins, fixed louvers, dark color glazing, frit glazing treatment, or additional glazing treatments—do not qualify as glare control devices. The acceptable ones are interior window blinds, shades, curtains, moveable exterior louvers, moveable screens, and moveable awnings.

- To maximize daylight in the interior spaces, transparent partitions—like interior windows placed in walls or doors—or interior glazing can be used. Using low-height partitions in open offices will also increase the amount of daylight.

- In all the options, all LEED BD+C projects except "LEED BD+C: Healthcare" should consider the **regularly occupied floor areas**, and the "LEED BD+C: Healthcare" projects should consider the **perimeter area**.

- In option 3, both the measurements should be taken after the project construction is complete and people have occupied the space. The measurements should be in a regularly occupied month.

- Option 1 and option 2 of this credit require a computer simulation. In option 3, the project teams will not create a simulation. Rather, they will conduct measurements on-site.

Quality Views—Credit

■ Applicable to: All the LEED BD+C Rating Systems

New Construction	1 point	Retail	1 point	Hospitality	1 point
Core and Shell	1 point	Data Centers	1 point	Healthcare	1 - 2 points
Schools	1 point	Warehouses & Dist. Centers	1 point		

CREDIT SUMMARY

Providing quality views is another factor to address occupant comfort and productivity. In offices, occupants who have a visual connection with outdoor environments demonstrate increased productivity. In hospitals, patients who have a decent view and access to nature can have reduced healing periods.[4] Project teams that consider the building orientation, interior layout, and building envelope to create quality views will therefore achieve a much greater level of occupant satisfaction for their projects.

This credit awards projects that provide a direct line of sight to the outdoors via vision glazing. Vision glazing should allow a clear image of outdoors and should also be free of frits, patterns, fibers, or tints that disturb color. In open offices, partial height/low height partitions can be used to achieve quality views, or the partitions can be eliminated altogether. Note that implementing these strategies will also support the previous "Daylight" credit.

The credit has different requirements for "LEED BD+C: Warehouses and Distribution Centers" and "LEED BD+C: Healthcare" projects.

CREDIT INTENT

To give occupants a connection with the outdoor environment by providing quality views.

CREDIT REQUIREMENTS

For all LEED BD+C projects, except "LEED BD+C: Warehouses and Distribution Centers" and "LEED BD+C: Healthcare":
Projects should achieve a direct line of sight to the outdoors via vision glazing for **75% of all regularly occupied floor area**. Vision glazing should **provide a clear image of the exterior** and should not be obstructed by frits, fibers, patterned glazing or added tints that distort color balance.

In addition, 75% of all regularly occupied floor area must meet at least two of the following four view criteria:

- Multiple lines of sight to vision glazing in different directions that are at least 90 degrees apart.
- Views that include at least two of the following:
  - Flora, fauna, or sky
  - Movement
  - Objects at least 25 feet (7.5 meters) from the exterior of the glazing
- Unobstructed views located within the distance of three times the head height of the vision glazing. (To satisfy this requirement, the project teams will first determine the head height of the vision glazing for each regularly occupied space. Next, in the floor plan, they will identify all the regularly occupied floor area that is within three times the head height of the perimeter. This area should not contain any obstruction.)
- Views with a **view factor of 3 or greater**, which is defined according to "**Windows and Offices: A Study of Office Worker Performance and the Indoor Environment.**" (View factor is a measure of the amount and quality of the outdoor views within a 90-degree cone of vision from an individual workstation. A view factor of 5 represents a high-quality view, and a view factor of 0 represents a poor-quality view.)

In the calculations, project teams should include all the permanent interior obstructions, while the movable furniture and partitions can be excluded. Views into interior atria can be used to meet up to **30%** of the required quality view area.

For "LEED BD+C: Warehouses and Distribution Centers":

"LEED BD+C: Warehouses and Distribution Centers" projects basically have the same view requirements as mentioned above. However, those requirements are only applicable to the **office portion** of the building.

For the bulk storage, sorting, and distribution areas, projects should meet the above view requirements for only **25% of the regularly occupied floor area**.

For "LEED BD+C: Healthcare":

Only the "LEED BD+C: Healthcare" projects have the opportunity to earn 2 points under this credit.

If the **inpatient units** in the hospital building meet the mentioned view requirements, the projects will earn 1 point.

To earn the other point, projects should configure the floor plan so that the floor area within **15 feet** (4.5 meters) of the perimeter exceeds the following perimeter area requirements and additionally complies with the view requirements mentioned above.

Total floor area (sqft)	Perimeter area (sqft)
Up to 15,000	7,348
20,000	8,785
25,000	10,087
30,000	11,292
35,000	12,425
40,000	13,500
45,000	14,528
50,000 and more	15,516

Table 37. Minimum compliant perimeter area relative to the total floor area

The "perimeter area" is the floor area within **15 feet** (4.5 meters) of the perimeter, which also provides an exterior view.

Think about two design alternatives in which the first one is a square floor plan and the second one is a narrow-rectangle floor plan. The square building will contain a big core area that will not be exposed to any views, and only the spaces at the perimeter will have access to outside views. In the narrow-rectangle building, if the corridor is placed in the middle of the floor plan, all the rooms can have access to quality views. The following illustrations demonstrate the difference between these design alternatives. The white portions show the spaces with outside views, while the black areas are the spaces without any views. Note that the total floor area is the same in both of the design alternatives.

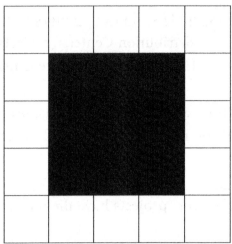

Square building configuration — 64% of the total floor area can have access to outside views

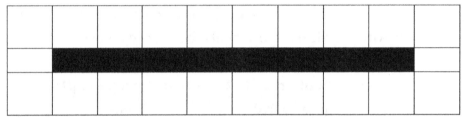

Narrow rectangle building configuration — more than 90% of the total floor area can have access to outside views

However, it is also important to note that the initial cost of the narrow-rectangle building will be higher than the square building. Since the narrow-rectangle building has more perimeter length, the building will contain more exterior elements.

The same rule will apply to two buildings with the same configuration but with different floor areas. If the total floor area of the narrow-rectangle building in the previous illustration increases (while maintaining the ratio), the total area with access to outdoor views will also decrease.

To summarize, the floor area and the floor layout are the top priorities to consider when designing for quality views.

All projects should produce documentation with the following:
- A list of all the regularly occupied spaces with the qualifying area in each space and view features
- Sections, elevations, diagrams, or photos showing that the sight lines to glazing do not encounter any permanent interior obstructions

🖹 Additionally, according to the relevant section of the credit requirements, projects should submit floor plans or diagrams identifying regularly occupied spaces and show the following items:

- Multiple sight lines for each regularly occupied space
- Sight lines and exterior features that are labeled
- Sight lines and areas indicating three times the head height
- Areas with a view factor of 3 or greater
- A method to determine the view factor for each typical building user location

EXEMPLARY PERFORMANCE

To qualify for exemplary performance under this credit, all LEED BD+C projects except "LEED BD+C: Warehouses and Distribution Centers" and "LEED BD+C: Healthcare" should meet the credit requirements for **90%** of all regularly occupied floor areas.

"LEED BD+C: Warehouses and Distribution Centers" projects should meet the credit requirements for **90%** of the regularly occupied floor areas for the office portion of the building and for **50%** of the regularly occupied floor area for the bulk storage, sorting, and distribution portions.

"LEED BD+C: Healthcare" projects should meet the credit requirements for **90%** of the regularly occupied floor area in the inpatient areas and should exceed the area requirements in table 37 by **10%** or more for the non-inpatient areas.

KEY THINGS TO REMEMBER

- View glazing should allow a clear image of the exterior and should not be obstructed by frits, fibers, patterned glazing, or added tints that distort color balance.
- For the bulk storage, sorting, and distribution areas, "LEED BD+C: Warehouses and Distribution Centers" projects should meet the credit's view requirements for only **25% of the regularly occupied floor area**.
- The "perimeter area" is the floor area within **15 feet** (4.5 meters) of the perimeter and which also provides an exterior view.
- LEED refers to "Windows and Offices: A Study of Office Worker Performance and the Indoor Environment" under this credit.

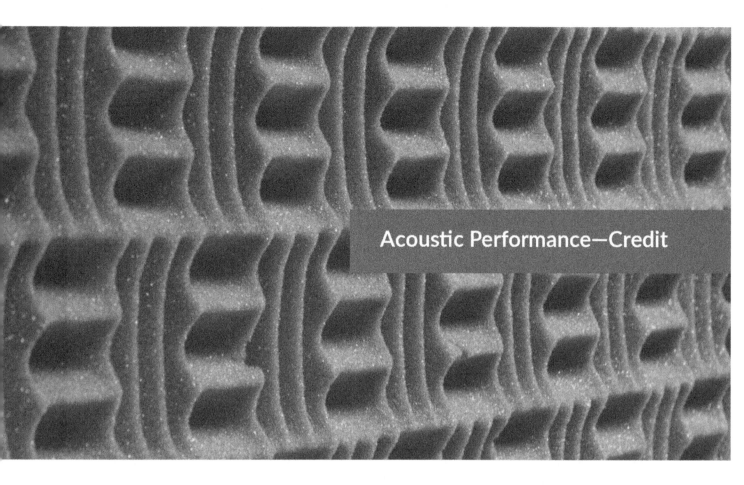

Acoustic Performance—Credit

- Applicable to: All the LEED BD+C Rating Systems except Core and Shell, and Retail

New Construction	1 point	Warehouses & Dist. Centers	1 point
Schools	1 point	Hospitality	1 point
Data Centers	1 point	Healthcare	1 – 2 points

CREDIT SUMMARY

Acoustic performance is essential in all building types for human comfort, privacy, productivity, and increased human health. Think about hearing everything from your neighbor next door because of the low acoustic quality of the interior partitions, which can easily lead to sleep disturbance and stress. In classrooms, students' concentration levels can easily be disturbed by outside noises. In hospitals with poor acoustic qualities, patients can face even more consequences.

This credit awards a point for establishing a high acoustic quality via **reducing HVAC background noise**, meeting the **sound transmission class** (STC) criteria by establishing sound isolation, requiring certain amounts of **reverberation time**, and meeting the sound reinforcement and masking systems criteria (if applicable).

The sound transmission class is a number that represents the overall ability of a material to reduce the transmission of noise.

To demonstrate, if we separate two rooms by a single layer of drywall on each side—a half inch of drywall on each side with batt insulation in the middle—the STC performance of the wall assembly will probably be around 40. However, if we use double-layer drywall and also double the batt insulation, the STC rating will jump to 55. To summarize, STC is calculated by averaging the sound transmission loss through an assembly.

Once more, reverberation time is the time span between when a sound is produced and when it dies away. Actually, sounds do not merely die away. In fact, they are absorbed by materials, furniture, and isolation products while they reach zero amplitude.

Masking systems or sound masking systems are made up of equipment used to reduce the background noise in spaces. Nowadays, masking systems are very popular for use in open offices in order to establish good acoustical quality.

For "LEED BD+C: Schools" and "LEED BD+C: Healthcare" projects, this credit has different requirements.

CREDIT INTENT

To provide workspaces and classrooms that promote building occupants' well-being, productivity, and communications through quality acoustic design.

CREDIT REQUIREMENTS

For all LEED BD+C projects, except "LEED BD+C: Schools" and "LEED BD+C: Healthcare": (This credit does not apply to "LEED BD+C: Core and Shell" and "LEED BD+C: Retail")

For all the occupied spaces, projects should meet the following requirements for "HVAC background noise," "sound isolation," "reverberation time," and "sound reinforcement/masking" (if installed in the project).

HVAC Background Noise:
For HVAC background noise, projects should achieve the maximum background noise levels from HVAC systems per **2011 ASHRAE Handbook, HVAC Applications, Chapter 48, Table 1; AHRI Standard 885-2008, Table 15** or a local equivalent.

Project teams should measure or calculate sound levels to confirm compliance. During the measurements, the sound-level meter used should conform to **ANSI S1.4 for type 1** (precision) or **type 2** (general purpose) sound measurement instrumentation, or it should conform to a local equivalent.

Additionally, projects should comply with the design criteria for HVAC noise levels resulting from the sound transmission paths listed in **2011 ASHRAE Applications Handbook, Table 6** or listed in a local equivalent.

Sound Transmission:

To address sound isolation, projects should first identify the occupied spaces and their adjacency combinations. Next, project teams should meet the composite sound transmission class (STC_C) ratings as listed in the following table or the local building code, whichever is more stringent.

Adjacency Combinations		STC_c
Residence, or hotel room	Residence or hotel room	55
Residence, or hotel room	Common hallway, stairway	50
Residence, or hotel room	Retail	60
Retail	Retail	50
Standard office	Standard office	45
Executive office	Executive office	50
Conference room	Conference room	50
Mechanical equipment room	Occupied area	60

Table 38. Maximum composite sound transmission class ratings for adjacent spaces

Before the substantial completion of construction, project teams should conduct measurements and confirm that the STC_C ratings on the previous table are met.

Reverberation Time:

Project teams should meet the reverberation time requirements adapted from **Performance Measurement Protocols for Commercial Buildings** according to the room and application type, and they should verify the reverberation time at 500 Hz, 1,000 Hz, and 2,000 Hz. (This is similar to the "Minimum Acoustic Performance" prerequisite, which also requires the verification of the reverberation time at 500 Hz, 1,000 Hz, and 2,000 Hz.)

In order to verify the reverberation time, project teams should either calculate or measure the reverberation time for each occupied space.

<u>Sound Reinforcement and Masking Systems:</u>

<u>Sound Reinforcement:</u>

For all large conference rooms and auditoriums serving more than 50 people, project teams should evaluate the need for sound reinforcement and AV playback capabilities. If sound reinforcement is needed, it should meet the following requirements:

- Have a minimum sound level of 70 dBA
- Maintain sound level coverage within +/- 3 dB at the 2,000 Hz octave band throughout the space
- Achieve a speech transmission index (STI) of at least 0.60 or common intelligibility scale (CIS) rating of a minimum of 0.77 at representative points within the area of coverage.

<u>Masking Systems:</u>

For projects that use masking systems, the masking system design levels should not exceed 48 dBA. Project teams should also ensure that loudspeaker coverage can provide uniformity of +/- 2 dBA and that speech spectra are masked.

Note that this credit actually does not require project teams to install sound reinforcement or masking systems. But if the project teams need to install them, then the installed equipment must meet the credit's requirements.

📄 As applicable, projects should provide the following documentation:

- <u>For HVAC background noise</u>: sound level values of the occupied spaces, noise reduction narrative, and calculation or measurement narrative
- <u>For sound transmission</u>: STC ratings for adjacent spaces and the calculation or the measurement narrative
- <u>For reverberation time</u>: reverberation time criteria for each room and the calculation or the measurement narrative
- <u>For sound reinforcement and masking systems</u>: an explanation of sound reinforcement methodology and system components and an explanation of masking system components.

For "LEED BD+C: Schools":
The "LEED BD+C: Schools" projects should meet the requirements below for HVAC "background noise" and "sound transmission."

HVAC Background Noise:
Projects should achieve a background noise level of **35 dBA or less** from the HVAC systems in <u>classrooms</u> and <u>other core learning spaces</u>. (In the "Minimum Acoustic Performance" prerequisite, this value was 40 dBA.)

Project teams should follow the recommended methodologies for mechanical system noise control in **ANSI Standard S12.60–2010, Part 1, Annex A.1; 2011 HVAC Applications ASHRAE Handbook, Chapter 48, Sound and Vibration Control, with errata; AHRI Standard 885–2008;** or a local equivalent for projects located outside the United States. (These are the same standards as in the "Minimum Acoustic Performance" prerequisite.)

Sound Transmission:
To address sound transmission, projects should design <u>classrooms</u> and <u>other core learning spaces</u> in order to meet the sound transmission class requirements of **ANSI S12.60–2010 Part 1** or a local equivalent. All the exterior windows must have an STC rating of at least **35** unless outdoor and indoor noise levels can be confirmed to justify a lower rating.

> 🗎 "LEED BD+C: Schools" projects should document the STC calculation or measurement method, a list of STC ratings, and the STC rating assembly source data.

For "LEED BD+C: Healthcare":
"LEED BD+C: Healthcare" projects have two options, and they can pursue either one of them or both of them. Under these options, projects should design the facility to meet or exceed the following sound and vibration requirements, which are adapted from "**2010 FGI Guidelines for Design and Construction of Health Care Facilities**" (2010 FGI Guidelines) and its reference document, "**Sound and Vibration Design Guidelines for Health Care Facilities**" (2010 SV Guidelines).

OPTION 1: SPEECH PRIVACY, SOUND ISOLATION, AND BACKGROUND NOISE – (1 Point)

Under this option, project teams should address "speech privacy and sound isolation," and "background noise" by meeting the following requirements:

Speech Privacy and Sound Isolation:

Project teams should achieve speech privacy, acoustical comfort, and minimal annoyance from noise-producing sources. Project teams should design the facility to meet the requirements outlined in the sections of "Table 1.2-3, Design Criteria for Minimum Sound Isolation Performance between Enclosed Rooms," and "Table 1.2-4 Speech Privacy for Enclosed Room and Open-Plan Spaces" (in the 2010 FGI Guidelines and 2010 SV Guidelines). Project teams should calculate or measure sound isolation and speech privacy descriptors achieved for representative adjacencies to confirm compliance.

Background Noise:

Project teams should consider the background noise levels generated by all building mechanical-electrical-plumbing systems, air distribution systems, and other facility noise sources. The design of the facility should meet the 2010 FGI Guidelines, "Table 1.2-2 Minimum-Maximum Design Criteria for Noise in representative interior rooms and spaces." Please note that, for the other rating systems, the background noise is referred to as "HVAC background noise." However, since healthcare facilities are more sensitive to noise, project teams should address all the MEP systems and other facility noise sources when designing for the background noise.

Project teams should either calculate or measure sound levels in representative rooms and spaces for each type to confirm compliance. They should use a sound level meter that conforms to **ANSI S1.4 for type 1** (precision) or **type 2** (general purpose) sound measurement instrumentation. For spaces not listed in Table 1.2-2, project teams should refer to the "2011 ASHRAE Handbook, Chapter 48, Sound and Vibration Control, Table 1."

📄 "LEED BD+C: Healthcare" project teams pursuing option 1 should document a list of spaces, adjacencies, and STC ratings, and they should submit the calculation results and the privacy index values for "Speech Privacy and Sound Isolation." For "Background Noise Levels," projects should submit the list of spaces, their design criteria, and the lab test reports, and they also should submit the simulation results or the measurement reports.

AND / OR

OPTION 2: ACOUSTICAL FINISHES AND SITE EXTERIOR NOISE — (1 Point)

Under this option, project teams should address "acoustical finishes" and "site exterior noise" by meeting the following requirements:

Acoustical Finishes:

Project teams should specify and use materials to meet the "2010 FGI Guidelines for Design and Construction of Health Care Facilities, Table 1.2-1, Design Room Sound Absorption Coefficients" and the "2010 Sound and Vibration Design Guidelines for Health Care Facilities." Project teams should either calculate or measure the average sound absorption coefficients for representative unoccupied rooms of each type in the building and confirm conformance.

Site Exterior Noise:

In order to address site exterior noise, project teams should minimize the noise produced by road traffic, aircraft flyovers, railroads, on-site heliports, generators, outdoor facility MEP, building services equipment, and more. Additionally, project teams should minimize the effects of the project (MEP equipment and activities) to the surrounding facility, and they are required to meet local applicable codes or "Table 1.2-1 of the 2010 FGI Guidelines," "Table 1.2-1, and the 2010 SV Guidelines," or "Table 1.3-1," whichever is more stringent.

Project teams should comply with the 2010 FGI Guidelines for the following noise sources:

- Heliports
- Generators
- Mechanical equipment
- Building services

Project teams should determine the exterior noise classification (A, B, C, or D) by measuring and analyzing data, and need to use the "2010 FGI Guidelines, Categorization of Health Care Facility Sites by Exterior Ambient Sound, Table A1.2a," and the "2010 SV Guidelines, Table 1.3-1."

The building envelope must be designed according to the composite STC rating based on the "2010 FGI Guidelines, Categorization of Health Care Facility Sites by Exterior Ambient Sound."

For exterior site exposure categories B, C, or D, project teams should calculate or measure the sound isolation performance of representative elements of the exterior building envelope to determine the composite sound transmission class rating for the representative facade sections. The above-mentioned measurements should generally conform to the "ASTM E966, Standard Guide for Field Measurements of Airborne Sound Insulation of Building Facades and Facade Elements."

📄 "LEED BD+C: Healthcare" projects pursuing option 2 should document the types of wall, ceiling, and floor finishes with their associated NRC values, and they should document the calculated average sound absorption coefficients for "Acoustical Finishes." For "Site Exterior Noise," projects should document the exterior building envelope STC rating, site noise exposure category, and the mitigation narrative for each 2010 FGI guideline.

EXEMPLARY PERFORMANCE

This credit does not qualify for exemplary performance.

KEY THINGS TO REMEMBER

- This credit requires implementing measures for HVAC background noise, sound transmission, reverberation time, sound reinforcement, and masking systems.
- The 2011 ASHRAE Handbook, HVAC Applications, is used to address HVAC background noise.
- Under the two options for the "LEED BD+C: Healthcare" rating system, projects should design the facility to meet or exceed the sound and vibration requirements that are adapted from "**2010 FGI Guidelines for Design and Construction of Health Care Facilities**" and its reference document, "**Sound and Vibration Design Guidelines for Health Care Facilities.**"
- Sound performance measurements under this credit cannot be performed after the substantial completion of construction.
- To address the HVAC background noise, all projects except "LEED BD+C: Schools" and "LEED BD+C: Healthcare" will use the **2011 ASHRAE Handbook, HVAC Applications, Chapter 48, Table 1; AHRI Standard 885-2008, Table 15.** The LEED BD+C: Schools will use the **ANSI Standard S12.60–2010, Part 1, Annex A.1; 2011 HVAC Applications ASHRAE Handbook, Chapter 48, Sound and Vibration Control, with errata; AHRI Standard 885–2008**, or a local equivalent for projects located outside the United States.
- Since healthcare facilities are more sensitive to noise, project teams for "LEED BD+C: Healthcare" facilities should address all the MEP systems and other facility noise sources when designing for background noise.
- For background noise, project teams should either calculate or measure sound levels in representative rooms and spaces of each type to confirm compliance by using a sound level meter that conforms to **ANSI S1.4 for type 1** (precision) or **type 2** (general purpose) sound measurement instrumentation.
- "LEED BD+C: Schools" projects should achieve a background noise level of **35 dBA** or less from the HVAC systems in <u>classrooms</u> and <u>other core learning spaces</u>.

CHAPTER 10

INNOVATION (IN)

The "Innovation" credit category encourages exploration and implementation of new green building technologies to create additional environmental benefits and to exceed the thresholds defined in the LEED credits.

Six total points are available in this credit category, which has four different strategies:

- Innovative Strategy
- Exemplary performance
- Pilot credits
- Including a LEED Accredited Professional on the project team

INNOVATIVE STRATEGY

LEED encourages projects to find new and unique ways of exceeding green building principles that have not been previously covered in the LEED rating systems. If projects can create their own innovation credits, they can then receive extra points under the "Innovation" credit.

An example might be a LEED-certified building that educates occupants and visitors about the positive effects that green buildings have on the environment—possibly using screens situated in common areas. The project teams can create a credit called "Green Education" and send it to GBCI as an innovation credit.

In another example, if the project teams choose to relocate or transplant trees on-site rather than removing them, they can choose to apply for an innovation credit.

The innovation credit created should meet the following criteria:

- Demonstrate a quantitative improvement in environmental performance by showing a comparison with its baseline values.
- Establish a comprehensive strategy that cannot be limited to the use of a single product and can be applied to the entire project.
- Create an innovation credit that is significantly better than the standard sustainable design practices.

Innovation—Credit

■ Applicable to: All the LEED BD+C Rating Systems

All the LEED BD+C Rating Systems	1 – 5 points

CREDIT SUMMARY

This credit is designed to encourage project teams to go beyond LEED requirements and innovate new ways to achieve sustainable design; to do so, this credit awards bonus points.

In order to achieve this credit, project teams can choose to create their own innovation credit and/or choose pilot credits to pursue from the LEED pilot credit library and fulfill its requirements and/or choose to achieve exemplary performance from the eligible credits. (Because pilot credit availability changes over time, it is recommended to register for a pilot credit as soon as the project teams decide to go ahead with it.)

Pilot credits are credits being tested for the updated version of LEED. According to the feedback received by USGBC from the projects that pursue these credits, these pilot credits can become actual credits of the updated LEED rating system, which would be LEED v5.

CREDIT INTENT

To encourage green building project teams to achieve exceptional or innovative performance.

CREDIT REQUIREMENTS

Project teams can use any combination of innovation, pilot, and exemplary performance strategies.

OPTION 1: INNOVATION — (1 Point)

Under this option, project teams should achieve significant and measurable environmental performance using an innovative strategy that is not addressed in the LEED green building rating system.

Project teams should identify the following:

- The intent of the proposed innovation credit
- Proposed requirements for compliance
- Proposed submittals to show compliance
- The design approach or strategies used to meet the proposed requirements

The proposed strategy of the innovation credit should meet the following criteria:

- Demonstrate a <u>quantitative</u> improvement in environmental performance. In other words, the project should establish a baseline of standard performance and compare the baseline with the final design performance.
- The strategy of the innovation credit should be comprehensive and should not address a limited portion of the project. In addition, the proposed credit should have <u>at least two</u> components and should not be limited to the use of a particular product or a design strategy.
- Finally, the proposed strategy should be significantly better than standard sustainable design practices.

Or under this option, projects can earn points by achieving the selected credits from <u>other</u> LEED rating systems.

For "LEED BD+C: Core and Shell" projects, the proposed innovation credit should cover both the core and shell portion including the common areas, and the tenant spaces. To enforce this requirement with the tenant spaces, project teams can include this scope in the tenant sales or lease agreements.

AND/OR

OPTION 2: PILOT — (1 Point)

Under this option, project teams should achieve **one** of the pilot credits from USGBC's LEED Pilot Credit Library.

Pilot credits are <u>specific</u> to the rating systems, and pilot credits open and close at varying intervals. Because pilot credit availability changes over time, it is recommended to register for a pilot credit as soon as the project teams decide to go ahead with it. After implementing the credit, the project teams should also provide feedback through the credit's feedback survey and provide any information that may be helpful for the future revisions of the credit.

AND/OR

OPTION 3: ADDITIONAL STRATEGIES — (1-3 Points)

Under this option, projects can receive more points for creating additional "Innovation" credits as required under option 1 and/or achieve additional pilot credits as required under option 2, and/or receive points for achieving exemplary performance for the qualifying credits.

Innovation — 1-3 Points
➤ Meet the requirements defined under option 1. No single innovation strategy can achieve more than one point.

Pilot — 1-3 points
➤ Meet the requirements of option 2.

Exemplary performance — 1-2 points
➤ Achieve exemplary performance in an existing LEED v4 credit that allows for exemplary performance.

📄 Project teams pursuing option 1 should provide documentation for the innovation narrative and any other supporting documentation.

📄 Project teams pursuing pilot credits should document pilot credit registration, pilot credit surveys, pilot credit specific submittals, and any other supporting documentation.

📄 Project teams achieving exemplary performance should provide documentation for an exemplary performance credit and submit supporting documentation.

EXEMPLARY PERFORMANCE

This credit does not qualify for exemplary performance.

KEY THINGS TO REMEMBER

- The "Innovation" credit contains 5 points, and the "Innovation" credit category contains 6 points (with the "LEED Accredited Professional" credit).
- Requirements for earning this credit under option 1.
- Pilot credits are <u>specific</u> to the rating systems, and pilot credits open and close at varying intervals.
- **The point values of all the options.** Even though option 3 awards three points for "Innovation" and "Pilot," it awards a maximum of **two points** for "Exemplary Performance."

LEED Accredited Professional—Credit

■ Applicable to: All the LEED BD+C Rating Systems

All the LEED BD+C Rating Systems	1 point

CREDIT SUMMARY

The "Innovation" credit category awards a point for having a LEED Accredited Professional (AP) with a specialty appropriate to the project as one of the principal participants of the project team. Legacy LEED APs (LEED APs without specialty) do not qualify in this credit.

The selected LEED AP with specialty principal should have the active credential at the time of the project's certification review.

CREDIT INTENT

To encourage the team integration required for LEED projects and to streamline the application and certification process.

CREDIT REQUIREMENTS

At least one principal participant of the project team must be a LEED Accredited Professional (AP) with a specialty appropriate for the project, or the project team must engage a LEED AP with specialty to support the project and participate in the certification process. A project employing a LEED AP O+M as a principal participant of the project team for a LEED BD+C project cannot earn the credit.

> 📄 Projects should document the full name and specialty credential of the LEED Accredited Professional.

EXEMPLARY PERFORMANCE

This credit does not qualify for exemplary performance.

KEY THINGS TO REMEMBER

- Legacy LEED APs (LEED APs without a specialty) do not qualify in this credit.
- Projects can receive only 1 point under this credit even they employ more than one LEED AP with a specialty appropriate for the project.
- The selected LEED AP with <u>appropriate</u> specialty to the project should have the active credential at the time of the project's certification review.

CHAPTER 11

REGIONAL PRIORITY (RP)

L EED projects span the entire globe. They exist in different climate zones, in different population densities, have different water and energy availabilities, and have different local problems to deal with. A credit may be much easier to achieve for a project in location A than in location B—even if it's the same project.

Since each location has different regional issues and different environmental problems, USGBC regional councils and chapters and the LEED International Roundtable have identified the environmental priorities in their locations.

In order to address the identified environmental priorities, the USGBC regional councils and chapters identified **six credits** from the existing LEED credits in each rating system that contribute more positive impacts to those regional issues for that particular location.

If a project decides to earn some of those credits, as a bonus, the project will also be awarded points from the "Regional Priority" credit, which is the only credit under the RP credit category. Projects can see the "Regional Priority" credits available for their location online at USGBC's website.

For example, a project located in Los Angeles, California, should first enter the exact project location in USGBC's "Regional Priority Lookup" page online. This web page will show the regional priority credits for that project's location. In this case, they are listed as follows:

- Optimize Energy Performance
- Surrounding Density and Diverse Use
- Access to Quality Transit
- Reduced Parking Footprint
- Rainwater Management
- Indoor Water Use Reduction

Let's say that the project has already earned the "Rainwater Management" and the "Access to Quality Transit" credits, which would also mean that the project would receive 2 additional bonus points from the "Regional Priority" credit in addition to the points received from the "Rainwater Management" and "Access to Quality Transit" credits.

For another location with low potable water availability, the "Indoor Water Use Reduction" and "Outdoor Water Use Reduction" credits could make up two of the six regional priority credits. Alternatively, if a specific location contains mostly sensitive lands, then the "Sensitive Land Protection" credit can be one of the six "Regional Priority" credits.

The "Regional Priority" credit contains 4 points, which means that if the project had achieved 4 out of the 6 "Regional Priority" credits, 4 points would thus be awarded. If the project had achieved 6 out of the 6 "Regional Priority" credits, again 4 points would be awarded. If the project had achieved 2 out of the 6 "Regional Priority" credits, 2 points would be awarded.

Regional Priority—Credit

■ Applicable to: All the LEED BD+C Rating Systems

All the LEED BD+C Rating Systems	1 - 4 points

CREDIT INTENT

To provide an incentive for the achievement of identified credits that address geographically specific environmental and public health priorities and social equity.

CREDIT REQUIREMENTS

There are six available "Regional Priority" credits for every location; those credits are identified by the USGBC regional councils and chapters. The project should earn **up to four** of those six credits. The "Regional Priority" credits have been identified by the USGBC regional councils and chapters and LEED International Roundtable as having additional regional importance for the project's region. To see the database of "Regional Priority" credits and their geographic applicability, go to USGBC's website, www.usgbc.org/rpc.

One point will be awarded for each "Regional Priority" credit achieved, up to a maximum of four. For credits with multiple thresholds (e.g., in the "Indoor Water Use Reduction" credit, thresholds change according to the percent reduction established in water savings), points will be awarded at particular levels of achievement.

This is similar to the point distribution of the "LEED for Neighborhood Development Location" credit. Projects located in LEED ND Platinum neighborhoods receive full points, and the projects located in LEED ND Silver neighborhoods earn fewer points.

> 📄 No documentation is necessary for the "Regional Priority" credit. Documenting the selected credits that also qualify as "Regional Priority" credits will result in the award of the points automatically.

EXEMPLARY PERFORMANCE

This credit does not qualify for exemplary performance.

KEY THINGS TO REMEMBER

- How points are distributed under this credit.
- For credits with multiple thresholds, points will be awarded at particular levels of achievement.
- The "Regional Priority" credit contains 4 points.
- "Regional Priority" credits are identified by the USGBC regional councils and chapters.

CHAPTER 12

EXAM REGISTRATION PROCESS

This chapter will provide information about the LEED AP BD+C exam. However, it is still recommended visit the USGBC website and download the latest LEED AP BD+C Candidate Handbook.

ELIGIBILITY REQUIREMENTS

Test takers must be 18 years of age or older and must also agree to the "Disciplinary and Exam Appeals Policy," which can be found on the GBCI website.

HOW TO REGISTER FOR THE EXAM?

1. If you have an existing USGBC site user account, log in to your credentials account to register for the exam at usgbc.org/credentials or create a new account if you don't have one.
2. Make sure that the name you enter exactly matches the name on the ID you will present at the test center. If it does not match, update your name on the website's user account "settings."

3. Review the address in the profile. (The certificate will be mailed to that address.)
4. Select the credential exam you wish to apply for and follow the instructions to complete the application.
5. You will be redirected to prometric.com/gbci to schedule your exam date and location.
6. When the exam is scheduled, you will receive a confirmation number onscreen and an email through Prometric.
   - Print and keep your confirmation number. You will need this confirmation number to confirm, cancel, or reschedule your appointment through Prometric's website, which is prometric.com/gbci.

Once you register and pay for your exam, you have one year to schedule your exam session. You may request one six-month extension of this one-year period.

WHERE TO TAKE THE EXAM?

The exam is administered by Prometric testing centers throughout the world.

EXAM FEES

The exam fee is $250 for USGBC members and $350 for nonmembers.

TESTING CENTER RULES

- At the Prometric testing center, all test takers should present a government-issued photo ID that also contains a signature.
- Nothing can be brought to the exam. Small lockers may be available at the testing center to store your wallet, cell phone, keys, and other small items. However, laptops, briefcases, or large purses shouldn't be taken to the testing center.
- Scrap paper and pencils will be provided by the test site staff and will be collected at the conclusion of the exam. No other paper can be brought into the exam room.
- To leave the room during the exam, test takers should get the test proctor's permission.
- Eating and drinking is not permitted in the exam room.

SPECIAL TESTING ACCOMODATIONS

Accommodations can be requested in case you have a documented disability that would prevent you from taking the exam under normal testing conditions. Prometric complies with the provisions of the Americans with Disabilities Act (ADA).

Any special accommodation should be indicated during exam registration. There is no additional charge for special accommodations.

ABOUT THE EXAM

The LEED AP BD+C exam contains two core parts. The first core part is the LEED Green Associate exam. The second core part is the LEED AP BD+C exam, which contains 100 randomly delivered multiple-choice questions that should be completed in two hours. LEED Green Associates will only need to take the second core part of the exam in order to earn the LEED AP BD+C credential.

The LEED AP exam can be taken in one sitting. In this case, the exam will take four hours. However, if the test taker passes the first part of the exam, which is the LEED Green Associate exam, and subsequently fails the second part, the test taker cannot earn the LEED Green Associate credential and must then retake the whole exam and pass both parts.

In the exam there will be both scored and unscored questions. Unscored questions are used to collect performance data for USGBC. Test takers will not know if a question will be scored or unscored. As there are both scored and unscored questions on the exam, and the questions are also scaled, there's no way to know how many correct answers you need in order to pass the exam.

In order to pass all the LEED Professional exams, candidates must score 170 points out of 200 possible points. 125 is the minimum score in all the LEED Professional exams. If you are taking the LEED AP exam combined, you should score 170 or higher points on both core parts of the exam. At the end of the exam, you will be able to see your score on screen.

If you have an appeal about the exam content, you can leave comments regarding any question in the exam in case you think there's a technical mistake; however, appeals must be made in the first fourteen days after the test. If your appeal is approved, you will be able to take the test again although your score for the first test will not change.

Make sure you read all the questions and choices very carefully! If a question seems to have more than one answer, make sure you thoroughly understand the question and pay special attention to the wording. It doesn't matter how well you know the exam content, if you don't read the content very carefully, the exam can easily trick you into selecting the wrong answer.

EXAM CONTENT

The LEED AP BD+C exam is intended to test knowledge and skills necessary to support the LEED certification process. The exam evaluates test takers' ability at three cognitive levels: recall items, application items, and analysis items.

Recall items assess a test taker's ability to recall factual information. Application items assess a test taker's ability to find a solution to a scenario according to the LEED principles and procedures. And analysis items assess a test taker's ability to break down the problem into its components to find a solution by evaluating the relationships of the components.

The exam questions reflect task domains and knowledge domains. Task domains include the tasks necessary to perform LEED effectively, such as team coordination, certification process, analyses required for LEED credits, and more. Knowledge domains include the LEED process, integrative strategies, credit categories, and more.

Below is the breakdown of the exam questions about knowledge domains:

- LEED process
- Integrative strategies
- Location and transportation
- Sustainable sites
- Water efficiency
- Energy and atmosphere
- Materials and resources
- Indoor environmental quality
- Project surroundings and public outreach

The segment about project surroundings and public outreach contains questions about values of sustainable design, regional design, environmental impacts, the necessity of green buildings, and more.

EXAM FORMAT

All the LEED credentialing exams are computer based. Exam questions and answer options will be displayed on screen.

Most of the exam questions are multiple-choice questions that ask to choose the correct answer out of the displayed choices. However, some questions will have more than one answer, in which case the test taker is asked to choose two out of four choices or three out of five. And there will be no partial credit for choosing only one correct answer.

Test takers can leave a question unanswered, flag questions for later review, and change the answer of any test question before the completion of the exam. If you have extra time at the end of your exam, it's highly recommended that you review all the questions.

On the exam, answer every single question since leaving a question blank will not award any points. And if you're unsure about the answer, mark the question and come back to review it later.

During the exam, if you forget something, some later questions or answer choices can make you remember the answer of that previous question.

EXAM TUTORIAL AND EXIT SURVEY

Before the exam, there will be a ten-minute tutorial to demonstrate the exam software. And at the end of the exam, there will be a ten-minute optional exit survey.

During the completion of the tutorial, you can write down any notes on the provided scratch paper that you think will be helpful during the exam.

WHAT TO EXPECT AT THE TEST CENTER

It is recommended that the test takers arrive thirty minutes prior to the scheduled exam appointment. Test takers who arrive later than their scheduled exam time will lose their seat.

Test center staff will escort the test taker to a workstation, and the test taker should remain seated during the exam unless authorized to leave by test center staff. If there is a problem with the computer or you need to take a break, raise your hand to notify the test center staff. However, the exam will not pause if you take a break.

All the test takers should also obey Prometric's security rules while at the test center.

AFTER THE EXAM

EXAM RESULTS

After the exam, your exam score will be displayed on screen, and the test center staff will provide a printed report of your results.

PASSING THE EXAM

As soon as you have passed the exam, you can use the title "LEED® AP BD+C" and/or the logo. As the LEED AP BD+C accreditation will supersede the LEED Green Associate accreditation, the LEED Green Associate title can no longer be used.

Your exam results will be processed within three days, and once the results are processed, a certificate can be requested.

A certificate will be available as a pdf soft copy that can be downloaded at any time for free and as a hard copy that can be requested from the USGBC website for a fee.

FAILING THE EXAM

The full exam fee will be charged for each scheduled exam session after failing an exam.

HOW TO MAINTAIN LEED CREDENTIALS

All the LEED Green Associates must earn fifteen continuing education (CE) hours within two years of earning their credential, while all the LEED APs with a specialty will need to earn thirty continuing education (CE) hours within two years of earning their credential.

HOW TO KNOW YOU ARE READY?

Before the exam, make sure you feel comfortable with the following:
- The prerequisite and credit summaries
- Everything mentioned under the "Key Things to Remember" sections at the end of every prerequisite/credit
- The case studies
- Appendices
- The terms in the "Glossary" section.

Some people may also choose to take practice tests to reinforce knowledge, however if you thoroughly studied this book and are also comfortable with the items listed above, you should not have any problems during the real exam.

Wish you all the best in your exam!

HOW TO ACCESS THE DIGITAL RESOURCES

Simply scan the QR code below with your phone, tablet, or any other capable device to access sample test questions online and familiarize yourself with the actual exam format.

To truly evaluate and sustain our performance, each of us needs feedback. That being said, please do submit any comments about this book, your test score, and/or any other feedback to the author online with this QR code.

PREREQUISITE & CREDIT SUMMARIES

INTEGRATIVE PROJECT PLANNING AND DESIGN—PREREQUISITE

Beginning in the <u>programming</u> and <u>predesign phase</u>, at a minimum, project teams should implement the following processes.

- <u>Owner's Project Requirements Document</u>: Projects should prepare the owner's project requirements (OPR) and a health mission statement to be incorporated into the OPR.
- <u>Preliminary Rating Goals</u>: Project teams should conduct a preliminary LEED meeting with a minimum of four key members and the owner or owner's representative to create a **LEED action plan**
- <u>Integrated Project Team</u>: Integrated project team should be assembled, which should include as many professionals as—the number cannot be fewer than **four** members—in addition to the owner or owner's representative
- <u>Design Charrette</u>: Project teams should conduct, at a minimum, a **four-hour charrette** that includes as many professionals as feasible.

INTEGRATIVE PROCESS—CREDIT

Project teams should perform the following analyses for both **energy-** and **water-related systems.**

1. **Energy related systems:**

   <u>Before completing the schematic design</u>, project teams should perform a **"simple box" energy modeling**. Project teams should assess **at least two strategies** associated with each of the following: site conditions, massing and orientation, basic envelope attributes, lighting levels, thermal comfort ranges, plug and process load needs, and programmatic and operational parameters.

Project teams should document how these analyses and findings informed the project's OPR, BOD, and design, including the following as applicable:

- Building and site program
- Building form and geometry
- Building envelope and facade specifications on different orientations
- Elimination and/or significant downsizing of building systems
- Other systems

2. Water related systems:

Projects should perform a **preliminary water budget analysis** <u>before completing the schematic design</u>. Project teams should evaluate all of the following: indoor water demand, outdoor water demand, process water demand, and supply sources.

The credit requires projects to find at least one nonpotable water source and reduce the burden on the municipality-supplied water or wastewater treatment systems by contributing **to at least two** of the water demand components listed above. Project teams should document how these analyses informed the project's OPR, BOD, and design, including the following as applicable:

- Plumbing systems
- Sewage conveyance and/or on-site treatment systems
- Rainwater quantity and quality management systems
- Landscaping, irrigation, and site elements
- Roofing systems and/or building form and geometry
- Other systems

With the completion of the preliminary energy and water research and analysis, the credit requires project teams to conduct a **goal-setting workshop**.

LEED FOR NEIGHBORHOOD DEVELOPMENT LOCATION—CREDIT

In order to be eligible for this credit, the project has to be located inside a boundary of one of the following:

a. LEED ND Pilot—Stage 2 LEED for Neighborhood Development Certified Plan
b. LEED ND Pilot—Stage 3 LEED for Neighborhood Development Certified Project
c. LEED 2009—Stage 2 Precertified LEED for Neighborhood Development Plan
d. LEED 2009—Stage 3 LEED ND Certified Neighborhood Development
e. LEED v4—LEED for Neighborhood Development Certified Plan
f. LEED v4—LEED for Neighborhood Development Certified Built Project

Basically, the LEED ND sites need to be <u>Stage 2</u> or <u>Stage 3</u> under the LEED Pilot or LEED 2009 rating systems or <u>Certified Plan</u> or <u>Certified Project</u> under the LEED v4 rating system. Conditional approvals or prereviewed LEED ND sites will not earn the credit.

SENSITIVE LAND PROTECTION—CREDIT

OPTION 1 – (1 Point)

Under this option, the development footprint must be located on previously developed land.

OR

OPTION 2 – (1 Point)

If the land is not previously developed, then the development footprint or <u>a portion</u> of it should not be located on land that falls under any of the following categories:

a. **Prime farmland**
b. **Floodplains**
c. **Habitat**
d. **Water bodies**: No development can be made within **100 feet** (30 meters) of water bodies, with the exception of some minor improvements.
e. **Wetlands**: No development can be made within **50 feet** (15 meters) of wetlands, with the exception of some minor improvements.

The following are the minor developments that are acceptable <u>within</u> water bodies and wetlands—with the requirement of <u>being available to all building users</u>:

- Brownfield areas can be remediated.
- Grading can be performed to allow for public access.
- Any activity to maintain or restore natural hydrology, or native natural communities can be implemented.
- Bicycle and pedestrian pathways, which can be constructed up to **12 feet wide** (3.5 meters), of which no more than **8 feet** (2.5 meters) can be impervious.
- One single-story structure per 300 linear feet (90 linear meters) on average, with the structure not exceeding 500 square feet (45 square meters).
- Trees that meet any of the following ratings can be removed:
  - Trees that are under 40% condition rating
  - Trees whose diameters are less than 6 inches (150 millimeters) at breast height
  - Hazardous trees
  - Up to 75% of dead trees
  - Up to 20% of the trees whose diameters are more than 6 inches (150 millimeters) at breast height, with a condition rating of 40% or higher

➤ Clearings that do not exceed 500 square feet (45 square meters). This is limited to one clearing per 300 linear feet (90 linear meters) on average.

HIGH PRIORITY SITE—CREDIT

OPTION 1: HISTORIC DISTRICT — (1 Point)

Under this option, the project site must be located on an infill location inside a historic district. After confirming the infill status, project teams should confirm that the land is inside a "historic district," which should be identified by the historic preservation entity that designates local historic districts.

OR

OPTION 2: PRIORITY DESIGNATION — (1 Point)

Under this option, the project site must be located in one of the following priority development areas:

➤ A site listed by EPA National Priorities List
➤ A Federal Empowerment Zone site
➤ A Federal Enterprise Community site
➤ A Federal Renewal Community site
➤ A site within a Department of the Treasury Community Development Financial Institutions Fund Qualified Low-Income Community
➤ A site in a US Department of Housing and Urban Development's Qualified Census Tract (QCT) or Difficult Development Area (DDA)
➤ For projects outside the United States, sites that meet the same types of specifications of a local equivalent program administered at the national level

OR

OPTION 3: BROWNFIELD REMEDIATION — (2 Points)

To pursue this option, the project site must be located on a brownfield and identified with soil or groundwater contamination, and the local, state, or national authority must require remediation at this site. **Project teams pursuing this option should remediate the brownfield to the satisfaction of the oversight authority.**

In order to identify contamination, project teams need to conduct a **Phase I** or **Phase II Environmental Site Assessment** (or a local equivalent for projects outside the United States) or consult a biologist or environmental scientist.

SURROUNDING DENSITY AND DIVERSE USES—CREDIT

For all LEED BD+C projects, except "LEED BD+C: Warehouses and Distribution Centers" and "LEED BD+C: Healthcare":

OPTION 1: SURROUNDING DENSITY — (2-3 Points)

Under this option, the project site should be located so that the **quarter-mile** (400 meter) radius of the project boundary meets the required values in table 2.

Only with regard to the "LEED BD+C: School" projects, project teams should neglect any physical education spaces (such as playgrounds or playing fields) from the development density calculations.

AND/OR

OPTION 2: DIVERSE USES — (1-2 Points)

Under this option, the building's **main entrance** should be within a **half mile** (800 meter) walking distance of the main entrance of **four to seven** (1 point) or **eight or more** (2 points) existing and publicly available diverse uses.

For "LEED BD+C: Warehouses and Distribution Centers" projects:

OPTION 1: DEVELOPMENT AND ADJACENCY — (2-3 Points)

Construct or renovate the project site on a previously developed site that was used for industrial or commercial purposes (2 points).

OR

Construct or renovate the project on a site that is both a previously developed and adjacent site; the adjacent sites must be used at the time for industrial or commercial purposes (3 points).

AND/OR

OPTION 2: TRANSPORTATION RESOURCES — (1-2 Points)

Under this option, project teams should construct or renovate the project on a site that satisfies **two** or **three** (1 point) or **four** (2 points) of the following transportation resources requirements:

- The site is located within a **10-mile** (16-kilometer) driving distance of a <u>main logistics hub</u>, defined as an <u>airport</u>, <u>seaport</u>, <u>intermodal facility</u>, or <u>freight village with intermodal transportation</u>.
- The site is located within a **1-mile** (1.6-kilometer) driving distance of an on-off ramp to a <u>highway</u>.
- The site is located within a **1-mile** (1.6-kilometer) driving distance of an access point to an active <u>freight rail line</u>.

➤ The site is served by an active <u>freight rail spur</u>.

<u>For "LEED BD+C: Healthcare" projects:</u>
OPTION 1: SURROUNDING DENSITY — (1 Point)

Under this option, the project site must be located on a site for which the surrounding existing density within a **quarter-mile** (400-meter) radius of the project boundary is:

➤ at least **7 dwelling units per acre** (17.5 DU per hectare) with a **0.5 floor-to-area ratio** (the counted density must be existing density, not zoned density); or

➤ at least **22,000 square feet per acre** (5,050 square meters per hectare) of buildable land.

For previously developed existing rural healthcare campus sites, projects should achieve a minimum development density of **30,000 square feet per acre** (6,890 square meters per hectare).

OR

OPTION 2: DIVERSE USES — (1 Point)

Under this option, the project site should be located so that the building's main entrance is within a **half-mile** (800 meter) walking distance of the main entrance of **at least seven** operational and publicly accessible diverse uses shown on table 3.

ACCESS TO QUALITY TRANSIT—CREDIT

<u>For all LEED BD+C projects, except "LEED BD+C: Schools" and "LEED BD+C: Healthcare":</u>
Project teams should locate **any functional entry** of the building within a **quarter-mile** (400 meter) walking distance of existing or planned bus, streetcar, or rideshare stops. Or **any functional entry** of the building must be located within a **half-mile** (800 meter) walking distance of existing or planned bus rapid transit stops, light or heavy rail stations, commuter rail stations, or commuter ferry terminals.

Projects served by two or more transit routes such that no one route provides more than **60%** of the documented levels can earn one additional bonus point up to the maximum number of points.

<u>For LEED BD+C: Schools projects:</u>
OPTION 1: TRANSIT-SERVED LOCATION — (1-4 Points)

This option basically requires the same criteria as listed previously for other LEED BD+C project types, however school projects are not required to evaluate weekend transit service as long as the students do not commute to school on weekends.

OR

OPTION 2: PEDESTRIAN ACCESS — (1-4 Points)

Under this option, "LEED BD+C: Schools" project teams should demonstrate that the required percentages of students live within a **three-quarter-mile** (1200 meter) walking distance (for grades 8 and below, or ages 14 and below), and a **1 1/2-mile** (2400-meter) walking distance (for grades 9 and above or ages 15 and above) of **any** functional entry of the school building.

For LEED BD+C: Healthcare projects:

This option basically requires the same criteria as listed previously for other LEED BD+C project types and in option 1 of "LEED BD+C: Schools". The only difference for healthcare projects is that the point values for this option will be awarded differently, and the number of weekend trips also needs to be addressed, unlike in option 1 of "LEED BD+C: Schools".

BICYCLE FACILITIES—CREDIT

See the summary section under the credit, and see the credit's formulas below the summary section.

REDUCED PARKING FOOTPRINT—CREDIT

This credit requires projects not exceed the **minimum local code requirements** for the parking capacity. Additionally, projects should provide parking capacity that is a percentage reduction below the base ratios of the **Parking Consultants Council, as shown in the Institute of Transportation Engineers' Transportation Planning Handbook, 3rd edition, tables 18-2 through 18-4**. Projects without off-street parking will earn the credit automatically.

Case 1: Baseline location
> Projects that have not earned points under "Surrounding Density and Diverse Uses" or "Access to Quality Transit" credits should achieve a **20%** reduction from the base ratios.

Case 2: Dense and/or transit-served location
> Projects that have earned 1 or more points under either the "Surrounding Density and Diverse Uses" credit or the "Access to Quality Transit" credit, should achieve a **40%** reduction from the base ratios.

Project teams need to provide preferred parking for carpools for **5%** of the total parking after the reductions have been made from the base ratios.

$$\text{Percent parking reduction} = \frac{\text{Total baseline capacity} - \text{Total provided capacity}}{\text{Total baseline capacity}} \times 100$$

GREEN VEHICLES—CREDIT

<u>For all LEED BD+C projects, except "LEED BD+C: Schools", and "LEED BD+C: Warehouses and Distribution Centers"</u>:

Project teams should designate **5% of all parking spaces** as <u>preferred parking</u> for sole use by green vehicles. Or instead of providing preferred parking to green vehicles, projects can provide a discounted parking rate of **at least 20%** to green vehicles. Next, project teams should pursue one of the following two options:

OPTION 1: ELECTRIC VEHICLE CHARGING — (1 Point)

Under this option, projects should install **electric vehicle supply equipment (EVSE) in 2% of all the parking spaces** used by the project.

The installed EVSE should have the following properties:

- Provide Level 2 charging capacity (208–240 volts) or greater
- Comply with the relevant regional or local standard for electrical connectors
- Be networked or accessible from the Internet and be capable of participating in a demand-response program or time-of-use pricing to encourage off-peak charging

OR

OPTION 2: LIQUID, GAS, OR BATTERY FACILITIES — (1 Point)

Under this option, projects should install **liquid** or **gas alternative fuel** fueling facilities or a **battery switching station** that should be capable of refueling a number of vehicles per day equal to at **least 2% of the total parking spaces**.

<u>For "LEED BD+C: Schools"</u>:
OPTION 1: GREEN PASSENGER VEHICLES — (1 Point)

Under this option, the school projects should designate **5% of all parking spaces** used by the project as preferred parking for green vehicles. Or instead of providing preferred parking to green vehicles, projects can provide a discounted parking rate of **at least 20%** to green vehicles. Next, the project teams should pursue one of the following two paths:

PATH 1: ELECTRIC VEHICLE CHARGING

Under this path, projects should, again, install **electric vehicle supply equipment (EVSE) in 2% of all the parking spaces** used by the project.

The installed EVSE should have the following properties:

- Provide Level 2 charging capacity (208–240 volts) or greater
- Comply with the relevant regional or local standard for electrical connectors
- Be networked or accessible from the Internet and be capable of participating in a demand-response program or time-of-use pricing to encourage off-peak charging

OR

PATH 2: LIQUID, GAS, OR BATTERY FACILITIES

Under this path, projects should install **liquid** or **gas alternative fuel** fueling facilities or a **battery switching station** that should be capable of refueling a number of vehicles per day equal to **at least 2% of the total parking spaces**.

OR

OPTION 2: GREEN BUSES AND SCHOOL-OWNED VEHICLES — (1 Point)

Under this option, school projects should develop and implement a **plan** for **every bus serving the school** in order to meet the required emissions standards within <u>seven years of the building certificate of occupancy</u>. If the school project teams choose to retrofit buses, the retrofitting must be approved by a relevant third party such as the **California Air Resources Board** or a local equivalent. Additionally, project teams should develop and implement a plan for **100%** of all other (nonbus) vehicles owned or leased to serve the school as green vehicles.

<u>For "LEED BD+C: Warehouses and Distribution Centers"</u>:
OPTION 1: ALTERNATIVE FUEL VEHICLES — (1 Point)

Project teams should provide an on-site fleet with at least **one yard tractor** powered by <u>electricity</u>, <u>propane</u>, or <u>natural gas</u>, and they should also provide <u>on-site charging</u> or <u>refueling stations</u> for the mentioned vehicle(s). Liquid or gas refueling stations should be separately ventilated if not located outdoors.

OR

OPTION 2: REDUCED TRUCK IDLING — (1 Point)

Project teams should provide an electrical connection for at least **50% of all dock door locations** to limit truck idling at the dock.

CONSTRUCTION ACTIVITY POLLUTION PREVENTION—PREREQUISITE

Projects should create and implement an erosion and sedimentation control plan (ESC) for all construction activities associated with the project. The plan should conform to the erosion and sedimentation requirements of the **2012 US Environmental Protection Agency (EPA) Construction General Permit (CGP)** or a local equivalent, whichever is more stringent, and it should describe the measures implemented.

If the local codes do require a CGP, projects can directly earn this prerequisite without any additional effort. However, if the local codes do not require a CGP, project teams should check and compare the local codes with the CGP and implement whichever is more stringent.

ENVIRONMENTAL SITE ASSESSMENT—PREREQUISITE

Project teams should conduct a Phase I Environmental Site Assessment, according to the **ASTM E1527-05 standard**, or a local equivalent, and they should determine if any environmental contamination exists on-site. If contamination is suspected, project teams can directly conduct a Phase II Environmental Site Assessment, according to the **ASTM E1903-11 standard** or a local equivalent.

If no contamination is found under the Phase I ESA, project teams will earn the prerequisite. However, if the Phase I ESA indicates existence of any recognized environmental condition, or if it suggests additional assessment, project teams must then conduct a Phase II ESA. And if any contamination is found, projects must remediate the site to meet <u>local</u>, <u>state</u>, or <u>national environmental protection agency regional residential standards</u>, using whichever standard is more stringent.

SITE ASSESSMENT—CREDIT

Projects should prepare and document a site survey or assessment that includes the following:

- **Topography**: This covers contour mapping, slope stability risks, and unique topographic features.

- **Hydrology**: This covers flood hazard areas, lakes, delineated wetlands, streams, shorelines, rainwater collection and reuse opportunities, and Urban Hydrology for Small Watersheds **Technical Release 55 (TR-55) initial water storage capacity of the site**.

- **Climate**: This pertains to the site's solar exposure, heat island effect potential, seasonal sun angles, prevailing winds, monthly precipitation, and temperature ranges.

- **Vegetation**: This covers the site's primary vegetation types, significant tree mapping, threatened or endangered species, unique habitat, greenfield area, and invasive plant species.

- **Soils**: Project teams should determine the soil classification with **Natural Resources Conservation Service soils delineation**, the US Department of Agriculture prime farmland status, healthy soils, disturbed soils, and previous development on-site.

- **Human use**: This includes views, the site's transportation infrastructure, adjacent properties, and construction materials with existing recycle or reuse potential.

- **Human health effects**: Project teams should evaluate the proximity of vulnerable populations that can be affected by the project, adjacent physical activity opportunities, and proximity to major sources of air pollution. Additionally, project teams should identify any source of noise, air, or water pollution that can affect the design.

SITE DEVELOPMENT – PROTECT OR RESTORE HABITAT—CREDIT

Projects should preserve and protect **40%** of the greenfield area on the site, <u>if it exists</u>, from all development and construction activity, and pursue one of the following options.

OPTION 1: ON-SITE RESTORATION – (2 Points)

By using native or adapted vegetation, projects should restore **30%** (including the building footprint) of all portions of the site that were previously disturbed. Projects that achieve **at least a density of 1.5 floor-to-area ratio** may also include <u>vegetated roof surfaces</u> in this calculation if native and adapted plants are used and the vegetated roof provides habitat and promotes biodiversity. Projects should restore all disturbed soils that will be revegetated to meet the following requirements:

- ➤ Soils (including imported soils) must be reused for functions similar to their original function.
- ➤ Imported topsoils, or soil blends designed to serve as topsoil, cannot include either of the following:

  - ▪ Soils defined regionally by the NRCS web soil survey as prime farmland, unique farmland, or farmland of statewide or local importance
  - ▪ Soils from other greenfield sites, unless they are a byproduct of a construction process

- ➤ Restored soil should meet the criteria of **reference soils** in categories 1, 2, and 3 and meet the criteria of either category 4 or 5:

  1) Organic matter
  2) Compaction
  3) Infiltration rates
  4) Soil biological function
  5) Soil chemical characteristics

Only for the "<u>LEED BD+C: School</u>" projects, the dedicated athletic fields that are used only for athletic purposes are excluded from the <u>soil restoration criteria</u>. Additionally, these areas cannot be counted toward the 30% minimum restoration requirement.

OR

OPTION 2: FINANCIAL SUPPORT – (1 Point)

Under this option, projects should provide financial support equivalent to at least $0.40 per square foot ($4 per square meter) for the total site area, including the building footprint.

Financial support must be provided to a land trust or conservation organization **within the same EPA Level III ecoregion** or the **project's state**. For projects in the United States, the land trust must also be accredited by the **Land Trust Alliance**, which is an organization that provides accreditation to land trust organizations. For projects outside the United States, the land trust or conservation organization must be located within **100 miles (160 kilometers)** of the project.

OPEN SPACE—CREDIT

Projects should provide outdoor space **more than or equal to 30% of the total site area**, including the building footprint. **A minimum 25% of the provided outdoor space must be vegetated** (turf grass does not count as vegetation) or should have overhead vegetated canopy.

The outdoor space must be physically accessible and be one or more of the following:

- Pedestrian-oriented paving or turf area with physical site elements that accommodate outdoor social activities for building occupants
- Recreation-oriented paving or turf area with physical site elements to encourage physical activity for building occupants
- Garden space with different vegetation types and species that provide opportunities for year-round visual interest
- Garden space dedicated to community gardens or urban food production
- Preserved or created habitat that meets the criteria of the "Site Development—Protect or Restore Habitat" credit and also includes elements of human interaction

For projects that achieve a density of 1.5 floor-area ratio (FAR), **extensive** or **intensive vegetated roofs** can be used for the minimum 25% vegetation requirement, and the roof's physically accessible paving areas can be used toward credit compliance. Wetlands or naturally designed ponds can be counted as open space as well. But their side slope gradients should average 1:4 (vertical: horizontal) or less, and they need to be vegetated. For projects that are part of a <u>multitenant complex</u>, open spaces can be at another location in the site master plan.

RAINWATER MANAGEMENT—CREDIT

OPTION 1: PERCENTILE OF RAINFALL EVENTS — (2-3 Points)
PATH 1: 95TH PERCENTILE — (2 Points)

Under this path, projects should manage on-site rainwater runoff from the developed site for the **95th percentile of regional or local rainfall events** by using <u>green infrastructure</u> and <u>low-impact development</u>, to best replicate the natural site hydrology.

Project teams will use the **daily rainfall data** and EPA methodology to determine the 95th percentile amount. The mentioned methodology is the **US Environmental Protection Agency Technical Guidance on Implementing the Stormwater Runoff Requirements for Federal Projects under Section 438 of the Energy Independence and Security Act.**

OR

PATH 2: 98TH PERCENTILE — (3 Points)

Project teams pursuing this path should achieve path 1. But in this instance, for the **98th percentile of regional or local rainfall events.**

OR

PATH 3: ZERO-LOT-LINE PROJECTS ONLY—85TH PERCENTILE — (3 Points)

Only for the zero-lot-line projects in urban areas with a minimum density of 1.5 floor-to-area ratio, project teams should manage the runoff from the developed site for the **85th percentile of regional or local rainfall events**, again by using low-impact development and green infrastructure to best replicate the natural site hydrology.

OR

OPTION 2: NATURAL LAND COVER CONDITIONS — (3 Points)

Under this option, project teams should manage the annual increase in rainwater runoff on-site, from the natural land cover condition to the post-developed condition for the 95th percentile of regional or local rainfall events. In order to pursue this option, project teams should have data showing the natural land cover conditions.

Only for the projects that are a part of a multitenant complex, the credit requirements can be met by using a **coordinated approach** for the multiple buildings within the project boundary. Distributed techniques based on a watershed approach are required. Project teams can use distributed LID strategies to manage runoff closest to its source.

HEAT ISLAND REDUCTION—CREDIT

OPTION 1: NON-ROOF AND ROOF — (2 Points)

$$\frac{\text{Area of non-roof measures}}{0.5} + \frac{\text{Area of high-reflectance roof}}{0.75} + \frac{\text{Area of vegetated roof}}{0.75} \geq \text{Total site paving area} + \text{Total roof area}$$

Projects should use any combination of the following strategies to satisfy the previous equation.

For the non-roof measures on-site:

- Use existing plants or install new plants that will provide shade over paving areas on the site within 10 years of planting. Install vegetated planters.
- Provide shade with structures covered by energy generation systems.
- Provide shade with architectural devices or structures that have a three-year aged solar reflectance value of at least **0.28.**
- Provide shade with vegetated structures.
- Use paving materials with a three-year aged solar reflectance value of at least **0.28.**
- Use an open-grid pavement system that is at least **50% unbound.**

For high-reflectance roofs:

Use roofing materials to meet the required SRI and three-year aged SRI values. Roof areas covered by mechanical equipment, skylights, or similar items will be excluded.

For vegetated roofs:

Projects can install intensive or extensive vegetated roofs.

OR

OPTION 2: PARKING UNDER COVER — (1 Point)

Under this option, projects should place at least **75%** of parking spaces under cover. Motorcycle spaces are included in the calculations; however, bicycle parking spaces are exempt. Any roof that is used to shade or cover parking must either

- have a three-year aged SRI of at least **32;**
- be a vegetated roof; or
- be covered by energy-generation systems.

LIGHT POLLUTION REDUCTION—CREDIT

Projects need to meet uplight and light trespass requirements by either using the backlight-uplight-glare (BUG) method in option 1 or the calculation method in option 2. Projects also need to meet internally illuminated signage requirements if signage exists on site.

Project teams should consider all the **exterior luminaires** inside the project boundary based on the following:

- The photometric characteristics of each luminaire when mounted in the same orientation and tilt as in the project design.
- The lighting zone of the project property at the time construction starts. Project teams need to classify the project under a lighting zone, using the lighting zones definitions provided in the **Illuminating Engineering Society of North America and Interna-**

tional Dark-Sky Association (IES/IDA) Model Lighting Ordinance (MLO) User's Guide.

Following are the types of lighting that are exempt from the credit requirements if they are controlled separately from the nonexempt lighting:

- ❧ Specialized signal, directional, and marker lighting for transportation
- ❧ Lighting solely used for facade and landscape lighting in MLO lighting zones 3 and 4 and that is automatically turned off from midnight to 6:00 a.m.
- ❧ Government-mandated roadway lighting
- ❧ Lighting for theatrical purposes, stages, and video performances
- ❧ Hospital emergency department and helipad lighting
- ❧ National flag lighting in MLO lighting zones 2, 3, or 4
- ❧ Internally illuminated signage (this has its own requirement)

Following are the exceptions which projects can modify their lighting boundary:

- ❧ If the property line is adjacent to a public area that is a parking lot, walkway, bikeway, or plaza, the lighting boundary can be moved 5 feet (1.5 meters) beyond the property line.
- ❧ When there are adjacent properties owned by the same entity, and those properties are contiguous to the property that the LEED project is within, the lighting boundary may be expanded to include those properties if they have the same or higher MLO lighting zone designation as the LEED projects.
- ❧ When a property line is adjacent to a street, alley, or transit corridor, the lighting boundary can be moved to the centerline of the street, alley, or transit corridor.

Uplight:

OPTION 1: BUG RATING METHOD

Projects should not exceed the following luminaire uplight ratings, based on the specific light source installed in the luminaire as defined in **IES TM-15-11, Addendum A.**

OR

OPTION 2: CALCULATION METHOD

Under this option, projects should not exceed the required percentages for total lumens emitted above horizontal. Unlike option 1, in this option project teams will calculate the cumulative (total) maximum allowable uplight percentages based on the lighting zone.

AND

Light Trespass:

OPTION 1: BUG RATING METHOD

Projects should not exceed the luminaire backlight and glare ratings as defined in **IES TM-15-11, Addendum A**, based on the mounting location and distance from the lighting boundary.

Projects should orient all luminaires **less than two mounting heights** from the lighting boundary such that the backlight points toward the nearest lighting boundary line. <u>Building-mounted luminaires with the backlight oriented toward the building are exempt from the backlight rating requirement</u>.

OR

OPTION 2: CALCULATION METHOD

Under the calculation method, projects should not exceed the required vertical illuminances at the lighting boundary.

Project teams will need to use lighting software and develop a photometric site plan to pursue this option (manually measuring it with a light meter may not be possible at all).

AND

Internally illuminated exterior signage:

Any internally illuminated exterior signage should not exceed a luminance of **200 cd/m²** (nits) **during nighttime hours** and **2,000 cd/m²** (nits) **during daytime hours**.

SITE MASTER PLAN—CREDIT

In order to be eligible for this credit, school projects should <u>plan for future developments</u> and additionally achieve **at least four** of the following credits: High-Priority Site, Site Development—Protect or Restore Habitat, Open Space, Rainwater Management, Heat Island Reduction, and Light Pollution Reduction.

Under this credit, projects should develop a site master plan in collaboration with the school authorities. The master plan should include both the current construction activity and future construction activities within the building's life span. Next, the project teams will need to recalculate the achieved credits mentioned above, at that point using the future development data from the master plan.

TENANT DESIGN AND CONSTRUCTION GUIDELINES—CREDIT

<u>Before a lease is signed</u>, project teams should create an illustrated document with the following content as applicable:

- A description of the sustainable design and construction features of the project and the project's sustainability goals and objectives, including those for tenant spaces
- Recommendations for sustainable products, materials, strategies, and services
- Information to support the tenants to coordinate space, design, and construction with the building systems when pursuing the LEED ID+C v4 prerequisites and credits listed under the credit.

Note that these guidelines will not be binding on lessees.

PLACES OF RESPITE—CREDIT

Projects should provide places of respite for <u>patients and visitors</u> equal to **5%** of the **net usable program area of the building**, and they should provide places of respite for <u>staff</u> equal to **2%** of the **net usable program area of the building**.

Places of respite should be ideally outdoors. However, maximum **30%** of the respite area can be located in interior atria, solaria, greenhouses, or conditioned spaces. To qualify as a place of respite in an interior space, **90%** of the space should achieve a direct line of sight to unobstructed views of nature.

Both the dedicated <u>indoor</u> and <u>outdoor</u> areas should meet the following requirements:

- The dedicated area should be accessible from within the building or located within **200 feet** (60 meters) of a building entrance or access point.
- No medical care should be delivered in the places of respite.
- Options for shade or indirect sunlight should be provided, and projects should install at least one seating space per 200 square feet (18.5 square meters) of each respite area, with one wheelchair space per five seating spaces.
- Horticulture therapy and other specific clinical or special-use gardens unavailable to all building occupants may not account for more than 50% of the required area.
- Universal-access natural trails, which are available to visitors, staff, or patients, cannot account for more than 30% of the required area.

<u>Outdoor</u> areas should additionally contain a minimum of **25%** vegetation at the ground plane or have an overhead vegetated canopy, and should not be within 25 feet of smoking areas.

DIRECT EXTERIOR ACCESS – CREDIT

Under this credit, projects should provide direct access to an exterior courtyard, terrace, garden, or balcony. The provided space must be at least **5 square feet** (0.5 square meters) per patient for **75%** of all <u>inpatients</u> and **75%** of <u>outpatients whose length of stay exceeds four hours</u>. The only exclusion to this rule is the patients whose length of stay exceeds four hours and whose treatment makes them unable to move. If there are private balconies in the patient rooms, these spaces will qualify if they are at least 5 square feet (0.5 square meters).

Exterior places of respite—which meet the requirements of the "Places of Respite" credit and that are also adjacent to clinical areas or have direct access from inpatient units—can be included in this credit as well.

Qualifying spaces must be designated as nonsmoking, and all the spaces must meet the requirements for outdoor air contaminant concentrations in option 2 of the "Enhanced Indoor Air Quality Strategies" credit.

JOINT USE OF FACILITIES – CREDIT

OPTION 1: MAKE BUILDING SPACE OPEN TO THE GENERAL PUBLIC

Under this option, with the collaboration of school authorities, project teams should ensure that at least three of the following types of spaces in the school are available to be shared by the general public: auditorium, gymnasium, one or more classrooms, playing fields/stadiums, and joint parking. Additionally, in the joint-use areas, access to toilets should be provided after normal school hours.

OR

OPTION 2: CONTRACT WITH SPECIFIC ORGANIZATIONS TO SHARE BUILDING SPACE

Under this option, with the collaboration of school authorities, a contract should be signed with the community or other organizations or businesses to provide at least two of the following types of dedicated-use spaces inside the building: commercial office, health clinic, community service centers, library or media center, police office, parking lot, and one or more commercial businesses. Additionally, in the joint-use areas, access to toilets should be provided after normal school hours.

OR

OPTION 3: USE SHARED SPACE OWNED BY OTHER ORGANIZATIONS

In this option, the students will use other facilities outside of their school building. With the collaboration of the school authorities, school project teams should ensure that at least two of the following six types of spaces that are owned by other organizations or agencies are accessible to students: auditorium, gymnasium, one or more classrooms, cafeteria, swimming pool, and playing fields/stadiums.

All the joint-use facilities should be accessible by foot, and there must be <u>direct pedestrian access</u> to these spaces from the school. Joint-use agreements should be signed with the other organizations or agencies that demonstrate how these spaces will be shared.

OUTDOOR WATER USE REDUCTION—PREREQUISITE

Projects should reduce outdoor water use through one of the options below. Nonvegetated surfaces (such as pavements) must be excluded from landscape area calculations. <u>Athletic fields</u> and <u>playgrounds</u>, if vegetated, and <u>food gardens</u> may be included or excluded in the prerequisite calculations at the project teams' discretion.

OPTION 1: NO IRRIGATION REQUIRED

If a project has a landscape that does not need any irrigation beyond a maximum of a <u>two-year establishment period</u>, documenting it will fulfill the prerequisite.

OR

OPTION 2: REDUCED IRRIGATION

Under this option, projects need to reduce the project's landscape water consumption by at least **30%** from the calculated baseline for the <u>site's peak watering month</u>. This reduction should be established by careful selection of the plant species and the irrigation systems according to their efficiency. For the landscape water requirement calculation, the EPA WaterSense Water Budget Tool will be used.

<u>Project teams cannot use nonpotable water sources</u> to establish the 30% outdoor water reduction. However, this can happen under the "Outdoor Water Use Reduction" credit.

INDOOR WATER USE REDUCTION—PREREQUISITE

<u>For Building Water Use</u>:
For all the following fixtures and fittings shown in table 16, projects should reduce aggregate water consumption by **20%** from their baseline number of units. The baseline flow and flush rates are specified by the **Energy Policy Act of 1992 (EPAct 1992)**.

For all newly installed toilets, urinals, private lavatory faucets, and showerheads (that are eligible), projects should use WaterSense-labeled products, or an equivalent labeling can be used for projects that are located outside the United States.

<u>For Appliance and Process Water Use</u>:

All the installed appliances and processes must meet the ENERGY STAR requirements.

BUILDING LEVEL WATER METERING—PREREQUISITE

Projects should install permanent water meters that can measure the **total potable water use** for the <u>building</u> and <u>associated grounds</u>. Metered data should be collected in <u>monthly</u> and <u>annual</u> summaries. (The meter readings can be automated or manual.)

For a <u>5-year period</u>, the project should commit to sharing the whole-project water use data with USGBC, beginning on the date that the project accepts <u>LEED certification</u> or <u>typical occupancy</u>, whichever comes first. (The only exception to data sharing is a change of building ownership or lessee during the first 5 years of data sharing).

OUTDOOR WATER USE REDUCTION—CREDIT

OPTION 1: NO IRRIGATION REQUIRED – (2 Points)

As the name of the option implies, if the project contains a landscape that does not need any irrigation beyond a maximum <u>two-year establishment period</u>, it will automatically fulfill this option.

OR

OPTION 2: REDUCED IRRIGATION – (2 Points)

Under this option, project teams should reduce the project's landscape water consumption by at least **50%** (1 point) or **100%** (2 points) from the calculated baseline for the site's <u>peak watering month</u>. This reduction should be established by careful selection of the plant species and by increasing the efficiency of the irrigation systems. The **US Environmental Protection Agency WaterSense Water Budget Tool** will be used for water budget calculations.

<u>Nonvegetated surfaces</u>, such as pavements, are excluded from landscape calculations. <u>Athletic fields</u>, <u>vegetated playgrounds,</u> and <u>food gardens</u> may be included or excluded from these calculations according to the project teams' decision.

Additional reductions beyond the prerequisite level of **30%** may be achieved with the use of any combination of efficiency, <u>alternative water sources,</u> and smart scheduling technologies. Alternative water sources can include graywater, reclaimed wastewater, swimming pool backwash water, captured rainwater, refrigeration system condensate, fluid cooler discharge, food steamer discharge, fire pump test water, industrial process water, municipally supplied treated wastewater, stormwater and foundation drain water, and ice machine condensate.

INDOOR WATER USE REDUCTION—CREDIT

For Building Water Use:
Projects should further reduce indoor water consumption from the calculated baseline in the "Indoor Water Use Reduction" prerequisite. Additional potable water savings above the prerequisite level (20%) can be established by using alternative water sources.

AND

For Appliances and Process Water Use:
Projects should install equipment fulfilling the minimum LEED requirements of any of the categories below. One point will be awarded for projects that fulfill the requirements of any of the following categories, while "LEED BD+C: Schools", "LEED BD+C: Retail", and "LEED BD+C: Healthcare" projects can earn an additional point for fulfilling the requirement of a second category.

> Category 1: Commercial Washing Machines
> Category 2: Commercial Kitchen Equipment
> Category 3: Laboratory and Medical Equipment
> Category 4: Municipal Steam Systems

COOLING TOWER WATER USE REDUCTION—CREDIT

Project teams should conduct a one-time potable water analysis for cooling towers and evaporative condensers to find the actual values of Ca, total alkalinity, SiO_2, CI^-, and conductivity. Then, the project teams should find the number of cooling tower cycles by dividing the "maximum allowed concentration level" of each parameter by the "actual concentration" level of each parameter found in the testing potable makeup water. Next, projects should limit the cooling tower cycles to avoid exceeding the maximum values for any of these parameters.

$$\textbf{Cycles of concentration} = \frac{\text{Maximum parameter concentrations in condenser water}}{\text{Actual parameter concentrations in makeup water}}$$

Projects that meet the requirements up to this point will earn one point under this credit. To gain an additional point, projects can use a minimum of **20%** of recycled nonpotable water in their cooling towers or can instead increase the cooling tower cycles beyond **10** by increasing the level of treatment in the condenser or makeup water.

WATER METERING—CREDIT

Project teams should install permanent water meters to **at least two** or more of the following water subsystems that are applicable:

- Irrigation: Meter water systems that serve at least **80%** of the irrigated landscape area, landscaping that requires no irrigation are exempt. However, if reclaimed water is used for irrigation, then 100% of the reclaimed water should be metered.

- Indoor plumbing fixtures and fittings: Meter water systems that serve at least **80%** of the total number of fixtures and fittings described in the "Indoor Water Use Reduction" prerequisite.

- Domestic hot water: Meter at least **80%** of the installed domestic hot water heating capacity, including tanks and on-demand heaters.

- Boilers with aggregate projected annual water use of 100,000 gallons (378,541 liters) or more, or boilers with more than 500,000 Btu/hr (150 kW): For multiple boilers, a single makeup meter can record the total flow.

- Reclaimed water: Meter all the reclaimed water. If the reclaimed water contains a makeup water connection, that should be metered as well.

- Other process water: Meter at least **80%** of process end uses, which can include humidification systems, clothes washers, dishwashers, pools, and more.

The submetering equipment to be used can be read manually, or it can be connected to the building automation system.

In addition to the requirements above, "LEED BD+C: Healthcare" projects should install water meters in any five of the following: purified water systems, filter backwash water, water use in laundry, water use in a laboratory, water use in a dietary department, water use in a central sterile and processing department, water use in physiotherapy/hydrotherapy treatment areas, water use in a surgical suite, cold water makeup for domestic hot water systems, and closed-loop hydronic system makeup water.

FUNDAMENTAL COMMISSIONING AND VERIFICATION—PREREQUISITE

Scope of the commissioning process:

Project teams should complete the following commissioning activities for the mechanical, electrical, plumbing, and renewable energy systems and assemblies according to **ASHRAE Guideline 0-2005** and **ASHRAE Guideline 1.1-2007 for HVAC&R systems**, as related to energy, water, indoor environmental quality, and durability.

For the building envelope, the requirements are limited including the envelope in the OPR and the BOD and review of the OPR, the BOD, and the project design.

NIBS Guideline 3-2012 for Exterior Enclosures can provide additional guidance on building envelope commissioning.

The project teams should first develop the **OPR** and the **BOD**. Next, the project teams should assign the commissioning authority. The CxA is the person who will manage the whole commissioning process. The CxA will complete the following tasks:

- Review the OPR, the BOD, and the project design
- Develop and implement the Cx plan
- Ensure that the Cx requirements are integrated into the construction documents
- Prepare construction checklists and system test procedures
- Confirm system test execution
- Maintain an issues and benefits log throughout the Cx process
- Prepare a final Cx report
- Report all the findings **directly to the owner** throughout the whole process

Qualifications of the Commissioning Authority (CxA):

By the end of the design development phase, the project teams should engage a commissioning authority. The qualified CxA should have completed commissioning for at least two similar projects from the early design phase to a minimum of ten months of occupancy.

The CxA can be

- A qualified employee of the owner;
- An independent consultant;
- An employee of the design or construction firm who is not a part of the project design or construction team (except that for projects smaller than 20,000 square feet, the CxA can be a qualified member of the design or construction team as well);
- A disinterested subcontractor of the design or construction team; and
- For small projects with computer room peak cooling loads less than 2,000,000 Btu/h (600 kW) or a total computer room peak cooling load less than 600,000 Btu/h (175 kW), the CxA may be a qualified member of the design or construction team.

Current Facilities Requirements (CFR) and Operations and Maintenance (O&M) plan:

Projects should prepare a **CFR** and **O&M plan**, which should contain all the information necessary to operate the building efficiently. The plan must include the following:

- A schedule for building occupancy
- A run-time schedule for equipment
- A sequence of operations for the building
- Setpoints for all the HVAC equipment
- Building lighting levels

- Any changes in schedules or setpoints for different seasons, days of the week, and times of day
- Minimum requirements for outside air
- A preventive maintenance plan for building equipment that is described in the systems
- A commissioning program to include periodic commissioning requirements, ongoing commissioning tasks, and continuous tasks for critical facilities

MINIMUM ENERGY PERFORMANCE—PREREQUISITE

For all LEED BD+C Rating Systems, except "LEED BD+C: Data Centers":
For all the options, project teams should first determine the climate zone of the project according to **ASHRAE 90.1-2010, Appendix B**. Projects outside the United States can refer to **ANSI/ASHRAE/IESNA Standard 90.1–2010, Appendixes B and D** and determine the appropriate climate zone for their project.

OPTION 1: WHOLE-BUILDING ENERGY SIMULATION

Under this option, project teams should create a building energy model and simulate the whole-building energy use. New construction projects should demonstrate a minimum **5%** improvement, major renovation projects should demonstrate a minimum **3%** improvement, and core and shell projects should demonstrate a minimum **2%** improvement.

Project teams should calculate the baseline building performance according to **ANSI/ASHRAE/IESNA Standard 90.1-2010, Appendix G with errata**.

In addition to the energy modeling requirements, projects' designs should meet the mandatory provisions of **ANSI/ASHRAE/IESNA Standard 90.1-2010, with errata**.

If the unregulated loads are not identical and the simulation program cannot model the energy savings, project teams should then follow the **exceptional calculation method (ANSI/ASHRAE/IESNA Standard 90.1-2010, G2.5)**.

Project teams may also use the COMNET Modeling Guidelines and Procedures for documenting the measures for reducing unregulated loads.

OR

OPTION 2: PRESCRIPTIVE COMPLIANCE: ASHRAE 50% ADVANCED ENERGY DESIGN GUIDE

Under this option, projects should comply with the mandatory and prescriptive provisions of **ANSI/ASHRAE/IESNA Standard 90.1-2010, with errata**. Next, projects should comply with the HVAC and service water heating requirements, equipment efficiencies, economizers, ventilation, and duct-and-damper requirements in "Chapter 4, Design Strategies and Recommendations by Climate Zone" of the corresponding **ASHRAE 50% Advanced Energy Design Guide.**

OR

OPTION 3: PRESCRIPTIVE COMPLIANCE: ADVANCED BUILDINGS™ CORE PERFORMANCE™ GUIDE

Under this option, projects should comply with the mandatory and prescriptive provisions of **ANSI/ASHRAE/IESNA Standard 90.1-2010, with errata.** Next, the projects should comply with the **Advanced Buildings™ Core Performance™ Guide (CPG).**

In this option, the energy performance target should be established using the EPA's **ENERGY STAR Target Finder,** and projects should achieve a minimum score of **90.**

For "LEED BD+C: Data Centers":

"LEED BD+C: Data Center" projects should comply with the mandatory provisions of **ANSI/ASHRAE/IESNA Standard 90.1-2010, with errata.** Next, project teams need to create a whole-building energy simulation in accordance with **ANSI/ASHRAE/IESNA Standard 90.1–2010, Appendix G, with errata,** and they should demonstrate a **5%** improvement in the proposed performance rating over the baseline performance rating.

To determine the total energy cost savings, project teams should create two separate models, one for building energy cost and the other for IT equipment energy cost. Two IT load models should be developed by using two scenarios, one for the maximum estimated IT load rating and the second for the startup IT rating expected at the time of commissioning.

Data center project teams should also determine the **power utilization effectiveness (PUE) value** of the proposed design. For the data center projects, a minimum of **2%** of the **5% energy savings** must come from building power and cooling infrastructure.

BUILDING-LEVEL ENERGY METERING—PREREQUISITE

Projects should install new building-level energy meters/submeters, or use existing ones, that can be aggregated to provide **total building energy consumption,** including electricity, natural gas, chilled water, steam, fuel oil, propane and biomass energy sources. Utility-owned meters capable of aggregating total building energy consumption are also acceptable. This prerequisite does not require metering of the locally generated energy sources dedicated to the project.

The total building energy consumption and the electrical demand data (if metered) should be shared with USGBC **at a minimum of one month intervals for a five year period or until**

the building changes ownership or lessee. Data sharing should start on the date the project accepts LEED certification or typical occupancy, whichever comes first.

"LEED BD+C: Core and Shell" projects should install **base building-level energy meters/submeters** that can be aggregated to provide base building-level data to represent total building energy consumption, including electricity, natural gas, chilled water, steam, fuel oil, propane, and biomass energy sources.

FUNDAMENTAL REFRIGERANT MANAGEMENT—PREREQUISITE

Projects should not use chlorofluorocarbon-based refrigerants in their HVAC&R systems. When reusing existing HVAC&R equipment, project teams should complete a **comprehensive CFC phase-out conversion** before the project completion. Phase-out plans going beyond the project completion date will be considered on their merits.

Existing small HVAC&R or other equipment, such as standard refrigerators and small water cooler units containing less than **0.5 pound** (225 grams) of refrigerant, are exempt from the prerequisite requirements.

ENHANCED COMMISSIONING—CREDIT

Qualifications of the Commissioning Authority (CxA):

As with the "Fundamental Commissioning and Verification" prerequisite, the qualified CxA should have completed commissioning for at least **two similar projects from the early design phase to the minimum ten months of occupancy.** But with this credit the CxA can only be an independent consultant, owner's employee, or a disinterested subcontractor of the design team. Note that in the prerequisite, the CxA can also be a disinterested subcontractor of the design and construction team, but in this credit, the CxA can only be a disinterested subcontractor of the design team.

OPTION 1: ENHANCED SYSTEMS COMMISSIONING — (3-4 Points)

PATH 1: ENHANCED COMMISSIONING — (3 Points)

As with the "Fundamental Commissioning and Verification" prerequisite, complete the commissioning process in accordance with **ASHRAE Guideline 0-2005** and **ASHRAE guideline 1.1-2007 for HVAC&R systems** with respect to the electrical, mechanical, plumbing, and renewable energy systems as they relate to energy, water, indoor environmental quality, and durability.

Under this credit, the CxA will **review the contractor submittals** and additionally do the following:

➤ Verify inclusion of **systems manual requirements** in construction documents to be issued for bid.

➤ Verify inclusion of **operator and building user training requirements** in construction documents to be issued for bid.

➤ Verify the **systems manual** updates and delivery and also verify that the necessary **operating documents** are delivered to the owner before building occupancy.

➤ Verify operator **and occupant trainings delivery and effectiveness.**

➤ Verify **seasonal testings.**

➤ Review the building operations **ten months** after the project's substantial completion

➤ Develop an **ongoing commissioning plan.**

OR

PATH 2: ENHANCED AND MONITORING BASED COMMISSIONING — (4 points)

In addition to all the requirements in "Path 1: Enhanced commissioning," projects should develop monitoring-based procedures and identify points to be measured in order to assess the performance of energy and water-consuming items. The enhanced Cx plan should be updated to cover the MBCx requirements. Project teams should address the following:

- Roles and responsibilities
- Measurement requirements, such as points, metering systems, or data access
- Points to be tracked
- Limits of acceptable values for the points tracked
- Elements used to evaluate performance
- Action plan for identifying and correcting errors
- Planning for repairs
- Training to prevent errors
- The analyses frequency in the first year of occupancy

The systems manual should be updated with any modifications or new settings.

Only for the "LEED BDC+C: Data Center" projects:
For projects choosing option 1 (either path) and have peak cooling loads less than 2,000,000 Btu/h (600 kW), or a total computer room peak cooling load less than 600,000 Btu/h (175 kW), the CxA must additionally:

➤ Perform at least one commissioning verification review of the OPR, the BOD, and the design documents before the development of mid-construction documents

- Evaluate and confirm the review comments in all the design submissions
- Conduct an additional full verification review with 95% completion of the design documents and the BOD.

For projects with peak cooling loads of <u>more than</u> 2,000,000 Btu/hr (600kW) or a total computer room peak cooling load of more than 600,000 Btu/hr (175 kW), the CxA should conduct **at least three verification reviews** of the <u>basis of design</u>. The first one should be before the start of design development, one should be before the midconstruction documents, and one final verification of the completed design documents should ensure that the owner's project requirements are met.

AND/OR

OPTION 2: ENVELOPE COMMISSIONING— (2 Points)

In the "Fundamental Commissioning and Verification" prerequisite, the building envelope should have been a part of the OPR and the BOD, while the OPR, the BOD, and the project design should have been reviewed with the inclusion of the building envelope. In this option, the project teams should complete the prerequisite's requirements as they apply to the building envelope (which also means that the Cx plan created under the prerequisite should also cover the building envelope) and additionally commission the building envelope in accordance with **ASHRAE Guideline 0-2005** and the **National Institute of Building Sciences (NIBS) Guideline 3-2012, Exterior Enclosure Technical Requirements for the Commissioning Process** as they relate to energy, water, indoor environmental quality, and durability.

The CxA should **review the contractor submittals** and additionally do the following:
- Verify **inclusion of systems manual requirements** in the construction documents
- Verify inclusion of **operator and building user training requirements** in the construction documents
- Verify **systems manual updates and delivery**
- Verify **operator and occupant training delivery and effectiveness**
- Verify **seasonal testings**
- Review the building operations **ten months after the project completion**
- Develop an **ongoing commissioning plan**

<u>Only for the LEED BD+C: Healthcare" projects</u>:
"LEED BD+C: Healthcare" projects may have additional testing procedures and requirements for the life safety equipment under this credit.

OPTIMIZE ENERGY PERFORMANCE—CREDIT

OPTION 1: WHOLE BUILDING ENERGY SIMULATION — (1-18 Points)

Under this option, projects should follow the criteria in option 1 of the "Minimum Energy Performance" prerequisite to further improve the building's energy performance. Projects will be awarded points according to their percentage of annual <u>energy cost savings</u>. A new construction project that makes a reduction of **6%** will get 1 point, and a project that makes a reduction of **50%** will get the full 18 points. Unlike in the "Minimum Energy Performance" prerequisite, under this option, projects using renewable energy sources can count the on-site renewable energy generated in the credit calculations.

OR

OPTION 2: PRESCRIPTIVE COMPLIANCE: ASHRAE ADVANCED ENERGY DESIGN GUIDE—(1-6 Points)

Projects pursuing this option should comply with applicable recommendations and standards in "Chapter 4, Design Strategies and Recommendations by Climate Zone," for the appropriate **ASHRAE 50% Advanced Energy Design Guide** and climate zone.

ADVANCED ENERGY METERING—CREDIT

Project teams should install advanced energy metering for the following:
- All whole-building energy sources used by the building
- Any individual energy end uses that consume **10% or more of the total annual consumption of the building**

The advanced energy metering should meet the following characteristics:
- Meters should be permanently installed and be able to record at intervals of one hour or less and transmit data to a remote location. The metering data should be remotely accessible, and all meters should be capable of reporting hourly, daily, monthly, and annual energy use.
- Electricity meters should record both the energy consumption and the energy demand. If appropriate, the whole-building electricity meters should record the power factor.
- The data collection system should be connected to a local area network, building automation system, wireless network, or comparable communication infrastructure.
- The system must be able to store all meter data for at least thirty-six months.

"LEED BD+C: Core and Shell" projects should install meters for future tenant spaces.

DEMAND RESPONSE—CREDIT

The intent of this credit is to encourage project teams to design the building and equipment to allow participation in demand-response programs through **load shedding** or **load shifting**.

CASE 1: DEMAND RESPONSE PROGRAM AVAILABLE — (2 Points)

- Design a real-time, "**fully automated**" DR system based on external initiation by a DR program provider. "**Semiautomated**" DR may also be utilized in practice. However, a "**manual**" demand-response system will not satisfy the credit.
- With the intention of multiyear renewal, enroll in a **minimum one-year** DR program for at least **10% of the estimated peak electricity demand**.
- Develop a plan for meeting the DR commitment during the DR event.
- Include the DR processes in the CxA's scope of work, including participation in at least one full test of the DR plan.

OR

CASE 2: DEMAND RESPONSE PROGRAM NOT AVAILABLE — (1 Point)

If a demand-response program is not available in the project's location, projects should provide infrastructure for **future demand-response programs** or **dynamic**, **real-time pricing programs** and complete the following activities:

- Install interval recording meters with communications and ability for the building automation system to accept an external price or control signal.
- Develop a comprehensive plan for shedding at least **10% of estimated peak electricity demand**.
- Include the CxA in the DR processes, including participation in at least one full DR testing.
- Contact the local utility to discuss participation in future DR programs.

RENEWABLE ENERGY PRODUCTION—CREDIT

Projects should use renewable energy systems to offset building energy costs. The percentage of renewable energy will be calculated with the following equation:

$$\textbf{\% renewable energy generated} = \frac{\text{Equivalent cost of usable energy produced by the renewable energy system}}{\text{Total building annual energy cost}}$$

The use of <u>solar gardens</u> or <u>community renewable energy systems</u> is also allowed if both of the requirements below are met:

➤ The project owns the system or leased the system for a period of at least **10 years**
➤ The system is located within the **same utility service area**

ENHANCED REFRIGERANT MANAGEMENT—CREDIT

<u>For all LEED BD+C projects, except "LEED BD+C: Retail"</u>:

OPTION 1: NO REFRIGERANTS OR LOW-IMPACT REFRIGERANTS — (1 Point)

Under this option, projects should not use any refrigerants or only use naturally occurring or synthetic refrigerants that have an <u>ODP</u> of **0** and a <u>GWP</u> of less than **50**.

As with the "Fundamental Refrigerant Management" prerequisite, existing HVAC&R equipment and other equipment such as refrigerators and small water coolers that contain less than 0.5 pound (225 grams) of refrigerant will be exempt from the credit calculations.

OR

OPTION 2: CALCULATION OF REFRIGERANT IMPACT — (1 Point)

Under this option, project teams should select refrigerants to be used in the HVAC&R equipment to minimize or eliminate the emission of compounds that contribute to ozone depletion and climate change by performing weighted average calculations for all the refrigerants used.

<u>For "LEED BD+C: Retail"</u>:

"LEED BD+C: Retail" projects should also meet either "Option 1" or "Option 2" for all their HVAC&R systems. However, stores that contain commercial refrigeration systems must also comply with the following requirements:

➤ Use only non-ozone depleting refrigerants.
➤ Use equipment with an average HFC refrigerant charge of no more than 1.75 pounds of refrigerant per 1,000 Btu/h total evaporator cooling load.
➤ Establish a predicted store wide annual refrigerant emissions rate of no more than 15%. Projects should conduct leak testing using the procedures in the EPA GreenChill's best practices guideline for leak tightness at installation.

Alternatively, for the newly constructed stores, projects with commercial refrigeration systems can provide proof of attainment of EPA GreenChill's <u>silver-level store certification</u>, instead of following the mentioned prescriptive criteria.

GREEN POWER AND CARBON OFFSETS—CREDIT

Projects should engage in a contract for a **minimum of 5 years,** to be delivered **at least annually**, from the qualified resources that have come online since January 1, 2005. The contract should specify the provision of at least **50%** or **100%** of the project's energy from green power, carbon offsets, and/or renewable energy certificates (RECs).

Green power and RECs should be **Green-e Energy-certified** or the equivalent. RECs can only be used to mitigate the effects of **scope 2** electricity use only. And carbon offsets may be used to mitigate **scope 1** or **scope 2** emissions on a **metric ton of carbon dioxide-equivalent** basis, and they can be used for both electricity and nonelectricity energy sources, such as natural gas. All the purchased carbon offsets should be **Green-e Climate-certified** or equivalent.

For projects located in the United States, the carbon offsets should be from greenhouse gas emission reduction projects within the United States, while for the projects outside the United States, purchasing carbon offsets from the country that the project is located in is not mandatory. Projects should determine the percentage of green power or offsets based on the **quantity** of energy consumed.

For "LEED BD+C: Core and Shell" projects **only**, the energy usage for the core and shell floor area will be defined by Building Owners and Managers Association (BOMA) standards, and the core and shell area should not be less than 15% of the project's floor area. If the core and shell area of the project is less than 15% of the project's floor area, then the project should address 15% of the total building area in the credit calculations.

STORAGE AND COLLECTION OF RECYCLABLES—PREREQUISITE

For all the LEED BD+C rating systems, except LEED BD+C: Retail, projects should provide dedicated areas that can be accessible by the waste haulers and building occupants for the collection and storage of recyclable materials for the entire building. Collection and storage areas can be located separately as well. Recyclable materials must include **mixed paper, corrugated cardboard, glass, plastics,** and **metals.** Additionally, projects should take the necessary actions for safe collection, storage, and disposal of two of the following: **batteries, mercury-containing lamps,** and **electronic waste.**

"LEED BD+C: Retail" projects only:
Retail projects should conduct a waste stream analysis and identify a project's top **five** recyclable waste streams (by weight or volume) using consistent metrics throughout. (The waste stream study period should be a minimum of 24 hours.)

Once the waste stream study is completed, project teams should list the top **four** recyclable waste streams and provide dedicated areas for separation, collection, and storage of the recyclables, which should also be accessible to the waste haulers and the building occupants. If project teams identify batteries, lamps containing mercury, or electronic waste as one the four waste streams, all necessary measures should be taken for safe collection, storage, and disposal (not recycling) of those items.

CONSTRUCTION AND DEMOLITION WASTE MANAGEMENT PLANNING— PREREQUISITE

Projects should develop and implement a **construction and demolition waste management plan** by meeting the following:

- Establish waste diversion goals by identifying at **least 5 materials** (both structural and nonstructural) targeted for diversion. Make an approximate calculation to show the percentage of these materials compared to the total construction waste. Units may be by weight or volume but must be consistent throughout the calculations.
- Specify whether the materials be separated or commingled and explain the diversion strategies planned. Describe how these materials will be transported to the recycling facilities and describe the recycling process.

Project teams should write down a final report showing all major waste streams generated, including their disposal and diversion rates. Below is the formula to be used for disposal and diversion-rate calculations:

Diversion rate = (Total waste diverted from landfill / Total waste produced by the project) x 100

Alternative daily cover (ADC) does not qualify as a material diverted from disposal in LEED calculations. (Even though ADC will not count as a diversion, it should still be included as a portion of the total construction waste generated.) And **land-cleaning debris**, which is created by the removal of rock, soil, stone, and vegetation, is not considered waste since the ingredients are all natural products. However, the handling of both alternative daily cover and land-cleaning debris, as well as all the other materials not contributing to diversion, should still be addressed in the construction and demolition waste management plan.

For this prerequisite and its credit, "Construction and Demolition Waste Management," projects that cannot implement reuse and recycling methods can consider waste-to-energy systems if the **European Commission Waste Framework Directive 2008/98/EC** and **Waste Incineration Directive 2000/76/EC** are followed. Waste-to-energy facilities must meet the applicable **European Committee for Standardization (CEN) EN 303** standards. Wood-based products will be exempt from this additional requirement for incineration and will be directly considered diversion.

PBT SOURCE REDUCTION – MERCURY—PREREQUISITE

In the project's recycling collection system, project teams should identify <u>the types of mercury-containing products and devices to be collected</u>, <u>identify the criteria for their handling by a recycling program</u>, and <u>identify the disposal methods for captured mercury</u>. Applicable mercury-containing devices include lamps (linear, circular fluorescent, HIDs, etc.), dental wastes, and more. For dental care facilities, projects should specify and install amalgam separation devices that meet the ISO 11143 standard.

Additionally, all healthcare projects should comply with **2010 FGI Guidelines for Design and Construction of Health Care Facilities, Section A1.3-4b, Mercury Elimination**, as outlined in the following section:

- <u>New construction projects</u>: Healthcare facilities cannot use mercury-containing equipment, including switching devices, thermostats, and other building system sources, with the exclusion of lamps.

- <u>Renovation projects</u>: Healthcare facilities should develop a **phase-out plan** to eliminate mercury-containing products and upgrade current mercury-containing lamps to high-efficiency, mercury-free or low-mercury lamp technology.

BUILDING LIFE-CYCLE IMPACT REDUCTION—CREDIT

OPTION 1: HISTORIC BUILDING REUSE – (5 Points)

Under this option, in order to avoid new construction, projects should be reusing a historic building with a "historic" designation, or the existing building should be inside a historic district. To qualify as a historic building, the building or the historic district must be listed or eligible for listing in the <u>local</u>, <u>state</u>, or <u>national register</u> of <u>historic places</u>. If the building does not have a "historic" designation but is located inside a historic district, it may qualify under this credit if it meets one of the four **US National Register of Historic Places** criteria or the **state** or **local historic criteria**.

Once the status of the building is confirmed, project teams should maintain the existing building <u>structure</u>, <u>envelope</u>, and <u>interior nonstructural elements</u> of the historic building or the contributing building inside a historic district. Project teams should not demolish any part of the historic building or the contributing building in a historic district unless it has structural problems or contains hazardous materials.

For buildings listed <u>locally</u>, the approval for any demolition should be granted by the <u>local historic preservation review board</u>. For the buildings listed in a state register or the US National Register of Historic Places, the approval for any demolition should be in a programmatic agreement with the state historic preservation office or National Park Service.

Any alteration, such as preservation, restoration, or rehabilitation, must be conducted according to the <u>local</u> or <u>national standards</u> for rehabilitation, wherever applicable. If the building is not subject to historic review, a **preservation professional** that meets the <u>United States' federal qualifications for historic architects</u> should be included in the project team, and the preservation professional must confirm conformance to the **Secretary of Interior's Standards for the Treatment of Historic Properties**. If the building is not subject to any historic review, the preservation professional must ensure conformance with the <u>Secretary of Interior's Standards for the Treatment of Historic Properties</u>.

OR

OPTION 2: RENOVATION OF ABANDONED OR BLIGHTED BUILDING — (5 Points)

Under this option, project teams should maintain at least **50%**, by <u>surface area</u>, of the existing building **structure** (e.g., foundation, floor, roof decking), **enclosure** (e.g., skin, framing), and **interior structural elements** (e.g., walls, doors, floor coverings, ceiling systems) for buildings that meet local criteria of <u>abandoned</u> buildings or are <u>considered blighted</u>.

The building must be renovated to a <u>state of productive occupancy</u> to fulfill this option. If there is any deterioration or damage, up to **25%** of the building surface area may be excluded from credit calculation. If the deteriorated or damaged part of the building is more than 25% of the building surface area, project teams should proceed with demolishing those parts and neglect pursuing this option. Additionally, window assemblies and any hazardous materials that are remediated as a part of the project should also be excluded from the calculations.

Following is the equation to be used for this option:

$$\text{Abandoned or blighted building reuse} = \left(\frac{\text{Surface area reused}}{\text{Existing building surface area} - \text{Hazardous or unsafe materials demolished area}} \right) \times 100$$

OR

OPTION 3: BUILDING AND MATERIAL REUSE — (2-4 Points)

Under this option, projects should be using existing buildings and materials, as well as using salvaged materials off-site. Projects will reuse or salvage building materials <u>on-site</u> or <u>off-site</u> as a percentage of the <u>surface area</u>. **Structural elements** (e.g. foundation, floors, roof decking), **enclosure materials** (e.g., skin, framing), and **permanently installed interior elements** (e.g., walls, doors, floor coverings, ceiling systems) should all be <u>included</u> in the credit calculations. Window assemblies and any hazardous materials that are remediated as a part of the project are excluded from the calculations.

Off-site products that are used for this credit **cannot contribute toward the** "Building Product Disclosure and Optimization—Sourcing of Raw Materials" credit.

Following is the equation to be used under this option:

$$\text{Existing building reuse} = \left(\dfrac{\text{Surface area reused from off-site} + \text{Surface area reused from on-site}}{\text{Existing building surface area} - \text{Hazardous materials surface area}} \right) \times 100$$

OR

OPTION 4: WHOLE-BUILDING LIFE-CYCLE ASSESSMENT — (3 Points)

For new construction (buildings or portions of buildings), project teams should conduct a life-cycle assessment of the project's structure and enclosure, which should demonstrate **a minimum of 10% reduction**, compared with the baseline building, in at least three of the six impact categories listed below, <u>one of which must be global warming potential</u>:

- ➻ Global warming potential (greenhouse gases), in CO_2e;
- ➻ Depletion of the stratospheric ozone layer, in kg CFC-11;
- ➻ Acidification of land and water sources, in moles H+ or kg SO_2;
- ➻ Eutrophication, in kg nitrogen or kg phosphate;
- ➻ Formation of tropospheric ozone, in kg NOx, kg O_3 eq, or kg ethene; and
- ➻ Depletion of nonrenewable energy resources, in MJ.

No impact category evaluated as part of the life-cycle assessment may increase by more than **5%** compared with the baseline building.

The LCA should cover the structure and enclosure, including the footings, foundations, structural wall assemblies from cladding to interior finishes, structural floors, ceilings (excluding finishes), and roof assemblies. The mechanical, electrical, and plumbing systems, as well as the excavation and other site development activities, should be <u>excluded</u> from the LCA. Additional building elements such as nonstructural walls or finishes can be included or excluded from the LCA in the project teams' discretion.

In the LCA calculations, the building should fully account for maintenance and replacement for at least **60 years**. Additionally, for the LCA calculations, data sets must be compliant with **ISO 14044**.

<u>For "LEED BD+C: Healthcare" projects only;</u>
For all options in this credit, if "LEED BD+C: Healthcare" projects have demolished building materials to create courtyards for increasing daylighting, those demolished parts can be considered as "retained" in the credit calculations. However, the new courtyards must meet the requirements of the "Daylight" credit.

BPDO: ENVIRONMENTAL PRODUCT DECLARATIONS

OPTION 1: ENVIRONMENTAL PRODUCT DECLARATION (EPD) — (1 Point)

Under this option, project teams should use at least **20 different permanently installed products**, sourced from at least **five different manufacturers** which meet one of the following disclosure criteria:

- Product-specific declarations: Only the products with a publicly available, critically reviewed life-cycle assessment conforming to **ISO 14044** and having at least a **cradle-to-gate scope assessment** will qualify under these criteria. For the purposes of credit-achievement calculations, these products will be valued as **one quarter (1/4) of a product**.

- Environmental Product Declarations: To qualify for an EPD, a product must conform to ISO 14025, 14040, 14044, and EN 15804 or ISO 21930, and the EPD should have at least a cradle-to-gate scope assessment. Next, for the purposes of credit achievement calculations, the EPDs will be valued according to their types as follows:

  a. **Industry-wide (generic) Type III third-party certification EPD**: This includes products with **industry-wide (generic) Type III third-party certification** (including external certification that the manufacturer is recognized as the participant by the program operator). These products will be valued as **one-half (1/2) of a product** for the purposes of credit-achievement calculations.

  b. **Product-specific Type III third-party certification EPD**: This includes products with **product-specific Type III third-party certification** (including external certification that the manufacturer is recognized as the participant by the program operator). These products will be valued as **one whole (1) product** for the purposes of credit achievement calculations.

- Other USGBC-approved program

Similar products from the same manufacturer can be counted as separate products as well, but their formulations must be different.

AND/OR

OPTION 2: MULTI-ATTRIBUTE OPTIMIZATION — (1 Point)

Under this option, **50%** (by cost) of the permanently installed products used in the project must comply with one of the following criteria.

- Third-party-certified products that demonstrate impact reduction below the industry average **in at least three** of the following five impact categories are valued at **100%** of their cost for credit-achievement calculations.

- Global warming potential (greenhouse gases), in CO_2e;
- Depletion of the stratospheric ozone layer, in kilograms of CFC-11;
- Acidification of land and water sources, in moles of H+ or kilograms of SO_2;
- Eutrophication, in kilograms of nitrogen or kilograms of phosphate;
- Formation of tropospheric ozone, in kilograms of NO_x or kilograms of ethane; and depletion of nonrenewable energy resources, in million joules (MJ).

→ Other USGBC-approved programs

For the credit achievement calculations, products that are sourced (extracted, manufactured, purchased) within **100 miles** (160 kilometers) of the project site will be valued at **200%** of their base contributing cost. And this will only happen under option 2, not option 1. Additionally, under option 2, structure and enclosure materials cannot constitute more than **30%** of the value of compliant building products.

As discussed, all the qualifying products must be <u>permanently installed</u> products for both options 1 and 2. For LEED, <u>mechanical</u>, <u>electrical</u>, <u>plumbing,</u> and <u>furniture</u> items are not considered permanently installed building products and are typically excluded from the credit calculations. However, if the project team considers them "permanently installed building products," they can be included in the credit calculations as long as they are also included in the other BPDO credits, which are "BPDO: Sourcing of Raw Materials" and "BPDO: Material Ingredients."

BPDO: SOURCING OF RAW MATERIALS—CREDIT

Project teams should achieve one or both of the following options for a maximum of 2 points.

OPTION 1: RAW MATERIAL SOURCE AND EXTRACTION REPORTING — (1 Point)

Under this option, project teams should use at least **20 permanently installed building materials** from at least **five different manufacturers**, which have:

- → publicly released a report from their raw material suppliers that includes raw material extraction locations;
- → a commitment to long-term ecologically responsible land use;
- → a commitment to meeting applicable standards or programs that address responsible sourcing criteria; and
- → a commitment to reducing environmental harms created from the extraction /manufacturing process.

Following are the valuation criteria for this option;

➤ Products sourced from manufacturers with self-declared reports are valued at **one-half (1/2) of a product** in the credit achievement calculations.

➤ Products with third-party verified corporate sustainability reports that include environmental impacts of extraction operations and activities related to the manufacturer's product and the product's supply chain are valued as **one whole (1) product** for credit-achievement calculation. Acceptable CSR frameworks include:

- Global Reporting Initiative (GRI) Sustainability Report
- Organisation for Economic Co-operation and Development (OECD) Guidelines for Multinational Enterprises
- UN Global Compact: Communication of Progress
- ISO 26000: 2010 Guidance on Social Responsibility
- Other USGBC-approved programs

Similar products with <u>distinct formulations</u> from the same manufacturer can be counted as separate products. All the reports documented for the credit achievement should be current at the products' time of installation.

AND/OR

OPTION 2: LEADERSHIP EXTRACTION PRACTICES — (1 Point)

Under this option, project teams should use products that meet <u>at least one</u> of the following responsible extraction criteria for at least **25%** (by cost) **of the total value of permanently installed building products** in the project.

➤ **Extended producer responsibility (EPR):** This includes products purchased from a manufacturer that is involved in an extended-producer-responsibility program or is directly responsible for extended producer responsibility. Products meeting this criterion are valued at **50%** of their cost in the credit-achievement calculations.

➤ **Bio-based materials:** Bio-based products that meet the <u>Sustainable Agriculture Network's Sustainable Agriculture Standard</u>. Bio-based raw materials must be tested using <u>ASTM Test Method D6866</u> and be legally harvested. **Hide products**, such as leather and other animal skin material, are <u>excluded</u>. Products meeting bio-based material criteria are valued at **100%** of their cost in the credit-achievement calculation.

➤ **Wood products:** Wood products must be certified by the **Forest Stewardship Council (FSC)** or another USGBC-approved equivalent. Products meeting wood products criteria are valued at **100%** of their cost in the credit-achievement calculation.

➤ **Materials reuse:** This criterion includes salvaged, refurbished, or reused products. Products meeting materials reuse criteria are valued at **100%** of their cost in the credit-achievement calculation. To determine the cost of the reused material, project teams can use the "actual cost" paid for the material or the replacement value, whichever is higher.

> **Recycled content:** For LEED, recycled content is the sum of <u>postconsumer recycled content</u> plus <u>one-half of the preconsumer recycled content</u>. This is based on <u>cost</u>. Products meeting recycled-content criteria are valued at **100%** of their cost in the credit achievement calculation. These products must conform to ISO 14021-1999.

> **Any other USGBC-approved program**

Materials sourced (extracted, manufactured, or purchased) within **100 miles** (160 kilometers) of the project site will be valued at **200%** of the base contributing cost.

The base location for the "reused" materials will be considered as follows: If the material is taken directly from another building, the base location will be that building. If the material is bought from a store, the base location will be the store.

<u>Structure</u> and <u>enclosure materials</u> cannot constitute more than **30% of the compliant building products** by cost.

BPDO: MATERIAL INGREDIENTS—CREDIT

Projects can earn a maximum of two points under this credit by achieving the requirements of two out of the following three options:

OPTION 1: MATERIAL INGREDIENT REPORTING — (1 Point)

Under this option, project teams should use at least **20 different permanently installed building products** from at least **five different manufacturers** that use any of the following programs to demonstrate the chemical inventory of the product to at least **0.1%** (1,000 parts per million) of its ingredients;

> **Manufacturer Inventory:** The manufacturer should have published the complete content inventory of the product by showing all the ingredients identified by name and <u>Chemical Abstract Service Registration Number</u> (CASRN). The manufacturer may decline to show the name and/or CASRN for materials that are defined as trade secrets or intellectual property, but it should still disclose the role, amount, and GreenScreen benchmark according to a GreenScreen v1.2 assessment

> **Health Product Declaration:** The manufacturer should provide an HPD for its end-use product, with full disclosure of known hazards in compliance with the Health Product Declarations open standard.

> **Cradle to Cradle Certified (C₂C):** The product should be certified to the <u>Cradle to Cradle v2 Basic level</u> or <u>Cradle to Cradle v3 Bronze level</u>.

> **Other USGBC-approved programs**

Similar products with <u>distinct formulations</u> from the same manufacturer can be counted as separate products.

AND/OR

OPTION 2: MATERIAL INGREDIENT OPTIMIZATION — (1 Point)

Under this option, project teams should use products from manufacturers that document the products' material ingredient optimizations using the following paths for at least **25%** (by cost) **of the total value of permanently installed products** in the project:

- **GreenScreen v1.2 Benchmark:** This covers the products that have fully inventoried chemical ingredients to 100 ppm, and the ingredients do not contain "Benchmark 1" hazards.

  - If any ingredients are assessed with the "**GreenScreen List Translator,**" project teams will value these products at **100%** of their costs.
  - If all ingredients have undergone a full "**GreenScreen Assessment,**" project teams will value these products at **150%** of their costs.

- **Cradle to Cradle Certified:** This covers the products that have Cradle to Cradle certification. The valuation criteria for these products in the credit calculations will change according to the certification levels as follows:

  - <u>Cradle to Cradle v2 Gold</u>: value these products at **100%** of their costs.
  - <u>Cradle to Cradle v2 Platinum</u>: value these products at **150%** of their costs.
  - <u>Cradle to Cradle v3 Silver</u>: value these products at **100%** of their costs.
  - <u>Cradle to Cradle v3 Gold or Platinum</u>: value these products at **150%** of their costs.

- **International Alternative Compliance Path—REACH Optimization:** Projects outside the United States can use products and materials that do not contain substances that meet REACH criteria for "substances of very high concern." If the product does not contain any ingredients listed on the <u>REACH Authorization</u> or <u>Candidate list</u>, the product will be valued at **100%** of its cost in credit calculations.

- **Other USGBC-approved programs**

AND/OR

OPTION 3: PRODUCT MANUFACTURER SUPPLY CHAIN OPTIMIZATION — (1 Point)

Unlike option 2, in which the criterion valuation factors vary according to the criterion met, every product meeting the requirements of this option will be valued at **100%** of its cost.

Under this option, project teams should use building products for at least **25%** (by cost) **of the total value of permanently installed products** in the project that

- ➥ are sourced from manufacturers that engage in validated and robust safety, health, hazard, and risk programs and also, at a minimum, document at least **99%** (by weight) of the ingredients used to make the building product or building material; and
- ➥ are sourced from manufacturers with independent <u>third-party verification</u> of their supply chain that at a minimum verifies the following:
  - ▪ Processes are in place to communicate and transparently prioritize chemical ingredients along the supply chain according to available hazard, exposure, and use information to identify those that require more detailed evaluation.
  - ▪ Processes are in place to identify, document, and communicate information on health, safety, and environmental characteristics of chemical ingredients.
  - ▪ Processes are in place to implement measures to manage health, safety, and environmental hazards and risks of chemical ingredients.
  - ▪ Processes are in place to optimize health, safety, and environmental impacts when designing chemical ingredients.

For both options 2 and 3, products that are sourced (extracted, manufactured, or purchased) within **100 miles (160 kilometers)** of the project site are valued at **200%** of their cost.

Under option 2 and option 3 is that <u>structure</u> and <u>enclosure materials</u> cannot constitute more than **30% of the compliant building products** by cost. Once this threshold is reached, these materials cannot be considered as compliant materials from that point forward.

PBT SOURCE REDUCTION - MERCURY—CREDIT

Project teams should specify and install fluorescent lamps with both low mercury content and long lamp life. Projects should not install any circular fluorescent lamps or probe start metal halide lamps. Probe start metal halide lamps have short lamp life. Instead, projects can use pulse start metal halide lamps.

Project teams should specify the use of those lamps that meet the credit criteria for increased lamp life, should specify linear and U-bend fluorescent lamps to meet the rated hours and ballast type criteria, and should also consider installing high-efficiency lamps with no mercury content, such as LEDs, to replace high-pressure sodium (HPS) lamps. Next, projects should create a lighting schedule and track purchased lamps during construction with a material checklist.

If lamps required by operating rooms, dental treatment rooms, dental labs, and other spaces in medical military spaces comply with UFC 4-501-01 but cannot satisfy the credit requirements, those lamps may be excluded from the credit. If the credit requirements conflict with the local code or regulations, the affected lamps may be excluded from the credit, but projects should retain a copy of the local code.

PBT SOURCE REDUCTION – LEAD, CADMIUM AND COPPER—CREDIT

<u>For lead</u>: Project teams should specify and use solder and flux to connect plumbing pipe on site that meet the **California AB1953** standard, which stipulates that solder should not contain more than 0.2% lead and flux should not contain more than a weighted average of 0.25% lead for wetted surfaces.

For water that is intended for human consumption, project teams should specify and use pipes, pipe fittings, plumbing fittings, and faucets that meet the **California AB1953 standard** of a weighted average lead content of the wetted surface area of no more than 0.25% lead.

Projects should use lead-free roofing, flashing, interior paint, and exterior paint. The use of interior or exterior paints containing lead is prohibited under this credit.

Renovation projects should ensure the removal and disposal of disconnected wires with lead stabilizers, according to the **2002 National Electric Code requirements**.

Only the lead used for radiation shielding and copper used for MRI shielding are exempt from the credit's requirements.

<u>For cadmium</u>: Projects should not use any interior or exterior paints containing intentionally added cadmium.

<u>For copper</u>: Project teams should reduce or eliminate joint-related sources of copper corrosion in the copper pipe applications by the use of mechanically crimped copper joint systems. And the project teams should ensure that all solder joints and flux comply with **ASTM B828 2002**, and **ASTM B813 2010** respectively.

FURNITURE AND MEDICAL FURNISHINGS—CREDIT

Under this credit, at least **30%** (1 point) or **40%** (2 points), by cost, of all the freestanding furniture and medical furnishings that meet the criteria in one of the following three options should be used by projects. Projects should include any built-in casework and built-in millwork in the calculations, even if they are manufactured off-site.

OPTION 1: MINIMAL CHEMICAL CONTENT

Under this option, all components that constitute **at least 5%,** by weight, of a furniture or medical furnishing assembly should contain less than **100 parts per million** (ppm) of at least four of the five chemical groups, as required by the credit.

AND/OR

OPTION 2: TESTING AND MODELING OF CHEMICAL CONTENT

Under this option, all components of a furniture or medical furnishing assembly, including textiles, finishes, and dyes, must contain **less than 100 parts per million** (ppm) of at least two of the five chemicals or materials listed under option 1 of the credit.

And any new furniture or medical furnishing assemblies must be in accordance with **ANSI/BIFMA Standard Method M7.1–2011**. Projects should comply with **ANSI/BIFMA e3-2010 Furniture Sustainability Standard, Sections 7.6.1 and 7.6.2** using either the concentration modeling approach or the emissions factor approach.

AND/OR

OPTION 3: MULTI-ATTRIBUTE ASSESSMENT OF PRODUCTS

Under this option, projects should use products that meet at least one of the criteria below. Each product can receive credit for each criterion met.

- **Product-specific declarations**: Products with a publicly available, critically reviewed life-cycle assessment conforming to ISO 14044 that have at least a cradle to gate scope are valued as one-quarter (1/4) of a product for the purposes of credit-achievement calculation.

- **Environmental Product Declarations**: These conform to ISO 14025, 14040, 14044, and EN 15804 or ISO 21930 and have at least a cradle to gate scope.

  - **Industry-wide (generic) EPD**: Products with third-party certification (Type III) are valued as one-half (1/2) of a product for purposes of credit-achievement calculation.

  - **Product-specific Type III EPD**: Products with third-party certification (Type III) are valued as one whole product for purposes of credit-achievement calculation.

- **Materials reuse**: Use salvaged or reused products.
- **Recycled content**: Use products with recycled content.
- **Extended producer responsibility**: Products purchased from a manufacturer that participates in an extended producer responsibility program or is directly responsible for extended producer responsibility.
- **Bio-based materials**: Bio-based products must meet the **Sustainable Agriculture Network's Sustainable Agriculture Standard**.
- **Wood products**: Wood products must be certified by the Forest Stewardship Council or USGBC-approved equivalent.

Just like in the BPDO credits, products sourced (extracted, manufactured, purchased) within 100 miles (160 kilometers) of the project site are also valued at 200% of their base contributing cost under this credit.

DESIGN FOR FLEXIBILITY—CREDIT

With the early commitment of the project team and the owner, projects should increase building flexibility by employing at least three of the following strategies:

- Install interstitial space and design distribution zone utility systems and equipment to serve the occupied zones. Also, have the capacity to control multiple zones in clinical spaces.
- Provide programmed **soft space**, such as administration or storage space, equal to at least **5%** of **departmental gross area** (**DGA**). Additionally, projects should determine a strategy for future accommodation of the displaced soft space.
- Provide shell space equal to at least **5%** of DGA.
- Determine horizontal expansion capacity for diagnostic and treatment uses or other clinical space equal to at least **30%** of existing floor area, excluding inpatient units, without demolition of the occupied space.
- Design for future vertical expansion on at least **75%** of the roof. The existing operations and service systems should be able to continue at or near capacity during the expansion.
- Assign spaces for future above-grade parking structures equal to **50%** of existing on-grade parking capacity, with direct access to the main hospital lobby or circulation.
- Use demountable partitions for **50%** of applicable areas.
- Use movable or modular casework for at least **50%** of casework and millwork.

CONSTRUCTION AND DEMOLITION WASTE MANAGEMENT—CREDIT

To earn this credit, project teams should recycle and/or salvage nonhazardous construction and demolition materials. Project teams should choose either one the following options:

OPTION 1: DIVERSION — (1-2 Points)

PATH 1: DIVERT 50% AND THREE MATERIAL STREAMS — (1 Point)

Under this path, projects should divert at least **50%** of the total construction and demolition material. Diverted materials should include **at least three material streams**.

OR

PATH 2: DIVERT 75% AND FOUR MATERIAL STREAMS — (2 Points)

Under this path, projects should divert at least **75%** of the total construction and demolition material. Diverted materials should include **at least four material streams**.

Diversion rate = (Total waste diverted from landfill / Total waste produced by the project) x 100

OR

OPTION 2: REDUCTION OF TOTAL WASTE MATERIAL — (2 Points)

Under this option, projects should not generate more than **2.5 pounds of construction waste per square foot (12.2 kilograms of waste per square meter) of the building's gross floor area.**

Waste per area = (Total construction and demolition waste generated / Project gross floor area) x 100

MINIMUM INDOOR AIR QUALITY PERFORMANCE—PREREQUISITE

Please review the whole prerequisite as it contains lots of details.

ENVIRONMENTAL TOBACCO SMOKE CONTROL—PREREQUISITE

Project teams should prohibit smoking inside the building and additionally prohibit smoking outside the building except in designated smoking areas located at least **25 feet (7.5 meters)** from all entries, outdoor air intakes, and operable windows. Furthermore, smoking should be prohibited outside the property line in the spaces used for business purposes.

Signage must be posted within **10 feet** (3 meters) of <u>all building entrances</u>, and it should indicate the no-smoking policy.

"LEED BD+C: School" projects must **prohibit smoking on the entire site** and post signage indicating the no-smoking policy.

<u>For residential projects only</u>:

OPTION 1: NO SMOKING

Project teams should meet the previous requirements just like the other rating systems, and they should prohibit smoking inside the <u>entire building</u>.

OR

OPTION 2: COMPARTMENTALIZATION OF SMOKING AREAS

If smoking will not be prohibited inside the whole building, residential projects should pursue this option. Projects must prohibit smoking inside all <u>common areas</u>, and this prohibition must be written in the building rental or lease agreements.

Since this option is for residential projects that will allow smoking inside the residential units, each unit must be compartmentalized to prevent excessive leakage between units. Plus, the following would apply:

- All exterior doors and operable windows in the residential units should be weather-stripped to minimize leakage from outdoors.
- All doors leading from residential units into common hallways should be weather-stripped.
- By sealing penetrations in the walls, ceilings, and floors and by sealing vertical chases, minimize uncontrolled pathways for the transfer of smoke.
- Demonstrate a maximum leakage of 0.23 cubic feet per minute per square foot at 50 Pa of the enclosure.

MINIMUM ACOUSTIC PERFORMANCE—PREREQUISITE

Every school project should first identify all <u>classrooms</u> and <u>other core learning spaces</u> and address the following requirements.

<u>**HVAC Background Noise:**</u> School projects should achieve a maximum background noise level of **40 dBA** from the HVAC systems in the classrooms and other core learning spaces. Projects should follow the recommended methodologies for the mechanical system noise control in **ANSI Standard S12.60–2010**, Part 1, Annex A.1; 2011 **HVAC Applications ASHRAE Handbook**, Chapter 48, Noise and Vibration Control (with errata); **AHRI Standard 885–2008** or a local equivalent for projects located outside the United States.

When the necessary measures are taken, project teams will measure the HVAC background noise according to the mentioned standards when no occupants are present, all the furnishings are installed, and the noises from other sources are minimized.

<u>**Exterior Noise:**</u> In school projects that are exposed to high noise levels—peak-hour L_{eq} above **60 dBA** during school hours—project teams should design acoustic treatment and other measures to reduce the noise intrusion from exterior sources and control the sound transmission between classrooms and other core learning spaces.

Projects that are located at least <u>one-half mile</u> (800 meters) from any significant noise source, such as airports, industry, highways, etc., are exempt from this requirement.

If there are noise-producing sources located within one-half mile (800 meters) of the project, the project teams should conduct acoustic readings during normal school hours. If the peak-hour L_{eq} is above 60 dBA, the team must implement noise reduction measures. After the necessary measures are taken, the project teams must again conduct acoustic readings and confirm that the peak-hour L_{eq} is below 60 dBA.

Reverberation Time: To address reverberation time, school projects should meet the following requirements according to their classroom and core learning space size.

For classrooms and core learning spaces that are less than 20,000 cubic feet (566 cubic meters):

Project teams should design classrooms and other core learning spaces with sufficient sound-absorptive finishes and comply with the reverberation time requirements specified in ANSI Standard S12.60–2010, Part 1, Acoustical Performance Criteria, Design Requirements and Guidelines for Schools, or a local equivalent for projects outside the United States.

Project teams should determine the sound absorption properties of the absorptive materials at 500 Hz, 1,000 Hz, and 2,000 Hz. Next, project teams should choose and pursue one of the following options.

OPTION 1:

Confirm that the total surface area of acoustic wall panels, ceiling finishes, and other sound-absorbent finishes equals or exceeds the total ceiling area of the room. The acoustic materials must have noise reduction coefficients (NRCs) of 0.70 or higher in order to be included in this calculation.

OR

OPTION 2:

Confirm through calculations that rooms are designed to meet reverberation time requirements as specified in the ANSI Standard S12.60-2010 standard. Reverberation time should be verified at 500 Hz, 1,000 Hz, and 2,000 Hz.

For classrooms and core learning spaces that are equal to or bigger than 20,000 cubic feet (566 cubic meters):

Project teams should meet the recommended reverberation times for classrooms and core learning spaces as specified in the NRC-CNRC Construction Technology Update No. 51, Acoustical Design of Rooms for Speech (2002), or a local equivalent for projects outside the United States. Reverberation time should be verified at 500 Hz, 1,000 Hz and 2,000 Hz.

Prerequisite Exceptions:

Projects with a limited scope of work or projects that must obey historic preservation requirements may be considered exempt from this prerequisite's requirements according to GBCI's considerations. This prerequisite does not cover auditoriums, natatoriums, music performance spaces, teleconferencing rooms, or special education rooms. It only covers classrooms and core learning spaces.

ENHANCED INDOOR AIR QUALITY STRATEGIES—CREDIT

OPTION 1: ENHANCED IAQ STRATEGIES – (1 Point)

In the **mechanically ventilated spaces**, project teams should comply with the following strategies as applicable:

A. Entryway systems;

B. Interior cross-contamination prevention; and

C. Filtration.

In the **naturally ventilated spaces**, project teams should apply the following strategies:

A. Entryway systems; and

B. Natural ventilation design calculations.

For the **mixed-mode systems**, project teams should apply the following strategies:

A. Entryway systems;

B. Interior cross-contamination prevention;

C. Filtration;

D. Natural ventilation design calculations; and

E. Mixed-mode design calculations.

A. <u>Entryway systems</u>: Under this strategy, projects should install **permanent entryway systems** at least 10 feet (3 meters) long in the primary direction of travel at the <u>regularly used exterior entrances</u>, in order to prevent dirt and particulates from reaching indoors. Some example entryway systems may be **grilles, grates, slotted systems,** and **rollout mats**, or any other entryway system with equivalent or better performance. Entryway systems should be maintained on a weekly basis.

"LEED BD+C: Warehouses and Distribution Centers" are not required to install entryway systems at the doors leading from the exterior to the loading dock or garage. However, entryway systems should be installed between these spaces and adjacent office spaces. "LEED BD+C: Healthcare" projects should additionally provide pressurized entryway vestibules at the building entrances with high-volume.

B. <u>**Interior cross-contamination prevention**</u>: Under this strategy, projects should exhaust spaces that may contain hazardous materials or chemicals (according to the exhaust rates determined in the "Minimum Indoor Air Quality Performance" prerequisite or a minimum of 0.5 cfm per square foot), in order to create negative pressure with respect to the adjacent spaces when the doors to the room are closed. These types of spaces should also contain self-closing doors and deck-to-deck partition or a hard-lid ceiling.

C. <u>**Filtration**</u>: Each ventilation system that supplies outdoor air to the occupied spaces should contain particle filters or air cleaning devices that has a **MERV rating 13 or higher**, in accordance with the **ASHRAE 52.2-2007**, or **Class F7 or higher** as defined by the CEN standard **EN 779-2002**, Particulate Air Filters for General Ventilation, Determination of the Filtration Performance.

All filters should be replaced after construction and before occupancy. For "LEED BD+C: Data Centers", the mentioned requirement will only be applicable to the regularly occupied spaces.

D. <u>**Natural ventilation design calculations**</u>: Under this strategy, the natural ventilation design for the occupied spaces should employ the appropriate strategies in **Chartered Institution of Building Services Engineers Applications Manual AM10, March 2005, Natural Ventilation in Non-Domestic Buildings, Section 2.4**.

E. <u>**Mixed-mode design calculations**</u>: The mixed-mode system design for the occupied spaces should comply with **CIBSE Applications Manual 13-2000, Mixed Mode Ventilation**.

AND/OR

OPTION 2: ADDITIONAL ENHANCED IAQ STRATEGIES − (1 Point)

For the **mechanically ventilated spaces**, project teams should comply with <u>one</u> of the following strategies:

A. Exterior contamination prevention;

B. Increased ventilation;

C. Carbon dioxide monitoring; or

D. Additional source control and monitoring.

For the **naturally ventilated spaces**, project teams should comply with <u>one</u> of the following strategies:

A. Exterior contamination prevention;

B. Additional source control and monitoring; or

C. Natural ventilation room by room calculations.

For the **mixed-mode systems**, project teams should comply with <u>one</u> of the following strategies:

A. Exterior contamination prevention;

B. Increased ventilation;

C. Additional source control and monitoring; or

D. Natural ventilation room-by-room calculations.

A. <u>**Exterior contamination prevention**</u>: Under this strategy, project teams should design the building to minimize and to control the entry of pollutants into the building. Through the **computational fluid dynamics modeling, Gaussian dispersion analyses, wind tunnel modeling,** or **tracer gas modeling,** project teams should ensure that the outdoor air contaminant concentrations at the outdoor air intakes are below the requirements listed in the following table:

Pollutants	Maximum concentration	Referenced Standard
The pollutants regulated by **National Ambient Air Quality Standards**	Allowable annual average OR 8- or 24-hour average where an annual standard does not exist OR Rolling 3 month average	National Ambient Air Quality Standards

B. <u>**Increased ventilation**</u>: This strategy requires projects to increase the breathing zone ventilation air rates by **at least 30%** above the minimum rates determined in the "Minimum Indoor Air Quality Performance" prerequisite, in all the occupied spaces.

C. <u>**Carbon dioxide monitoring**</u>: In all the densely occupied spaces, projects should monitor carbon dioxide levels. For LEED, densely occupied spaces the areas that contain at least 25 people per 1,000 square feet (93 square meters). Carbon dioxide monitoring devices should have an audible or visual indicator, or alert the building automation system if the carbon dioxide concentrations exceeds the setpoint by **10%** (carbon dioxide setpoint should be calculated using the methods in ASHREA 62.1-2010, Appendix C).

D. **Additional source control and monitoring**: For all the spaces that area likely to contain contaminants, project teams should address additional contaminants besides carbon dioxide. Firstly, the project teams should plan to reduce the likelihood of contaminant release. Next, monitoring systems with sensors and alarm should be installed to monitor the presence of specific contaminants.

E. **Natural ventilation room by room calculations**: Under this strategy, projects should implement **CIBSE AM10, Section4, Design Calculations** to confirm that room-by-room airflows will provide effective natural ventilation.

LOW EMITTING MATERIALS—CREDIT

OPTION 1: PRODUCT CATEGORY CALCULATIONS — (1–3 Points)

Under this option, project teams should identify all applicable products according to the product categories and obtain manufacturer documentation to confirm compliance. Table 30 shows the product categories and their requirements.

Following are the emission and content requirements specified on table 30.

- **General emissions evaluation**: This criterion requires products to be tested and determined compliant in accordance with the **California Department of Public Health (CDPH) Standard Method v1.1-2010.**

- **VOC content requirements for wet-applied products**: Wet-applied products must meet the previous "General emissions evaluation" requirements and additionally meet the applicable limits of the **California Air Resources Board (CARB) 2007, Suggested Control Measure for Architectural Coatings**, or the **South Coast Air Quality Management District (SCAQMD) Rule 1113.**

- **Composite wood evaluation**: Composite wood products should have low formaldehyde emissions and must meet the **California Air Resources Board** formaldehyde requirements.

- **Furniture evaluation**: New furniture and furnishings items should be tested according to the **ANSI/BIFMA Standard Method M7.1-2011**, and meet the **ANSI/BIFMA e3-2011 Furniture Sustainability Standard Sections 7.6.1 and 7.6.2.**

- **Additional insulation requirements (for LEED BD+C: Healthcare and School only)**: Batt insulation should not contain formaldehyde.

- **Exterior applied products (for LEED BD+C: Healthcare and School only)**: Sealants, adhesives, roofing, coatings, and waterproofing materials applied on-site should meet the VOC limits of **California Air Resources Board 2007 Suggested Control Measure for Architectural Coatings** and **South Coast Air Quality Management District, Rule 1168.**

OR

OPTION 2: BUDGET CALCULATION METHOD — (1–3 Points)

This option does not contain product categories, rather it organizes the **building interior** into six assemblies (the sixth assembly is only for "LEED BD+C: School" and "LEED BD+C: Healthcare" projects): floorings, ceilings, walls, thermal and acoustic insulation, furniture, and exterior applied products (for "LEED BD+C: Schools" and "LEED BD+C: Healthcare" only).

For each assembly type, projects should determine the percentage of compliant materials. The compliant materials should meet the emission and content requirements mentioned under "Option 1".

If 90% of an assembly meets the criteria, the whole assembly will be counted as 100% compliant. If less than 50% of an assembly meets the criteria, the whole assembly will be counted as 0% compliant.

CONSTRUCTION INDOOR AIR QUALITY MANAGEMENT PLAN—CREDIT

Projects should develop and implement an **indoor air quality** (IAQ) **management plan** for both the <u>construction</u> and <u>preoccupancy phases</u> of the building. The plan must address all of the following:

- During construction, projects should meet or exceed all applicable control measures of the **Sheet Metal and Air Conditioning National Contractors Association (SMACNA) IAQ Guidelines for Occupied Buildings under Construction, 2nd edition, 2007, ANSI/SMACNA 008–2008, Chapter 3**.
- Projects should protect absorptive materials, which are installed or stored on-site, from moisture damage.
- Permanently installed air-handling equipment should not be operated during construction unless it is operated with filtration media having a minimum efficiency reporting value of **8**, as determined by **ASHRAE 52.2–2007**, with errata,(or as defined in the CEN Standard EN779-2002, Particulate Air Filters for General Ventilation, Determination of the Filtration Performance with filtration media class of **F5 or higher**). The filtration media are installed at each return air grille and return or transfer duct inlet opening. Project teams should ensure that there is no bypass around the filtration media. Just before the occupancy, all the filtration media should be replaced with the designed filtration media.
- The use of tobacco products inside the building and within **25 feet** (7.5 meters) of the building entrance <u>during construction</u> should be prohibited.

Only for "LEED BD+C: Healthcare" projects:

Healthcare projects should develop an **environmental quality management plan** (**EQMP**) instead of developing an indoor air quality (IAQ) management plan, and they should address the following requirements;

- **Moisture:** Project teams should develop and implement a **moisture control plan** to protect building materials from moisture damage. Any material susceptible to microbial growth should be replaced with new, undamaged material.

- **Particulates:** Projects should not operate permanently installed air handling equipment during construction unless filtration media with a certain minimum efficiency are installed at each return air grille and return or transfer duct inlet opening such that there is no bypass around the filtration media. The filtration media must have a minimum efficiency reporting value of **8**—as determined by **ASHRAE 52.2–2007**, with errata (or equivalent filtration media with a class of **F5 or higher**, as defined by CEN Standard EN 779–2002, Particulate Air Filters for General Ventilation, Determination of the Filtration Performance). Immediately before occupancy, project teams should replace all filtration media with the final design filtration media.

- **VOCs:** Project teams should take all necessary measures to minimize exposure of absorbent materials to VOC emissions. Project teams should complete painting and sealing before installing the nonemitting materials so that those materials will not accumulate contaminants. Fuels, solvents, and other sources of VOCs should be stored separately from the absorbent materials.

- **Outdoor emissions:** For renovation projects involving waterproofing, repairing asphalt roofing, sealing parking lots, or other outdoor activities that generate high VOC emissions, project teams should develop a plan to manage fumes and avoid infiltration to the occupied spaces. Project teams should comply with the procedures established by **NIOSH**, Asphalt Fume Exposures during the Application of Hot Asphalt to Roofs (Publication 2003–112).

- **Tobacco:** During construction, project teams should prohibit the use of tobacco products inside the building and within **25 feet** (7.5 meters) of the building entrance.

- **Noise and vibration:** Project teams should develop a plan based on the British Standard (BS 5228) to reduce noise emissions and vibrations from construction equipment and other nonroad engine, by specifying low-noise emission design or the lowest decibel level available that meets performance requirements in the British Standard. Construction crews must wear ear protection in areas where sound levels exceed **85 dB** for extended periods.

- **Infection control:** For renovations and additions adjacent to occupied facilities or for phased occupancy in new construction, project teams should follow the **FGI 2010 Guidelines for Design and Construction of Health Care Facilities** and the **Joint**

Commission on Standards to evaluate infection control risk. After the evaluation, the required precautions should be documented in a project-specific plan. Projects should use the infection control risk assessment standard published by the **American Society for Healthcare Engineering** and the **Centers for Disease Control and Prevention** (**CDC**) as a guideline to evaluate risk and to take necessary mitigation measures during construction.

INDOOR AIR QUALITY ASSESSMENT—CREDIT

Project teams should choose one of the following options and implement its requirements right after construction ends and the building is completely cleaned. All interior finishes (doors, carpets, ceilings, furnishings, etc.) must be installed, and major VOC punch list items should be completed by the time one of the options below is performed.

OPTION 1: FLUSH-OUT — (1 Point)

PATH 1: BEFORE OCCUPANCY

Under this path, the flush out must be completed before the occupancy. Projects should install new filtration media after the construction and perform a building flush-out. During the flush-out, **14,000 cubic feet of outdoor air per square foot of gross floor area** should be supplied to the space while maintaining an internal temperature between **60° F and 80° F** (15° C–27° C) and relative humidity no higher than **60%**. The flush-out should be completed in every space of the building.

If the project teams use the permanent HVAC system for the flush-out, they will also need to replace the used filters (this is applicable to both path 1 and path 2).

OR

PATH 2: DURING OCCUPANCY

Under this path, before the occupancy, a minimum of **3,500 cubic feet of outdoor air per square foot of gross floor area** must be provided to the space while maintaining an internal temperature between **60° F and 80° F** (15° C–27° C) and relative humidity no higher than **60%**. This flush-out process should continue until a total of **14,000 cubic feet of outdoor air per square foot of gross floor area** is delivered to the space. After a minimum of 3,500 cubic feet of outdoor air per square foot of gross floor area is provided, the space must be ventilated at a minimum rate of **0.30 cubic foot per minute (cfm) per square foot of outdoor air,** or it should be ventilated at the **design minimum outdoor air rate** deter-

mined in the "Minimum Indoor Air Quality Performance" prerequisite, whichever is greater.

During each day of the flush-out, the ventilation should start **three hours before the
occupancy** and **continue during the occupancy**.

OR

OPTION 2: AIR TESTING — (2 Points)

Under this option, project teams will need to conduct air testing to determine if the contamination levels are above or below the credit's threshold values. If the contamination exceeds the
credit's threshold values, project teams should clear the contamination and conduct another
test.

To pursue this option, right after construction and **before occupancy**, under the ventilation
conditions typical for occupancy, project teams should conduct **baseline indoor air quality
testing** by using methods set forth by the USGBC; those are the **ASTM**, **EPA**, and **ISO** methods. The laboratory that will conduct the tests should be accredited under ISO/IEC 17025 for
the test methods they use.

The test will evaluate the concentrations of the following:

- Formaldehyde
- Particulates
- Ozone
- Total volatile organic compounds (TVOCs)
- Carbon monoxide (CO)
- Target chemicals listed in the California Department of Public Health (CDPH) Standard
  Method v1.1, Table 4-1, except formaldehyde

The measurements for the test must take place during normal occupied hours but <u>before
the occupancy</u>. The building ventilation system should be running at the normal daily start
time and operated at the minimum outdoor airflow rate, just as it would during the occupied
hours, throughout the test.

Project teams should choose the testing locations with the greatest VOC concentration levels, and the tests must be conducted by accredited personnel. There must be at least one test in
each floor of the building. If there are identical spaces, the project team can conduct the test in
every one out of seven rooms, thereby avoiding testing in each identical space. During the test,
the measurement equipment must be positioned between **3** and **6 feet** (90 and 180 centimeters)
above the floor, which is the breathing zone.

THERMAL COMFORT—CREDIT

Project teams must meet the requirements for both <u>thermal comfort design</u> and <u>thermal comfort control</u>.

Thermal comfort design:

<u>For all LEED BD+C projects, except "LEED BD+C: Warehouses and Distribution Centers"</u>:

OPTION 1: ASHRAE STANDARD 55-2010

Under this option, project teams should design <u>HVAC systems</u> and the <u>building envelope</u> to meet the requirements of **ASHRAE Standard 55–2010, Thermal Comfort Conditions for Human Occupancy, with errata** or a local equivalent.

OR

OPTION 2: ISO AND CEN STANDARDS

Under this option, project teams should design the <u>HVAC systems</u> and the <u>building envelope</u> to meet the requirements of the following applicable standard:

- **ISO 7730:2005, Ergonomics of the Thermal Environment, analytical determination and interpretation of thermal comfort** using calculation of the predicted mean vote (PMV) and predicted percentage of dissatisfied (PPD) indices and local thermal comfort criteria.
- **CEN Standard EN 15251:2007, Indoor Environmental Input Parameters for Design and Assessment of Energy Performance of Buildings**, addressing indoor air quality, thermal environment, lighting, and acoustics, Section A2.

"LEED BD+C: Data Center" projects should meet one of these options only for the <u>regularly occupied spaces</u>.

<u>For "LEED BD+C: Warehouses and Distribution Centers"</u>:
For the office portions of the building, "LEED BD+C: Warehouses and Distribution Centers" projects should meet the requirements above like the other rating systems.

Additionally, for the regularly occupied spaces of the building's <u>bulk storage</u>, <u>sorting</u>, and <u>distribution areas</u>, project teams should implement one or more of the following design alternatives:

- Radiant flooring
- Circulating fans
- Passive systems, such as heat venting, nighttime air, or wind flow
- Localized active cooling (refrigerant- or evaporative-based systems) or heating systems

> Localized, hard-wired fans that provide air movement for occupants' comfort

> Other equivalent thermal comfort strategies

Thermal comfort control:

For all LEED BD+C projects, except "LEED BD+C: Healthcare"

To address thermal comfort controls, projects should provide individual thermal comfort controls to at least **50% of the individual occupant spaces**. Additionally, projects should provide group thermal comfort controls for all shared multioccupant spaces.

The acceptable thermal comfort controls would be adjustable underfloor diffusers, operable windows, task mounted controls, or more. Any thermal comfort control without any accessible control or adjustable control cannot satisfy the credit's requirements.

All the thermal comfort controls provided should allow occupants to adjust at least one of the following in their local environment: air temperature, radiant temperature, air speed, and humidity.

For "LEED BD+C: Retail" projects, project teams should meet the mentioned requirements for **50%** of the individual occupant spaces in office and administrative areas.

For the projects under the "LEED BD+C: Hospitality" rating system, LEED assumes that these projects already provide adequate thermal comfort controls to the guest rooms, and therefore it excludes them from credit calculations.

For "LEED BD+C: Healthcare":

To address thermal comfort controls, "LEED BD+C: Healthcare" projects should provide individual thermal comfort controls for **every patient room** and at least **50% of the remaining individual occupant spaces**. Additionally, projects should provide group thermal comfort controls for all shared multioccupant spaces.

Again, all the thermal comfort controls provided, whether in individual spaces or shared multioccupant spaces, should allow occupants to adjust at least one of the following in their local environment: air temperature, radiant temperature, air speed, and humidity.

INTERIOR LIGHTING—CREDIT

For all LEED BD+C projects, except "LEED BD+C: Retail" and "LEED BD+C: Healthcare":

OPTION 1: LIGHTING CONTROL — (1 Point)

Under this option, project teams should provide individual lighting controls that enable occupants to adjust the lighting to suit their preferences for at least **90% of the individual occu-**

pant spaces. The individual lighting should contain at **least three lighting levels (on, off, midlevel)**, and the midlevel should be between 30% and 70% of the maximum illumination level (daylight contributions are not included).

Additionally, for **all the shared multioccupant spaces**, projects should meet all of the following requirements:

- ➤ Provide <u>multizone control systems</u> that enable occupants to adjust the lighting to meet the group needs and preferences with at least three lighting levels or scenes (on, off, midlevel).

- ➤ Lighting for any presentation or projection wall should be separately controlled by the occupants.

- ➤ Switches or manual controls must be in the same space with the controlled luminaires. The person operating the controls should be able to have a direct line of sight to the controlled luminaires.

For the projects under the "LEED BD+C: Hospitality" rating system, LEED assumes these projects already provide adequate lighting controls to the guest rooms and therefore <u>excludes</u> the guest rooms from the credit calculations.

AND/OR

OPTION 2: LIGHTING QUALITY — (1 Point)

Under this option, project teams should choose four of the following eight strategies.

1. Use lighting fixtures with a luminance of less than **2,500 cd/m² between 45 and 90 degrees from nadir** <u>in the regularly occupied spaces.</u>

2. Use light sources with a **color rendering index (CRI) of 80 or higher** <u>for the entire project.</u>

3. For at least 75% of the total connected lighting load, use light sources that have a rated life (or L70 for LED sources) of at least **24,000 hours** (at 3 hours per start, if applicable).

4. Use <u>direct-only overhead lighting</u> for **25% or less of the total connected lighting load** for <u>all regularly occupied spaces</u>.

5. For at least 90% of the regularly occupied floor area, projects should meet or exceed the following thresholds for area-weighted average surface reflectance: 85% for ceilings, 60% for walls, and 25% for floors.

6. Select furniture (if included in the scope of work) to meet the following thresholds for area-weighted average surface reflectance: 45% for work surfaces and 50% for movable partitions.

7. For at least 75% of the regularly occupied floor area, the ratio of average <u>wall surface illuminance</u> (excluding fenestration) to average <u>work surface illuminance</u> should not ex-

ceed **1:10**. Projects must also meet strategy 5, strategy 6, or demonstrate an area-weighted surface reflectance of at least 60% for walls.

8. For at least **75% of the regularly occupied floor area**, the ratio of average <u>ceiling illuminance</u> (excluding fenestration) to <u>work surface illuminance</u> should not exceed **1:10**. Projects must also meet strategy 5, strategy 6, or demonstrate an area-weighted surface reflectance of at least 85% for ceilings.

<u>For "LEED BD+C: Retail"</u>:

Retail projects only have one option, and they should provide <u>individual lighting controls</u> to **at least 90% of the individual occupant spaces** in <u>office</u> and <u>administrative areas</u>.

In the sales area, projects should provide controls that can reduce the ambient light levels to a midlevel. The midlevel should be between 30% and 70% of the maximum illumination level (daylight contributions are not included).

<u>For "LEED BD+C: Healthcare"</u>:

Healthcare projects should provide individual lighting controls for at least **90% of individual occupant spaces in staff areas**. For at least **90%** of patient positions, projects should provide lighting controls that are readily accessible from the patient's bed. In the <u>multioccupant patient spaces</u>, the controls must be individual lighting controls. In private rooms, project teams should additionally provide <u>exterior window shades</u>, <u>blinds</u>, or <u>curtain controls</u> that are readily accessible from the patient's bed.

In all the shared multioccupant spaces (not the multioccupant <u>patient</u> spaces), projects should provide multizone control systems that enable occupants to adjust the lighting to meet group needs and preferences, with at least three lighting levels or scenes (on, off, midlevel). Again, the midlevel should be between 30% and 70% of the maximum illumination level (daylight contributions are not included).

DAYLIGHT—CREDIT

Projects pursuing any option should provide **manual or automatic glare control devices with manual overrides for all the regularly occupied spaces**.

Project teams should select either one of the three options below.

OPTION 1: SIMULATION: SPATIAL DAYLIGHT AUTONOMY AND ANNUAL SUNLIGHT EXPOSURE — (2-3 Points)

Under this option, project teams should implement a computer simulation and demonstrate that **spatial daylight autonomy 300/50%** (sDA300/50%) of at least **55%**, **75%**, or **90%** is achieved. All LEED BD+C projects except "LEED BD+C: Healthcare" should consider the **regularly occupied floor areas** in the simulation, while the "LEED BD+C: Healthcare" projects should consider the **perimeter area** determined under the "Quality Views" credit.

By performing computer simulations, project teams should also demonstrate that **annual sunlight exposure 1000,250** (ASE1000,250) of **no more than 10%** is achieved for each analysis area. Project teams should use the regularly occupied floor spaces that are daylit per the sDA300/50% simulations.

For both simulations, an hourly time-step analysis based on meteorological data should be used, and projects should include <u>any permanent interior obstructions</u> to sunlight in the project model. <u>Movable furniture</u> and <u>partitions</u> can be excluded.

OR

OPTION 2: SIMULATION: ILLUMINANCE CALCULATIONS — (1-2 Points)

With the use of computer modeling, project teams should demonstrate that the illuminance levels in the regularly occupied floor area would be **between 300 lux and 3,000 lux for 9:00 a.m. and 3:00 p.m.** (both on a clear-sky day at the equinox). Points will be awarded according to the compliant floor area percentages. As is the case in option 1, all LEED BD+C projects except "LEED BD+C: Healthcare" should consider the **regularly occupied floor areas** while the "LEED BD+C: Healthcare" projects should consider the **perimeter area**.

Project teams should calculate the illuminance intensity for sun (direct component) and sky (diffuse component) to be used during the simulation. In order to calculate them, project teams will need to use the meteorological year data of the nearest available weather station. Next, project teams will select one day within **15 days of September 21** and the other day within **15 days of March 21** that will represent the <u>clearest sky condition</u>. After the two days are determined, the project teams will calculate and use the average of the hourly illuminance values for these two selected days.

With this data, project teams will conduct a simulation and calculate the percentage of floor area between 300 lux and 3,000 lux, at 9:00 a.m. and 3:00 p.m. to determine the point(s) earned. <u>Blinds</u> or <u>shades</u>, <u>moveable furniture</u>, and <u>partitions</u> may be excluded from the model. <u>Any permanent interior obstructions</u> to sunlight should be included.

OR

OPTION 3: MEASUREMENT — (2-3 Points)

Under this option, projects should achieve illuminance levels **between 300 lux** and **3,000 lux** for the percentage of floor area shown on table 36. One thing to note is that, in order to determine these illuminance levels, project teams will not create a simulation. Instead, they will conduct measurements on-site after the construction is complete and people have occupied the space.

As is the case for all the options in this credit, all LEED BD+C projects except "LEED BD+C: Healthcare" should consider the **regularly occupied floor areas** while the "LEED BD+C: Healthcare" projects should consider the **perimeter area**.

Between 9:00 a.m. and 3:00 p.m.—with furniture, fixtures and equipment all in place—project teams should measure the illuminance levels at appropriate work plane height. There must be two measurements. The first measurement should be in any **regularly occupied month**, while the second measurement should be in a regularly occupied month as specified in table 35. Regularly occupied month means that the measurement must be conducted during the building's regularly occupied periods.

Points will be awarded according to the compliant floor area percentages.

QUALITY VIEWS—CREDIT

For all LEED BD+C projects except "LEED BD+C: Warehouses and Distribution Centers" and "LEED BD+C: Healthcare":

Projects should achieve a direct line of sight to the outdoors via vision glazing for **75% of all regularly occupied floor area**. Vision glazing should **provide a clear image of the exterior** and should not be obstructed by frits, fibers, patterned glazing or added tints that distort color balance.

In addition, 75% of all regularly occupied floor area must meet at least two of the following four view criteria:

- ➤ Multiple lines of sight to vision glazing in different directions that are at least 90 degrees apart.
- ➤ Views that include at least two of the following:
  - a) Flora, fauna, or sky
  - b) Movement
  - c) Objects at least 25 feet (7.5 meters) from the exterior of the glazing
- ➤ Unobstructed views located within the distance of three times the head height of the vision glazing.
- ➤ Views with a **view factor of 3 or greater**, which is defined according to "**Windows and Offices: A Study of Office Worker Performance and the Indoor Environment.**"

In the calculations, project teams should include all the permanent interior obstructions, movable furniture and partitions can be excluded. Views into interior atria can be used to meet up to **30%** of the required quality view area.

For "LEED BD+C: Warehouses and Distribution Centers":

"LEED BD+C: Warehouses and Distribution Centers" projects basically have the same view requirements as mentioned previously. However, those requirements are only applicable to the **office portion** of the building. For the bulk storage, sorting, and distribution areas, projects should meet the above view requirements for only **25% of the regularly occupied floor area**.

For "LEED BD+C: Healthcare":

Only the "LEED BD+C: Healthcare" projects have the opportunity to earn 2 points under this credit. If the **inpatient units** in the hospital building meet the mentioned view requirements, the projects will earn 1 point.

To earn the other point, projects should configure the floor plan so that the floor area within **15 feet** (4.5 meters) of the perimeter exceeds the perimeter area requirements in table 37 and additionally complies with the view requirements mentioned previously. The "perimeter area" is the floor area within **15 feet** (4.5 meters) of the perimeter, which also provides an exterior view.

ACOUSTIC PERFORMANCE—CREDIT

For all LEED BD+C projects, except "LEED BD+C: Schools" and "LEED BD+C: Healthcare":

For all the occupied spaces, projects should meet the following requirements for "HVAC background noise," "sound isolation," "reverberation time," and "sound reinforcement/masking" (if installed in the project).

HVAC Background Noise: For HVAC background noise, projects should achieve the maximum background noise levels from HVAC systems per **2011 ASHRAE Handbook, HVAC Applications, Chapter 48, Table 1; AHRI Standard 885-2008, Table 15** or a local equivalent.

Project teams should measure or calculate sound levels to confirm compliance. During the measurements, the sound-level meter used should conform to **ANSI S1.4 for type 1** (precision) or **type 2** (general purpose) sound measurement instrumentation, or it should conform to a local equivalent.

Sound Transmission: To address sound isolation, projects should first identify the occupied spaces and their adjacency combinations. Project teams should meet the composite sound transmission class (STC$_C$) ratings as listed in table 38. Before the substantial completion of construction, project teams should conduct measurements and confirm that the specified STC$_C$ ratings are met.

<u>Reverberation Time</u>: Project teams should meet the reverberation time requirements adapted from **Performance Measurement Protocols for Commercial Buildings** according to the room and application type.

In order to verify the reverberation time, project teams should either calculate or measure the reverberation time for each occupied space.

<u>Sound Reinforcement and Masking Systems</u>:

<u>Sound Reinforcement</u>: For all large conference rooms and auditoriums serving more than 50 people, project teams should evaluate the need for sound reinforcement and AV playback capabilities. If sound reinforcement is needed, it should meet the following requirements:
- Have a minimum sound level of 70 dBA
- Maintain sound level coverage within +/- 3 dB at the 2,000 Hz octave band throughout the space
- Achieve a speech transmission index (STI) of at least 0.60 or common intelligibility scale (CIS) rating of a minimum of 0.77 at representative points within the area of coverage.

<u>Masking Systems</u>: For projects that use masking systems, the masking system design levels should not exceed 48 dBA. Project teams should also ensure that loudspeaker coverage can provide uniformity of +/- 2 dBA and that speech spectra are masked.

<u>For "LEED BD+C: Schools"</u>:
The "LEED BD+C: Schools" projects should meet the following requirements for HVAC "background noise" and "sound transmission."

<u>HVAC Background Noise</u>: Projects should achieve a background noise level of **35 dBA or less** from the HVAC systems in <u>classrooms</u> and <u>other core learning spaces</u>. Project teams should follow the recommended methodologies for mechanical system noise control in **"ANSI Standard S12.60–2010, Part 1, Annex A.1;" "2011 HVAC Applications ASHRAE Handbook, Chapter 48, Sound and Vibration Control, with errata;" "AHRI Standard 885–2008;"** or a local equivalent for projects located outside the United States.

<u>Sound Transmission</u>: To address sound transmission, projects should design classrooms and other core learning spaces in order to meet the sound transmission class requirements of **ANSI S12.60–2010 Part 1** or a local equivalent. All the exterior windows must have an

STC rating of at least **35** unless outdoor and indoor noise levels can be confirmed to justify a lower rating.

For "LEED BD+C: Healthcare":

"LEED BD+C: Healthcare" projects have two options, and they can pursue either one of them or both of them. Under these options, projects should design the facility to meet or exceed the following sound and vibration requirements, which are adapted from **2010 FGI Guidelines for Design and Construction of Health Care Facilities** (2010 FGI Guidelines) and its reference document, **Sound and Vibration Design Guidelines for Health Care Facilities** (2010 SV Guidelines).

OPTION 1: SPEECH PRIVACY, SOUND ISOLATION, AND BACKGROUND NOISE — (1 Point)

Under this option, project teams should address "speech privacy and sound isolation," and "background noise" by meeting the following requirements:

Speech Privacy and Sound Isolation: Project teams should achieve speech privacy, acoustical comfort, and minimal annoyance from noise-producing sources. Project teams should design the facility to meet the requirements outlined in the sections of "Table 1.2-3, Design Criteria for Minimum Sound Isolation Performance between Enclosed Rooms," and "Table 1.2-4 Speech Privacy for Enclosed Room and Open-Plan Spaces" (in the 2010 FGI Guidelines and 2010 SV Guidelines). Project teams should calculate or measure sound isolation and speech privacy descriptors achieved for representative adjacencies to confirm compliance.

Background Noise: Project teams should consider the background noise levels generated by all building mechanical-electrical-plumbing systems, air distribution systems, and other facility noise sources. The design of the facility should meet the 2010 FGI Guidelines, "Table 1.2-2 Minimum-Maximum Design Criteria for Noise in representative interior rooms and spaces."

Project teams should either calculate or measure sound levels in representative rooms and spaces for each type to confirm compliance. They should use a sound level meter that conforms to **ANSI S1.4 for type 1** (precision) or **type 2** (general purpose) sound measurement instrumentation. For spaces not listed in Table 1.2-2, project teams should refer to the "ASHRAE 2011 Handbook, Chapter 48, Sound and Vibration Control, Table 1."

AND / OR

OPTION 2: ACOUSTICAL FINISHES AND SITE EXTERIOR NOISE – (1 Point)

Under this option, project teams should address "acoustical finishes" and "site exterior noise" by meeting the following requirements:

Acoustical Finishes: Project teams should specify and use materials to meet the "2010 FGI Guidelines for Design and Construction of Health Care Facilities, Table 1.2-1, Design Room Sound Absorption Coefficients" and the "2010 Sound and Vibration Design Guidelines for Health Care Facilities." Project teams should either calculate or measure the average sound absorption coefficients for representative unoccupied rooms of each type in the building and confirm conformance.

Site Exterior Noise: In order to address site exterior noise, project teams should minimize the noise produced by road traffic, aircraft flyovers, railroads, on-site heliports, generators, outdoor facility MEP, building services equipment, and more. Additionally, project teams should minimize the effects of the project (MEP equipment and activities) to the surrounding facility, and they are required to meet local applicable codes or "Table 1.2-1 of the 2010 FGI Guidelines," "Table 1.2-1, and the 2010 SV Guidelines," or "Table 1.3-1," whichever is more stringent.

Project teams should comply with the 2010 FGI Guidelines for the following noise sources:

- Heliports
- Generators
- Mechanical equipment
- Building services

INNOVATION—CREDIT

Project teams can use any combination of innovation, pilot, and exemplary performance strategies.

OPTION 1: INNOVATION — (1 Point)

Under this option, project teams should achieve significant and measurable environmental performance using an innovative strategy that is not addressed in the LEED green building rating system.

Project teams should identify the following:

- The intent of the proposed innovation credit
- Proposed requirements for compliance
- Proposed submittals to show compliance
- The design approach or strategies used to meet the proposed requirements

The proposed strategy of the innovation credit should meet the following criteria:

- Demonstrate a <u>quantitative</u> improvement in environmental performance. In other words, the project should establish a baseline of standard performance and compare the baseline with the final design performance.
- The strategy of the innovation credit should be comprehensive and should not address a limited portion of the project. In addition, the proposed credit should have <u>at least two</u> components and should not be limited to the use of a particular product or a design strategy.
- Finally, the proposed strategy should be significantly better than standard sustainable design practices.

AND/OR

OPTION 2: PILOT — (1 Point)

Under this option, project teams should achieve **one** of the pilot credits from USGBC's LEED Pilot Credit Library.

AND/OR

OPTION 3: ADDITIONAL STRATEGIES — (1-3 Points)

Innovation — 1-3 Points

Pilot — 1-3 points

Exemplary performance — 1-2 points

LEED ACCREDITED PROFESSIONAL—CREDIT

At least one principal participant of the project team must be a LEED Accredited Professional (AP) with a specialty appropriate for the project, or the project team must engage a LEED AP with specialty to support the project and participate in the certification process. A project employing a LEED AP O+M as a principal participant of the project team for a LEED BD+C project cannot earn the credit.

REGIONAL PRIORITY—CREDIT

There are six available "Regional Priority" credits for every location; those credits are identified by the USGBC regional councils and chapters and LEED International Roundtable. The project should earn **up to four** of those six credits. The "Regional Priority" credits have been identified by the USGBC regional councils and chapters and LEED International Roundtable as having additional regional importance for the project's region.

One point will be awarded for each "Regional Priority" credit achieved, up to a maximum of four. For credits with multiple thresholds (e.g., in the "Indoor Water Use Reduction" credit, thresholds change according to the percent reduction established in water savings), points will be awarded at particular levels of achievement.

APPENDIX A – SUMMARY OF ASHRAE STANDARDS

Name of the Standard / Program	Keywords	Related Prerequisites / Credits
ASHRAE Guideline 0-2005	Commissioning essentials	Prerequisite — Fundamental Comm. and Ver., Credit — Enhanced Commissioning
ASHRAE Guideline 1.1-2007	HVAC & R technical requirements for commissioning	Prerequisite — Fundamental Comm. and Ver., Credit — Enhanced Commissioning
ANSI/ASHRAE/IESNA Standard 90.1.-2010, Appendix G with Errata	Used for the whole building energy simulation under option 1	Prerequisite — Minimum Energy Perf., Credit — Optimize Energy Perf.
ANSI/ASHRAE/IESNA Standard 90.1-2010, with errata	Used for all options	Prerequisite — Minimum Energy Perf., Credit — Optimize Energy Perf.
ASHRAE Advanced Energy Design Guide	Used under option 2	Prerequisite — Minimum Energy Perf., Credit — Optimize Energy Perf.
ASHRAE 90.1-2010, Appendix B	Energy standard for buildings, also used to identify project's climate zone	Prerequisite — Minimum Energy Performance
ANSI/ASHRAE/IESNA Standard 90.1–2010, Appendixes B and D	Energy standard for buildings, also used to identify international project's climate zone	Prerequisite — Minimum Energy Performance
ANSI/ASHRAE/IESNA Standard 90.1-2010, G2.5	Used for the exceptional calculation method	Prerequisite — Minimum Energy Performance

Name of the Standard / Program	Keywords	Related Prerequisites / Credits
ASHRAE 62.1-2010	Ventilation for acceptable indoor air quality	Prerequisite — Minimum Air Quality Perf., Credit — Enhanced IAQ Strategies
ASHRAE Standard 170–2008	Used to address the mechanical ventilation requirements of the healthcare projects	Prerequisite — Minimum Air Quality Performance
ASHRAE 52.2-2007	Air filter standards	Credit — Enhanced Indoor Air Quality Strategies, Credit — Construction Indoor Air Quality Management Plan
ASHRAE Standard 55–2010	Thermal comfort conditions for human occupancy	Credit — Thermal Comfort
2011 ASHRAE Handbook	Handbook about the HVAC applications, in the credit it relates to the HVAC background noise	Credit — Acoustic Performance

APPENDIX B – IMPORTANT STANDARDS AND PROGRAMS

Name of the Standard / Program	Keywords	Related Prerequisites / Credits
ANSI Consensus National Standard Guide 2.0	Useful for implementing a successful integrative process	Prerequisite—Integrative Project Planning and Design, Credit—Integrative Process
US Department of Agriculture, US Code of Federal Regulations Title 7, Volume 6	Defines prime farmlands	Credit—Sensitive Land Protection
Natural Resources Conservation Service (NRCS)	Soil survey	Credit—Sensitive Land Protection, Credit—Site Assessment
Federal Emergency Management Agency (FEMA)	Defines flood hazard areas	Credit—Sensitive Land Protection
US Endangered Species Act	Defines threatened and endangered species	Credit—Sensitive Land Protection
NatureServe	Classifies species and ecological communities	Credit—Sensitive Land Protection
International Union of Conservation of Nature Red List	Alternative to NatureServe	Credit—Sensitive Land Protection
US EPA National Priority List	Defines National Priority sites	Credit—High Priority Site
US Housing and Urban Development	Defines Federal Empowerment Zone, Federal Enterprise Community, and Federal Renewal Community	Credit—High Priority Site

Name of the Standard / Program	Keywords	Related Prerequisites / Credits
US Department of Treasury, Community Development Financial Institutions Fund	Provides funds for low-income communities	Credit—High Priority Site
Parking Consultants Council, Transportation Planning Handbook, 3rd edition	Provides base parking capacity ratios for buildings	Credit—Reduced Parking Footprint
American Council for an Energy-Efficient Economy (ACEEE)	Defines green vehicles (should score a minimum of 45 on ACEEE to qualify)	Credit—Green Vehicles
Illuminating Engineering Society of North America (IESNA)	Develops lighting specifications	Credit—Light Pollution Reduction
2012 US EPA, Construction General Permit (CGP)	Sets requirements for the erosion and sedimentation control (ESC) plan	Prerequisite—Construction Activity Pollution Prevention
TR-55 initial water storage capacity	Projects can model the watersheds to calculate the storm water runoff volume, peak rate of discharge and storage volumes	Site Assessment—Credit
Land Trust Alliance	Provides accreditation to land trust organizations	Credit—Site Development - Protect or Restore Habitat
US Environmental Protection Agency Technical Guidance on Implementing the Stormwater Runoff Requirements for Federal Projects under Section 438 of the Energy Independence and Security Act	Methodology used for the rainwater management calculations	Credit—Rainwater Management
National Climatic Data Center	Provides historical rainfall data	Credit—Rainwater Management

Name of the Standard / Program	Keywords	Related Prerequisites / Credits
Illuminating Engineering Society and International Dark Sky Association (IES/IDA) Model Lighting Ordinance (MLO) User Guide	Used to determine the lighting zone of the project	Credit—Light Pollution Reduction
US Environmental Protection Agency WaterSense Water Budget Tool	Calculates landscape water requirements (LWR)	Prerequisite, Credit—Outdoor Water Use Reduction
Energy Policy Act of 1992 (EPAct 1992)	Specifies baseline flow and flush rates	Prerequisite, Credit—Indoor Water Use Reduction
WaterSense	A program developed by EPA to identify high-performance, water-efficient fixtures and fittings	Prerequisite, Credit—Indoor Water Use Reduction
ENERGY STAR Portfolio Manager™	Interactive, online management tool that enables projects to track and assess energy and water consumption	
ENERGY STAR TargetFinder™	Allows projects to set target goals for building design's energy demands	
Home Energy Saver™	A do-it-yourself energy audit, which is developed by the US Department of Energy for existing buildings to analyze, reduce, and manage their energy use	
Montreal Protocol	Banned the production of chlorofluorocarbon (CFC) refrigerants and also phasing out hydrochlorofluorocarbon (HCFC) refrigerants	
Advanced Buildings™ Core Performance Guide™	Energy design guide	Prerequisite—Minimum Energy Performance
National Institute of Building Sciences (NIBS) Guideline 3-2012, Exterior Enclosure Technical Requirements for the Cx Process	Used for the envelope Commissioning	Credit—Enhanced Commissioning

Name of the Standard / Program	Keywords	Related Prerequisites / Credits
US Department of Energy's Commercial Buildings Energy Consumption Survey (CBECS)	Database used to estimate a building's total energy cost	Credit—Advanced Energy Metering, Credit—Renewable Energy Production, Credit—Green Power and Carbon Offsets
US EPA GreenChill	Provides best practices guideline for leak tightness at installation. Provides store certification.	Credit—Enhanced Refrigerant Management
Green-e	The leading certification program for the green power generation in the United States	Credit—Green Power and Carbon Offsets
Green-e Energy	Green power certification Program	Credit—Green Power and Carbon Offsets
Green-e Climate	Carbon offset certification program	Credit—Green Power and Carbon Offsets
US National Register of Historic Places	Identifies the "historic" designation criteria	Credit—Building Life-Cycle Impact Reduction
Secretary of Interior's Standards for the Treatment of Historic Properties	Sets standards for the treatment of historic properties	Credit—Building Life-Cycle Impact Reduction
Forest Stewardship Council (FSC)	A voluntary program which sets standards to wood product manufacturers to ensure responsible forest management in order to prevent deforestation and loss of habitat	Credit—BPDO Sourcing of Raw Materials
Extended Producer Responsibility (EPR)	Is a product stewardship policy approach that holds consumer goods companies responsible for managing their own products and packaging when consumers are finished with them	Credit—BPDO Sourcing of Raw Materials

Name of the Standard / Program	Keywords	Related Prerequisites / Credits
Sustainable Agriculture Network's Sustainable Agriculture Standard	Standard for bio-based Materials	Credit—BPDO: Sourcing of Raw Materials, Credit—Furniture and Medical Furnishings
Cradle to Cradle Certification (C2C)	Assesses the ingredients of a product according to environmental and human health hazards	Credit—BPDO Material Ingredients
GreenScreen	A method used to identify chemicals of high concern and safer alternatives	Credit—BPDO Material Ingredients
REACH Optimization	European Union's legislation that requires all chemicals sold to be evaluated based on their hazard profiles	Credit—BPDO Material Ingredients
Chartered Institution of Building Services Engineers (CIBSE) Applications Manual	About ventilation strategies	Prerequisite—Minimum Indoor Air Quality Performance, Credit—Enhanced Indoor Air Quality Strategies
National Ambient Air Quality Standards	Standards for exterior contamination prevention	Credit—Enhanced Indoor Air Quality Strategies
California Department of Public Health (CDPH) Standard Method v1.1	General emissions evaluation and VOC testing procedures	Credit—Low Emitting Materials, Credit—Indoor Air Quality Assessment
California Air Resources Board (CARB) 2007, Suggested Control Measure for Architectural Coatings	VOC content requirements for wet-applied products	Credit—Low Emitting Materials
South Coast Air Quality Management District (SCAQMD) Rule 1113	VOC content requirements for wet-applied products	Credit—Low Emitting Materials

Name of the Standard / Program	Keywords	Related Prerequisites / Credits
ANSI/BIFMA Standard Method M7.1-2011	Furniture evaluation	Credit—Low Emitting Materials
Sheet Metal and Air Conditioning National Contractors Association (SMACNA) guidelines	Describes the necessary control measures to be taken during construction to protect indoor air quality	Credit—Construction Indoor Air Quality Management Plan
Windows and Offices; A Study of Office Worker Performance and the Indoor Environment	Defines view factors	Credit—Quality Views

APPENDIX C – PREREQUISITES/CREDITS AND THEIR APPLICABLE RATING SYSTEMS

P/C	Name of the Prerequisite/Credit	Applicable to:
Prerequisite	Integrative Project Planning and Design	Healthcare
Credit	Integrative Process	All LEED BD+C Rating Systems
Credit	LEED for Neighborhood Development Location	All LEED BD+C Rating Systems
Credit	Sensitive Land Protection	All LEED BD+C Rating Systems
Credit	High Priority Site	All LEED BD+C Rating Systems
Credit	Surrounding Density and Diverse Uses	All LEED BD+C Rating Systems
Credit	Access to Quality Transit	All LEED BD+C Rating Systems
Credit	Bicycle Facilities	All LEED BD+C Rating Systems
Credit	Reduced Parking Footprint	All LEED BD+C Rating Systems
Credit	Green Vehicles	All LEED BD+C Rating Systems
Prerequisite	Construction Activity Pollution Prevention	All LEED BD+C Rating Systems
Prerequisite	Environmental Site Assessment	Schools and Healthcare
Credit	Site Assessment	All LEED BD+C Rating Systems
Credit	Site Development–Protect or Restore Habitat	All LEED BD+C Rating Systems
Credit	Open Space	All LEED BD+C Rating Systems
Credit	Rainwater Management	All LEED BD+C Rating Systems
Credit	Heat Island Reduction	All LEED BD+C Rating Systems

P/C	Name of the Prerequisite/Credit	Applicable to:
Credit	Light Pollution Reduction	All LEED BD+C Rating Systems
Credit	Site Master Plan	Schools
Credit	Tenant Design and Construction Guidelines	Core and Shell
Credit	Places of Respite	Healthcare
Credit	Direct Exterior Access	Healthcare
Credit	Joint Use of Facilities	Schools
Prerequisite	Outdoor Water Use Reduction	All LEED BD+C Rating Systems
Prerequisite	Indoor Water Use Reduction	All LEED BD+C Rating Systems
Prerequisite	Building-Level Water Metering	All LEED BD+C Rating Systems
Credit	Outdoor Water Use Reduction	All LEED BD+C Rating Systems
Credit	Indoor Water Use Reduction	All LEED BD+C Rating Systems
Credit	Cooling Tower Water Use	All LEED BD+C Rating Systems
Credit	Water Metering	All LEED BD+C Rating Systems
Prerequisite	Fundamental Commissioning and Verification	All LEED BD+C Rating Systems
Prerequisite	Minimum Energy Performance	All LEED BD+C Rating Systems
Prerequisite	Building Level Energy Metering	All LEED BD+C Rating Systems
Prerequisite	Fundamental Refrigerant Management	All LEED BD+C Rating Systems
Credit	Enhanced Commissioning	All LEED BD+C Rating Systems
Credit	Optimize Energy Performance	All LEED BD+C Rating Systems
Credit	Advanced Energy Metering	All LEED BD+C Rating Systems
Credit	Demand Response	All LEED BD+C Rating Systems
Credit	Renewable Energy Production	All LEED BD+C Rating Systems
Credit	Enhanced Refrigerant Management	All LEED BD+C Rating Systems
Credit	Green Power and Carbon Offsets	All LEED BD+C Rating Systems
Prerequisite	Storage and Collection of Recyclables	All LEED BD+C Rating Systems
Prerequisite	Construction and Demolition Waste Management Planning	All LEED BD+C Rating Systems
Prerequisite	PBT Source Reduction–Mercury	Healthcare
Credit	Building Life-Cycle Impact Reduction	All LEED BD+C Rating Systems
Credit	BPDO–Environmental Product Declarations	All LEED BD+C Rating Systems

P/C	Name of the Prerequisite/Credit	Applicable to:
Credit	BPDO–Sourcing of Raw Materials	All LEED BD+C Rating Systems
Credit	BPDO–Material Ingredients	All LEED BD+C Rating Systems
Credit	PBT Source Reduction–Mercury	Healthcare
Credit	PBT Source Reduction–Lead, Cadmium, and Copper	Healthcare
Credit	Furniture and Medical Furnishings	Healthcare
Credit	Design for Flexibility	Healthcare
Credit	Construction and Demolition Waste Management	All LEED BD+C Rating Systems
Prerequisite	Minimum Indoor Air Quality Performance	All LEED BD+C Rating Systems
Prerequisite	Environmental Tobacco Smoke Control	All LEED BD+C Rating Systems
Prerequisite	Minimum Acoustic Performance	Schools
Credit	Enhanced Indoor Air Quality Strategies	All LEED BD+C Rating Systems
Credit	Low–Emitting Materials	All LEED BD+C Rating Systems
Credit	Construction Indoor Air Quality Management Plan	All LEED BD+C Rating Systems
Credit	Indoor Air Quality Assessment	All LEED BD+C Rating Systems, except Core and Shell
Credit	Thermal Comfort	All LEED BD+C Rating Systems, except Core and Shell
Credit	Interior Lighting	All LEED BD+C Rating Systems, except Core and Shell
Credit	Daylight	All LEED BD+C Rating Systems
Credit	Quality Views	All LEED BD+C Rating Systems
Credit	Acoustic Performance	All LEED BD+C Rating Systems, except Core and Shell and Retail
Credit	Innovation	All LEED BD+C Rating Systems
Credit	LEED Accredited Professional	All LEED BD+C Rating Systems
Credit	Regional Priority	All LEED BD+C Rating Systems

P/C	Name of the Prerequisite/Credit	Design/Construction
Prerequisite	Integrative Project Planning and Design	Design
Credit	Integrative Process	Design
Credit	LEED for Neighborhood Development Location	Design
Credit	Sensitive Land Protection	Design
Credit	High Priority Site	Design
Credit	Surrounding Density and Diverse Uses	Design
Credit	Access to Quality Transit	Design
Credit	Bicycle Facilities	Design
Credit	Reduced Parking Footprint	Design
Credit	Green Vehicles	Design
Prerequisite	Construction Activity Pollution Prevention	Construction
Prerequisite	Environmental Site Assessment	Design
Credit	Site Assessment	Design
Credit	Site Development–Protect or Restore Habitat	Design
Credit	Open Space	Design
Credit	Rainwater Management	Design
Credit	Heat Island Reduction	Design
Credit	Light Pollution Reduction	Design
Credit	Site Master Plan	Design
Credit	Tenant Design and Construction Guidelines	Design
Credit	Places of Respite	Design
Credit	Direct Exterior Access	Design
Credit	Joint Use of Facilities	Design

P/C	Name of the Prerequisite/Credit	Design/Construction
Prerequisite	Outdoor Water Use Reduction	Design
Prerequisite	Indoor Water Use Reduction	Design
Prerequisite	Building-Level Water Metering	Design
Credit	Outdoor Water Use Reduction	Design
Credit	Indoor Water Use Reduction	Design
Credit	Cooling Tower Water Use	Design
Credit	Water Metering	Design
Prerequisite	Fundamental Commissioning and Verification	Construction
Prerequisite	Minimum Energy Performance	Design
Prerequisite	Building Level Energy Metering	Design
Prerequisite	Fundamental Refrigerant Management	Design
Credit	Enhanced Commissioning	Construction
Credit	Optimize Energy Performance	Design
Credit	Advanced Energy Metering	Design
Credit	Demand Response	Construction
Credit	Renewable Energy Production	Design
Credit	Enhanced Refrigerant Management	Design
Credit	Green Power and Carbon Offsets	Construction
Prerequisite	Storage and Collection of Recyclables	Design
Prerequisite	Construction and Demolition Waste Management Planning	Construction
Prerequisite	PBT Source Reduction–Mercury	Design
Credit	Building Life-Cycle Impact Reduction	Construction
Credit	BPDO–Environmental Product Declarations	Construction
Credit	BPDO–Sourcing of Raw Materials	Construction
Credit	BPDO–Material Ingredients	Construction
Credit	PBT Source Reduction–Mercury	Design
Credit	PBT Source Reduction–Lead, Cadmium, and Copper	Construction
Credit	Furniture and Medical Furnishings	Construction
Credit	Design for Flexibility	Design
Credit	Construction and Demolition Waste Management	Construction
Prerequisite	Minimum Indoor Air Quality Performance	Design
Prerequisite	Environmental Tobacco Smoke Control	Design
Prerequisite	Minimum Acoustic Performance	Design

P/C	Name of the Prerequisite/Credit	Design/Construction
Credit	Enhanced Indoor Air Quality Strategies	Design
Credit	Low–Emitting Materials	Construction
Credit	Construction Indoor Air Quality Management Plan	Construction
Credit	Indoor Air Quality Assessment	Construction
Credit	Thermal Comfort	Design
Credit	Interior Lighting	Design
Credit	Daylight	Design
Credit	Quality Views	Design
Credit	Acoustic Performance	Design
Credit	Innovation	Design/Construction
Credit	LEED Accredited Professional	Design/Construction
Credit	Regional Priority	Design/Construction

40/60 rule: A method used to choose the appropriate rating system for the project if the project seems to fit under multiple rating systems.

Active daylighting: Is a system that tracks and collects the sunlight using mechanical devices, but they may not function well on cloudy days.

Adapted plants: Types of plants that do not occur naturally in a specific location; however, they can nonetheless adapt easily to the climate of the region.

Adjacent site: A site containing a previously developed site at its minimum 25% of the boundary bordering parcels.

Albedo: A type of reflectivity measurement from "0" to "1," which "0" represents black surfaces that absorb all the solar radiation, while "1" represents white surfaces that reflects all the solar radiation.

Alternative compliance paths (ACPs): Enable international projects to earn the appropriate prerequisites/credits by allowing them to meet international standards or their local standards instead of United States based standards.

Alternative fuel vehicles: Vehicles that consume nongasoline, low-polluting fuels like hydrogen, electricity, propane, compressed natural gas, liquid natural gas, methanol, or ethanol.

Alternative fuel: Low-polluting fuels like hydrogen, electricity, propane, compressed natural gas, liquid natural gas, methanol, or ethanol.

Alternative water source: Nonpotable water from on-site surfaces, or freshwater sources, such as graywater, on-site reclaimed water, collected rainwater, captured condensate, and rejected water from reverse osmosis systems. Water from public utilities is excluded.

Basis of design (BOD): Describes the information necessary to accomplish the owner's project requirements, which includes system requirements, design criteria, standards, and guidelines, developed by the architect/engineer.

Bio-based materials: Are products other than food that are biological products, renewable agricultural materials or forestry materials. Biobased materials are derived from biomass. Plants and animals can be an example of biobased materials, however, hide products, such as leather and other animal skin material are excluded in LEED calculations.

Biofuel: Fuels produced from organic material. Biofuel includes untreated wood waste, landfill gas, agricultural crops or waste, animal waste, and other types of organic waste.

Bioswale: A stormwater control feature which uses a combination of engineered basin, soils and vegetation.

Blackwater: Is the term to describe the used water that has come into contact with waste. Thus, the water collected from the urinals and toilets can be classified as blackwater.

Blowdown: Removal of the cooling tower's water in order to minimize deposit of scales.

Brownfield site: A previously developed site that was contaminated with waste or pollution. A site that is left from an abandoned building in which the contamination is not yet known can also be classified as a brownfield site.

BUG rating method: A luminaire classification system that classifies a luminaire according to backlight, uplight, and glare.

Building automation system (BAS): A computer-based monitoring system which can monitor, coordinate and control every individual building system.

Building exterior: Defined as everything from the waterproofing membrane, inclusive of the waterproofing membrane.

Building footprint: Describes the area that the building sits on.

Building interior: Defined as everything inside the waterproofing membrane.

Built environment: Refers to all the man-made surroundings that are needed for human activity, from roads, to buildings, to neighborhoods.

Carbon neutrality: To emit no more carbon emissions than can realistically be offset.

Carbon offset: Is a reduction of carbon dioxide (CO_2) made in order to compensate, or offset an equivalent carbon dioxide (CO_2) emission made elsewhere.

Chain of custody (CoC): Procedure of tracking a product from extraction/harvesting to its distribution. An example may be the FSC certification, which provides chain-of-custody certification for wood-based products.

Charrettes: Are intense workshops that are generally held at the beginning of the project and during the project milestones.

Chlorofluorocarbon (CFC)-based refrigerant: A refrigerant in fluid state containing hydrocarbons, which absorb heat at low temperatures and reject heat at higher temperatures.

Clean waste: Materials that are left over from construction and demolition that are nonhazardous.

Closed system: System that does not produce any waste product at the end by circulating the same median.

Commingled waste: Single-streamed waste for recycling.

Commissioning (Cx): Is a systematic investigation by skilled personnel that compares building performance with the project goals, design specifications, and, most importantly, the owner's project requirements (OPR).

Conventional irrigation: Common system used for irrigation, such as irrigation through sprinkler heads above the ground.

Corporate Sustainability Reports (CSR): Provides information about the manufacturer or raw-material supplier of a product that has been verified to employ sustainable principles during the creation of their products.

Cradle-to-cradle: Evaluates materials to have infinite life cycles through recycling to form a closed system.

Cradle-to-grave: Investigates materials from their extraction to their disposal.

Cradle-to-gate assessment: Evaluates a product's partial life cycle from its resource extraction/harvesting to becoming a manufactured product ready for sale at the factory gate.

Current facility requirements (CFR): Requirements to fulfill the owner's operational needs.

Demand response (DR): An intentional reduction in the electricity usage in response to a demand response (DR) event, or changes in the price of electricity.

Demand response event (curtailment event): The period that the utility company asks for a reduction in electricity usage from its program participants.

Development footprint: Named for the sum of all the areas that are affected by the project's activity in the project site. Permeable pavements, at least 50% permeable, are exempt.

District energy system (DES): A central energy conversion plant that provides thermal energy, shared by a group of buildings.

Diverse use: Publicly available businesses that provide daily need goods or services. According to USGBC, diverse uses do not include ATMs, vending machines and touch screens.

Diversion rate: Percentage of waste materials diverted from landfill.

Drip irrigation systems: Are the types of microirrigation systems that drip water to the roots of plants to minimize the use of irrigation water and fertilizers. They are the most water-efficient systems and have very short payback periods.

Dry ponds (detention ponds): Hold the excess rainwater for some time, thereby allowing the rainwater to slowly seep into the ground without contamination. Dry ponds are excavated areas that detain and slow down stormwater but are dry at other times.

EDUCATION @USGBC: Education portal of USGBC.

Embodied energy: The total energy consumed resulting from a product's manufacturing, transportation, installation, and use.

Emergent properties: Emergence of certain properties in the systems as a result of interaction of individual elements.

Emissivity (infrared or thermal emittance): Is a measure that shows how much heat or infrared radiation a material can shed back into the atmosphere.

Energy rater: Professionals with a HERS rater credential that conducts the performance testing in LEED for Homes projects.

Energy use intensity (EUI): A measurement unit that describes the building's energy usage relative to its size.

Environmental Product Declaration (EPD): Disclosure that looks at the entire life cycle of a product and assesses the cost of the product on the environment. Products that contain an EPD will give information about a product's impact on global warming, ozone depletion, water pollution, greenhouse gas emission, human toxicity, and more.

Erosion and sedimentation control (ESC) plan: A plan developed to prevent erosion, sedimentation, and stormwater pollution to the water bodies, wetlands, and the whole neighborhood.

Evapotranspiration: Is the term used for the return of water to the atmosphere through evaporation from plants.

Extended Producer Responsibility (EPR): Is a product stewardship policy approach that holds companies producing consumer goods responsible for managing their own products and packaging when consumers are finished with them.

Extensive vegetated roofs: Are the types of roofs that do not include a variety of plants and require little maintenance. Their soil layer is thinner compared with the intensive roofs since they are more designed for the smaller-sized vegetation.

Floor-to-area ratio (FAR): Is calculated by dividing the total square feet of a building by the total square feet of the lot of the building.

Flush-out: Is the process of supplying good amounts of fresh air to the building before or during occupancy to take away the contaminated air and establish the desired level of indoor air quality.

Foot-candle: A measure of the amount of illumination that falls on a surface, equal to one lumen per square foot.

Functional entry: Any building opening that is open and used by pedestrians during business hours.

Gallons per flush (gpf): A unit of measurement used to calculate the water usage of flush fixtures such as toilets and urinals.

Gallons per minute (gpm): A unit of measurement used to calculate the water usage of flow fixtures such as sink faucets, shower heads, and aerators.

Geothermal heat pumps: Also known as "geoexchange", or "ground source heat pumps," geothermal heat pumps are central heating and/or cooling systems that transfer heat to or from the ground. In winter, this system uses the earth as a heat source while in summer, the earth is used as a heat sink.

Graywater: Is the untreated household water that did not come into contact with toilet waste. Used water from bathtubs, showers, bathroom washbasins, and water from clothes washers and laundry tubs can be examples of graywater and may be used as a flush water in toilets or urinals. This definition can change depending on the local codes.

Green building: According to the US Environmental Protection Agency, green building is the practice of creating structures and using processes that are environmentally responsible and resource-efficient throughout a building's life cycle, from siting to design, construction, operation, maintenance, renovation, and deconstruction. This practice expands and complements the classical building design concerns of economy, utility, durability, and comfort.

Green cleaning program : Specifies the green building products to be used (such as products that meet Green Seal, Environmental Choice, or EPA standards), chemicals allowed to be used inside the building, training of the cleaning personnel for the use of chemicals and green cleaning practices, indoor pest control plans, and energy-efficient cleaning equipment.

Green cleaning: The use of environmentally friendly products by also employing environmentally friendly cleaning principles in cleaning.

Green infrastructure: Infrastructure to direct the rainwater collected from the impervious surfaces to the vegetation and soil surfaces without routing them to the storm sewer system.

Green power: Off-site renewable energy.

Green vehicles: Vehicles that achieve a minimum green score of 45 on the American Council for an Energy Efficient Economy (ACEEE) annual vehicle rating guide (or a local equivalent for projects outside the United States.)

Greenfield: The term used to define undeveloped land.

Greenwashing: Refers to the presentation of a product or a material as being more environmentally friendly than it actually is.

Halons: Chemicals used in fire suppression systems.

Hard cost: Costs that physically contribute to the construction, such as labor costs, the cost of construction materials, and equipment.

Health Product Declaration (HPD): Disclosure that provides a product's material ingredients, list of potential chemicals, related concerns, and additional health information.

Heat island effect: Dark colored, nonreflective surfaces absorb heat during hot weather and release it into the atmosphere, and this releasing of heat is called the heat island effect.

Home Energy Rater (HERS Rater): Energy rater credential administered by the Residential Energy Services Network (RESNET).

Home size adjustment (HSA): In the LEED for Homes rating system, points are adjusted in all the categories according to the square footage of the home. Thus, homes that are bigger need to earn more points to achieve a LEED certification while smaller-sized homes can become LEED-certified by earning fewer points. Other LEED rating systems do not have size adjustments.

Impervious surface: A surface that contains less than 50% perviousness.

Indoor air quality management plan: A plan developed to protect the indoor air quality for construction workers and building occupants.

Infill sites: Or infill developments, are sites that at least 75% of their site area were either previously developed or were already being used for other purposes in the urban areas.

Inherently nonemitting materials: Materials with very low or no VOC content.

Integrated pest management (IPM): A sustainable approach that combines knowledge about pests, nature, pest prevention, and control methods that minimize pest infestation and damage while minimizing hazards to the building occupants, the property itself, and the environment.

Integrated process: Emphasizes the importance of connection and communication among all the professionals and stakeholders in the project.

Intensive vegetated roofs: Contain wider variety of plants and which contain more soil depth to support those plants.

Invasive plants: The types of plants that spread and damage the environment by taking over the adjacent existing native and adapted plants.

Land trust: A nonprofit organization that works on conserving lands.

Landscape water requirement (LWR): Is the amount of water that the landscape of the site will require during the site's peak watering month.

LEED AP with specialty: LEED credential, created for professionals with advanced knowledge in green building practices and specialized in a particular LEED rating system.

LEED Campus Program: Used to certify multiple projects that are located on a single campus and which are owned by the same entity.

LEED combined review: A type of LEED certification review in which the documentation for all the design and construction prerequisites/credits are submitted for review at the end of the construction phase (for LEED BD+C and LEED ID+C rating systems).

LEED Fellow: LEED credential created to designate the most exceptional professionals in the green building industry, it is the most prestigious designation awarded.

LEED for Homes Green Rater: Professional who provides in-field verification to LEED for Homes projects. (The other rating systems do not require any in-field verification.)

LEED for Homes Provider Organization: Responsible to oversee all the certification process and incorporate the LEED for Homes rating system requirements into the project's design and construction.

LEED Green Associate: LEED credential created for professionals with a proven, up-to-date understanding of green building principles and practices.

LEED impact categories: Also called system goals, are the key elements that every LEED project aims to accomplish, and it consists of 7 items.

LEED project boundary: Portion of the site submitted for LEED certification. Defined by the platted property line of the project, including all land and water within it.

LEED recertification: Necessary for LEED O+M projects to continue their certification every 5 years. LEED certification granted to projects under the other LEED rating systems do not need a recertification.

LEED split review: A type of LEED certification review in which the design prerequisites/credits are submitted for review during the design phase, and both the additional design prerequisites/credits and all the construction prerequisites/credits are submitted at the end of the construction phase (for LEED BD+C and LEED ID+C rating systems).

LEED Pro Reviewer: Professionals that evaluate the educational LEED courses on EDUCATION @USGBC.

LEED Volume Program: A streamlined certification process for organizations that plan to certify more than 25 prototype-based construction projects within 3 years.

Leverage point: The point where any action taken in the system can bring about significant results.

Life-cycle approach: Evaluates the entire life of a project, product, or service.

Life-cycle assessment (LCA): Evaluates all the environmental effects of a product quantitatively for the whole lifetime of that material.

Life-cycle costing (LCC): Assesses a product's total cost for the whole lifetime of the product by evaluating both the initial price and the operating costs.

Light shelves: Are horizontal, light-reflecting overhangs that are positioned to reflect the daylight into the desired area of the building.

Light tubes: Also called sun tubes or sun pipes, are structures that are used to transport sunlight inside a building.

Linear approach: An approach of the conventional building process, in which a project team member completes a work individually and then passes it to the next person.

Load shedding: Is the intentional action by the power utility to reduce the load in the power system in order prevent a total failure of the system.

Load shifting: Is storing the energy generated during off-peak hours, in order to use it during the peak-demand hours.

Long-term bicycle storage: Protected storage from rain and snow for the use of residents and employees.

Low-impact development (LID): An approach to mimic natural systems and to manage the stormwater closest to its source.

Makeup water: Water used to replace the lost water in open systems.

Masking systems: Or sound masking systems, are equipments used to reduce the background noise in spaces.

Minimum efficiency reporting value (MERV): Rates the air filters according to their performance on removing particles from air.

Minimum program requirements (MPRs): Provide guidance on the types of projects that are eligible for LEED certification, protect the integrity of the LEED program, and reduce the number of issues that arise during the certification process.

Monitor based commissioning (MBCx): Is the process of utilizing a software that will monitor real-time data from the building automation system and building meters.

Mulching: A protective layer applied to the surface of soil that will help to keep the roots of the plants cool and therefore prevent evaporation.

Native plants (indigenous plants): Are the type of plants that occur and develop naturally in a specific location.

Natural refrigerants: Refrigerants that occur in nature's biological and chemical cycles without human involvement, such as carbon dioxide (CO_2), water (H_2O), ammonia (NH_3), air, and hydrocarbons such as propane, ethane, and butane.

Negative feedback loops: A change brings an additional change in the opposite direction. If a room gets warmer than the set temperature, the thermostat will send a signal to the air conditioning, and the air conditioning will stop blowing warm air.

Net-zero energy project: A project that only use its own generated renewable energy.

Nonpoint source pollution: Type of pollution in which its source cannot be identified and which generally results from multiple sources.

Nonpotable water: Water that does not meet the human consumption standards.

Nonprocess energy (regulated energy): The energy consumed by the items that are used to condition spaces and maintain comfort and amenities for building occupants.

Open systems: Systems that constantly consume other items, use them, and produce waste at the end.

Open-grid pavement: A pavement system with at least 50% unbound.

Passive daylighting: Is a system that both collects the sunlight using static and nonmoving items such as windows, glass doors, some skylights, light tubes, and light shelves.

Pilot Credits: Credits being tested for the updated version of LEED.

Places of respite: An area in a natural environment, dedicated to connecting patients and visitors, in the hospitals.

Plug loads (receptacle load): Represents the electrical use by all the equipment that is connected to the electrical system via electrical receptacles.

Positive feedback loop: A producing B, which in turn produces more of A. An example of this would be an interest-earning savings account. As the account grows, more interest is earned which in turn brings further account growth.

Postconsumer recycled content: Is the recycled content of a used material. For example, recyclable printer paper can be sent to recycling after being used and can become a part of new printer paper. Other types of materials with postconsumer recycled content can be aluminum cans, water bottles, most glass, wood and steel products, newspapers, and more.

Potable water: Water that is approved for human use that meets or exceeds US Environmental Protection Agency drinking water quality standards (or a local equivalent outside the United States.)

Preconsumer recycled content: Is the content of a material that is recycled before getting used by any consumer. An example may be a sawdust generated during the manufacturing of a wood product that is recycled to be used inside an MDF board (medium density fiberboard).

Preferred parking: Parking spaces that are closest to the main entrance of a building.

Prerequisites: The minimum requirements that all buildings under a certain rating system must meet in order to achieve LEED certification.

Previously developed site: A site that contains at least 75% previously developed land.

Prime farmland: Land that is used for producing food, feed, forage, fiber, and oilseed crops or is available for these uses, as determined by the US Department of Agriculture's Natural Resources Conservation Service.

Prius effect: People can respond to something only if they have real-time information about it.

Process water: Is the type of water used by mechanical or other types of systems in buildings such as cooling towers or medical equipment in hospitals.

Radon: Is a radioactive gas that is naturally found in the soils, rocks, and water bodies that is harmful to human health.

Rainwater harvesting: An aspect of rainwater management that collects and filters the rainwater to be reused as an alternative to potable water.

Rapidly renewable materials: Natural materials that can replenish within 10 years.

Reclaimed water: Is the former blackwater that has been treated and purified for reuse.

Reference soils: Are the native soils of a site.

Refrigerant: Substances used to transfer heat.

Regenerative design: Is a type of building design that creates no waste and also provides more output than consumed input.

Renewable energy certificates (RECs): Or green tags, represent a tradable, nontangible commodity associated with the qualities of renewable energy generation. REC is a proof that, when purchased, an amount of energy was created using renewable energy sources.

Renewable energy: A type of energy that is derived from renewable sources. Renewable energy includes solar, wind, wave, biomass, and geothermal power, plus certain forms of hydropower.

Reverberation time: Is the time span between when a sound is produced and when it dies away.

Scope 1 energy: Relates to the direct energy from the owned or controlled sources.

Scope 2 energy: Energy that relates to the purchased energy.

Scope 3 energy: Relates to the energies that are not owned or directly controlled.

Sensitive lands: Ecologically sensitive areas such as prime farmland, floodplain, habitat, water bodies, or wetland.

Short-term bicycle storage: Typically used by visitors for less than two hours that typically does not provide enclosed parking.

Simple box energy modeling: A preliminary building model used to assess the building's energy loads.

Site assessment: Is a part of the integrative process, which clearly shows the project teams the properties of the site, including its topography, hydrology, climate, soil types, water availability, and human health effects.

Skylights: Are horizontal elements in the roof of the buildings that are made of opaque materials (mostly glass) to allow sunlight into the building.

Smart growth: A neighborhood development approach that protects undeveloped lands and contributes to project development in locations near jobs, schools, shops, and other diverse uses.

Soft cost: Covers everything needed for developing a project that does not physically contribute to the building. All the management and supervision costs, design costs, permits, and taxes can be seen as the soft costs.

Softscape: Part of a landscape that consists of live horticultural elements.

Solar reflectance (SR) value: Shows the solar energy that is reflected by a surface on a scale of 0 to 1. A black surface will have a SR of 0while a white surface will have a SR of 1.

Solar reflectance index (SRI) value: Indicates a material's ability to stay cool by reflecting solar radiation and emitting thermal radiation. Thus, both the solar reflectance and emissivity of a material will be combined to rank the material.

Source reduction: Refers to the exact sizing of the materials to be produced through prefabrication, modular construction, or similar methods, in order to prevent waste.

Spatial daylight autonomy (sDA): Is a metric used to describe annual sufficiency of ambient daylight in building interiors.

Stakeholder meetings: Meetings that are conducted among the project team, stakeholders, neighbors, and community members in order to understand and discuss community needs, issues, and concerns.

Suburban sprawl: The expansion of populations away from central urban areas into low-density areas.

Systems thinking: Refers to the understanding of each and every system of a building while also understanding their relationships and looking at the project as a whole.

Vision glazing: The term used for windows that provide exterior views.

Water balance approach: Aims to balance the water supply with water consumption.

Wet pond (retention pond): Pond designed to hold a specific amount of water indefinitely.

Xeriscaping: Type of landscaping that does not need any irrigation.

Zero-lot project: A type of project which the building footprint covers the whole lot.

REFERENCES

CHAPTER 2

1   J.F. Kenny, N.L. Barber, S.S. Hutson, K.S. Linsey, J.K. Lovelace, & M.A. Maupin. Estimated use of water in the United States in 2005: US Geological Survey Circular 1344, (2009).

2   D.M. Roodman & N. Lenssen "A Building Revolution: How Ecology and Health Concerns Are Transforming Construction," Worldwatch Paper 124 (Worldwatch Institute, 1995).

3   Energy Information Administration, EIA Annual Energy Outlook (EIA, 2008).

4   US Department of Energy Annual Outlook 2008.

5   Turner, C. & Frankel, Energy Performance of LEED for New Construction Buildings (2008), http://www.newbuildings.org/sites/default/files/Energy_Performance_of_LEED-NC_Buildings-Final_3-4-08b.pdf.

6   US Environmental Protection Agency, Report to Congress on Indoor Air Quality, volume 2, EPA/400/1-89/001C (EPA, 1989).

CHAPTER 4

1   US Energy Information Administration, Emissions of Greenhouse Gases Report (December 8, 2009), http://www.eia.doe.gov/oiaf/1605/ggrpt/.

2   International Council on Clean Transportation, Passenger Vehicles, (accessed March 22, 2013).

3   EPA, http://www.epa.gov/climatechange/ghgemissions/sources/transportation.html.

CHAPTER 5

1   Yang, X., Y.Hou, and B. Chen, Observed Surface Warming Induced by Urbanization in East China, J. Geophys. Res., 116(2011), D14113, doi:10.1029/2010JD015452.

CHAPTER 7

1   C. Turner and M. Frankel, Energy Performance of LEED for New Construction Buildings (March 4, 2008),
http://www.newbuildings.org/sites/default/files/Energy_Performance_of_LEED-NC_Buildings-Final_3-4-08b.pdf.

CHAPTER 8

1   US Environmental Protection Agency, http://epa.gov/osw/conserve/rrr/imr/cdm/pubs/cd-meas.pdf.

2   US Environmental Protection Agency, http://epa.gov/osw/nonhaz/municipal/pubs/msw2009rpt.pdf.

3   http://preservationnation.org/information-center/sustainable-communities/green-lab/lca/The_Greenest_Building_lowres.pdf

4   nps.gov/nr/publications/bulletins/nrb15/nrb15_2.htm.

5   "Healthy Business Strategies for Transforming the Toxic Chemical Economy," Clean Production Action (2006), http://www.cleanproduction.org/library/CPA-Healthybusiness-1.pdf.

6   Anastas and Warner, Green Chemistry: Theory and Practice (New York: Oxford University Press, 2000)

CHAPTER 9

1   Wyon, D. 1996. "Individual Microclimate Control: Required Range, Probable Benefits, and Current Feasibility." In Proceedings of Indoor Air 1996: Seventh International Conference of Indoor Air Quality and Climate, vol.1, Nagoya, Japan, pp.1067-1072.

2   Boyce, Peter, Reviews of Technical Reports on Daylight and Productivity (Rensselaer Polytechnic Institute, 2004); Heschong Mahone Group, Daylighting in Schools: An Investigation into the Relationship between Daylighting and Human Performance (1999).

3   Edwards, L., and P. Torcellini. A Literature Study of the Effects of Natural Light on Building Occupants (Golden, Colorado: NREL, 2002).

4   Ulrich, Roger, et al., "A Review of the Research Literature on Evidence-Based Healthcare Design," Health Environments Research and Design Journal 1(3) (2008), (http://www.herdjournal.com).

Made in the USA
Monee, IL
14 March 2024

54980486R00345